BEETLES

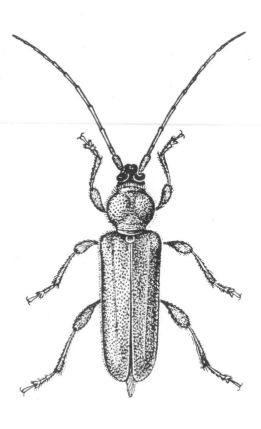

BEETLES

Text by K. W. Harde

Illustrations by F. Severa

BLITZ EDITIONS

Text by K. W. Harde
English edition edited by P. M. Hammond
Translated by Margot Schierlová
Illustrations by František Severa
Graphic design by Miloš Lang

Designed and produced by Aventinum Publishing House, Prague, Czech Republic
This English edition published 1998 by Blitz Editions, an imprint of Bookmart Ltd.
Registered Number 2372865
Trading as Bookmart Limited
Desford Road, Enderby, Leicester LE9 5AD

The original German edition was published by
Franckh'sche Verlagshandlung,
W. Keller u. Co., Stuttgart,
under the title Der Kosmos-Käferführer

ISBN 1-85605-448-9
Printed in the Czech Republic by Polygrafia, a.s., Prague
3/07/13/51-02

Contents

Introduction

By any account beetles are a particularly successful group of organisms. The approximately 370,000 species described to date outnumber all the known species of vascular plants; there are six or seven described beetle species for every one of vertebrates! Even so, beetle species already named represent only the tip of an iceberg. No student of the Coleoptera doubts that at least an equal number of beetle species remains to be described, but even a very approximate estimate of total numbers is difficult to make. Study of the immensely rich insect faunas of tropical rain forests is in its infancy, but recent investigation of selected tropical areas has led some entomologists to predict that as many as 5 million beetle species still await discovery.

Beetles belong to the group of insects known as the Endopterygota, those having a 'complete' metamorphosis, with a distinct pupal stage intervening between life as a larva and as a sexually mature adult. As in other endopterygotes the larvae of beetles represent the principal feeding stage. As well as having a very different structure, adult beetles tend to have quite different habits. This division of an individual's life into two completely separate phases seems to provide a recipe for success. Several other characteristics are likely to have been particularly advantageous to beetles in the course of their evolution and diversification. Among these are the features by which, as adults, they are generally most readily recognised. Most beetles have an extremely robust and hard external skeleton and possess a pair of horny wing-cases (elytra). The tough carapace not only helps in protecting them from potential predators, but also from a variety of other environmental hazards, such as excessive heat or aridity. It may be noted that adult beetles are especially numerous in habitats where an ability to push or burrow through densely packed substrates is at a premium. In such circumstances they are less likely to be crushed or damaged than a softer bodied insect. Adults of the majority of beetle species have membranous flight wings and are able to fly. Their wings often escape notice because, when not in use, they are folded away beneath the elytra, often in a complex manner. The protection afforded by the elytra is important as it enables adult beetles to have the best of both worlds. They are able to fly and so disperse themselves widely to occupy new habitats and, at the same time, they are able to crawl or burrow into cracks and crevices, into soil or wood, without risk of damage to their delicate organs of flight.

Beetles are to be found in virtually every terrestrial ecosystem, and there is very little in the way of potential nourishment which is not consumed by one species or another. However, their major impact on the world about us is through three types of activity: direct feeding on plants (including fungi), breaking down animal and plant debris, and preying on other invertebrates. A fairly large number of beetle species may be classified as pests. However, their depredations are frequently on a relatively minor scale, and they tend, as a group, to receive less attention from agriculturalists and applied entomologists than do certain other insect groups. Insects with sucking mouthparts, such as aphids or biting flies, are often important vectors of animal or plant diseases. This seems to be less frequently the case with beetles, although bark beetles and certain groups of weevils provide notable exceptions.

Apart from their directly economic and general ecological significance beetles claim the attention of scientists because of their enormous diversity of life-style and behaviour. An excellent account of this diversity — very much a summary, although the book runs to 800 pages — is to be found in *The Biology of Coleoptera* (R. A. Crowson, 1981). In this work Dr Crowson notes that the Coleoptera 'provide excellent illustrations and test cases for almost every general evolutionary principle, and future study of the group may well lead to the formulation of new generalisations'. This may not be a vain hope. After all, the evolutionary studies of such great biologists of the past as Charles Darwin and Alfred Russel Wallace began with an interest in the diversity of beetles!

Beetles are, of course, not without their aesthetic appeal. A number are of relatively large size, have striking forms and bright, often metallic, colours. Add to this the fact that they are easy to collect and preserve, and it is not difficult to see why they have become popular with amateur students of entomology. In this respect, at least in Europe, they rank second only to the Lepidoptera. Compared with many other insect groups the beetles of northern and central Europe are relatively well-known. Reasonably up-to-date identification works are available for the beetles of many European countries. However, because of the large number of species involved, to be comprehensive such works have to be large, often running to several volumes, and are generally costly. They are also, at least in part, usually too technical for the beginner. A good source of information concerning available identification works for beetles, on a world basis with emphasis on those in English, is *Animal Identification, Volume 3, Insects* (D. Hollis ed., 1980). The more important specialist identification works relevant to the beetles found in the British Isles, northern and central Europe, are noted below.

Although equal in importance to the adult stage the early stages of beetles are much less well known. Even some extremely common (if small) species found in the British Isles are unknown as larvae (e. g. *Stilbus testaceus,* p. 196: 3, and *Sericoderus lateralis,* p. 130: 8). Family level keys to larvae are included in *The natural classification of the families of Coleoptera* (R. A. Crowson, 1967). This book also contains the best available comprehensive treatment of beetle classification. The most reliable general work enabling the identification of larvae to genus or species is that of Klausnitzer (1978), although this is largely concerned with species living on the ground or in the soil, and is in German. Other useful works on larvae are those of Böving & Craighead (1931) and Peterson (1951), and further publications dealing with the larvae of particular beetle families may be located by referring to the volume edited by Hollis (1980) mentioned above. However, it must be said that few of these works are at all suitable for the beginner.

A final subject worthy of brief mention here is that of the insect group often known as the Strepsiptera. These curious insects, parasitic as larvae, mostly on bees or wasps, are considered by some entomologists to comprise a separate order. Today, most coleopterists place them as a family of beetles (Stylopidae), despite their rather unlikely appearance. However, only the winged and somewhat fly-like adult males are at all likely to be encountered by the non-specialist, and these rather rarely. A key to the central European species is given by R. Kinzelbach in Volume 3 of the standard work of Freude *et al.* (1969), but these little-known insects are not included in the present work.

The beetles of central Europe

In faunistic terms central Europe extends from Alsace in the west to Czechoslovakia and Poland in the east, and from Schleswig-Holstein in the north to Austria and the centre of Switzerland in the south. Entomologically speaking this area is one of the most thoroughly investigated parts of the world. Its beetle fauna comprises some 8,000 species.

The foundations of our knowledge of central European beetles were laid in the early nineteenth century, culminating in the production of C. G. Calwer's *Käferbuch* (various editions between 1858 and 1916). This popular but, for its time, accurate work included good coloured illustrations of a large proportion of the central European fauna. Between 1892 and 1904 L. Ganglbauer published his *Käfer Mitteleuropas,* a scholarly work in 4 wolumes, containing identification keys and descriptions of species, but no illustrations. In large part Ganglbauer's volumes were soon superseded as Edmund Reitter's equally comprehensive work — *Die Käfer des deutschen Reiches* (The Beetles of Germany) — appeared in parts between 1908 and 1916. This five-volume work (with an extra volume contributed by Adolf Horion in 1935) remained the standard account until recently. In addition to identification keys, Reitter included information on the distribution and biology of the species, and each volume contained a number of colour plates. Another influential work which deserves mention is that of Kuhnt (1912) who by means of a continuous key, containing short couplets, and illustrated by numerous marginal line figures, ingeniously managed to include all species of beetle known to occur in Germany in one volume. All of these works, of course, are in German, but their influence spread well beyond the confines of German-speaking countries. Their contents provided a basis for studies of the beetle faunas of other parts of Europe, and were extensively drawn upon by authors in other countries.

By the 1960s the standard central European works of Reitter and others were seriously out-of-date, but a modern and reliable replacement was in the offing. The first of 11 volumes of *Die Käfer Mitteleuropas* (The Beetles of Central Europe) was published in 1964 by H. Freude, K. W. Harde and G. A. Lohse. The work is now nearing completion (the tenth volume was published in 1981), and is likely to remain the standard comprehensive treatment of north and central European beetles for some time to come.

Die Käfer Mitteleuropas contains no coloured illustrations as an aid to identification, largely because these would have greatly increased the already high printing costs of the 11 volumes. Nevertheless, coloured pictures undoubtedly help to guide the beginner, who might otherwise be lost in long and complicated identification keys, towards a correct identification. This field guide, including as it does a large proportion of the beetle species to be found in central and north European countries, fills a gap in the literature available for this area. It may be used on its own, or in conjunction with more specialist works.

The British beetle fauna

Approaching 4,000 species of beetle are known to occur in the British Isles. This may seem a large number, but the most striking feature of the British beetle fauna, when placed in an European context, is its limited size. No more than half of the species found in a country such as Germany are also to be found in Britain. However, more than 90 % of British beetles are known from central Europe and very few are totally absent from France. Several thousand species occurring in the latter country (a large proportion of them in the south) are unknown in Britain. Overlap of the British and Scandinavian beetle faunas is also considerable, although the list of species found in the Scandinavian countries includes some 1,500 which are absent from the British Isles. Such disparities have a fortunate consequence for the study of beetles in Britain. Scandinavian, French or central European beetle books, such as the standard work of Freude *et al.* (1964, etc.), may be used with some confidence to identify beetles found in Britain. The more manageable size of the British fauna also has advantages for its study in depth. In many respects British beetles are better known than those of any other country of comparable size.

The absence from the British Isles of many beetle species which occur not far away on the European mainland is not hard to explain. Many favour a more continental climate, with greater extremes of summer and winter temperatures, than that of Britain. Some of these are species of the steppes, whose ranges extend into central and northern Europe from the east, but stop short of the most westerly parts of the continent. A good number of British 'absentees' are forest-dwellers, many of them, in such families as Anobiidae, Buprestidae and Cerambycidae, with wood-feeding larvae. For such species, and others associated with forest fungi, an Atlantic climate (relatively high rainfall and cool summers) appears to be unsuitable. Summer temperatures, even in the south of England, are simply not high enough for another large group of species; many species of Anthicidae, Scarabaeidae, Tenebrionidae and other families which are common further to the south in France, Switzerland and the southern parts of central Europe, are unable to survive in north-western Europe. Britain also lacks a number of species which inhabit the arctic and subarctic regions of northern Europe, although some of these are also found to the south in the mountains of central Europe, such as the Alps. It may be noted that many additional species of this type were present in Britain during past periods of cooler climate, but were lost from the British fauna by about 10,000 years ago, as warmer conditions signalled the end of the last glacial period. Some essentially boreal species persist in the northern parts of the British Isles where they may be confined to just a few mountain peaks. Apart from directly climatic considerations, other beetles find no place in the British fauna because their host-plants or special habitats are absent. In Britain there is no equivalent to the high mountain peaks of the Alps, or the large natural forests of spruce found on the European mainland.

However, the composition of the British beetle fauna is not a mere reflection of topography and the present climate and flora. It has also been moulded by historical processes which continue to exert their effect today. The gross climatic fluctuations of the past hundred thousand or so years have meant the repeated elimination from these islands of many species. With the return of conditions suitable for their survival in the British Isles recolonisation of these shores by many has been achieved. In some cases, however, this has been hindered or delayed by the fragmentation of once continuous stretches of suitable terrain or the complete disappearance of former land bridges. A good deal is now known of past changes in the composition of the British beetle fauna, especially that of the past few thousand years. Much of the available information comes from studies of beetle remains preserved in deposits such as peat beds, an area of study pioneered in Britain. Over the past 4 or 5 thousand years the role of man-made environmental change has been predominant in determining which beetle species have been lost from the fauna and which new arrivals have become established. The development of the British beetle fauna over the past 10,000 years or so has been reviewed at some length by Hammond (1974), whose account should be consulted for details.

The distribution of beetle species within the British Isles mirrors, on a smaller scale, that through north-western Europe as a whole. Almost half of the species known to occur in the British Isles are confined to the southern half or so of these islands. Several hundred do not occur outside of the southern counties of England. While as many as 3,000 beetle species are to be found in a richly wooded southern county such as Hampshire, only 600 or so have been recorded from the Outer Hebrides, an area which is comparable in size. Ireland occupies much the same position in respect to the rest of the British Isles as Great Britain does to continental Europe. More than one-third of British species are thought to be absent from Ireland, including many widespread forest-dwelling species and almost all members of such families as Buprestidae and Cerambycidae. Although not as rich in species as the south, the northern parts of Britain have their own specialities. Some of the 200 or so 'northern' species have a very restricted distribution, in the Scottish Highlands. Others extend further to the south, especially on the west side of the country, and may also be found in the Welsh hills and mountains.

Many other parts of Britain and Ireland have their own special species. Some are restricted to the East Anglian fens and broads, others to particular areas of the coast, or to remnants of the ancient forest that once covered much of Britain. The most notable of old forest areas, such as Windsor Forest and the New Forest, harbour a number of beetle species known to occur nowhere else in the British Isles. With the draining of the Fens, clear-felling of much woodland, the development of lowland heaths, areas of downland and stretches of coastline for agricultural or other purposes, the special habitats of many beetles have disappeared over the past century or so. This is not a new development, but a continuation of environmental change wrought by man in Britain over several thousand years. However, the pace of such change may have quickened, and as many as 100 species of beetle may have become extinct in the British Isles during the past 200 years. At least a further 200 species, many of them with very specialised habits, are now greatly threatened. Their extinction is only a matter of time.

Pioneer studies of the local beetle fauna began early in Britain. The most influential early work was that of James Stephens, whose 5 volumes of *'Mandibulata'* were published between 1828 and 1832. Although a bold attempt to cover the full range of British species, the work is today of merely historical interest. The first 'modern' British beetle books, with good keys, accurate descriptions, useful information concerning habits and habitats, and excellent coloured illustrations, are those of Canon W. W. Fowler; *The Coleoptera of the British Islands* appeared, in 5 volumes, between 1886 and 1891. A supplementary volume, with descriptions of extra species and a good deal of additional information concerning distribution, was produced later by Fowler and Donisthorpe (1913). Only one really comprehensive British work has been published since Fowler's time. Joy's *A Practical Handbook of British Beetles* (1932) is a much less full treatment of its subject matter than the work of Fowler, although more up-to-date in most respects. It comprises two volumes − one of text (mostly identification keys), and one of line illustrations. 'Fowler' and 'Joy' remain the standard works for the serious student of British beetles, but both are long out of print, and they are expensive as well as difficult to obtain on the second-hand market. Fortunately, a new (facsimile) edition of Joy's work was published in 1976, and may be obtained at what, by modern standards, is a reasonable price. In 1952 these standard works began to be replaced by a series of *Handbooks for the Identification of British Insects,* published by the Royal Entomological Society of London. Each part in this series deals with a particular group of species, usually those of one family or a group of small families; some 37 beetle families have been completed to date. When the full range of families has been treated the British beetle fauna will be as well served by identification works as that of any European country.

In the meantime those wishing to identify British beetles accurately have to make do with the rather out-of-date works of Fowler and Joy, supplemented, where available, by R.E.S.L. Handbooks. Not surprisingly, modern continental works are widely consulted by British coleopterists. Frequent use is made of various Scandinavian works and the available parts of the *Faune de France* series, as well as the important work of Freude *et al.* (1964, etc.) discussed above. To keep up-to-date the serious student also needs to remain abreast of the specialist literature. Useful papers appear in many different journals, but the majority of those relating specifically to the British beetle fauna are to be found in the *Entomologist's Monthly Magazine*, the *Entomologist's Gazette* or the *Entomologist's Record and Journal of Variation*. The more important papers for identifying British beetles which have appeared in these and other journals are listed in a useful bibliography by Kerrich *et al.* (1978). Two other works of importance to British coleopterists are deserving of special mention. Adolf Horion's *Faunistik der Mitteleuropäischen Käfer* (1941-on) remains the only source of data concerning distribution, habitats and general biology of European beetle species, which covers a wide range of families in depth. The 12 volumes of this work are in German. Finally, an up-to-date check-list of species recorded from the British Isles is almost indispensable to the serious student of British beetles. This need has been met by a recent publication of the Royal Entomological Society (Pope, 1977). Additions and corrections to this list are being made continually, and are published regularly in *Antenna,* the house journal of the R.E.S.L.

The study of British beetles is currently in an expansive phase, with additional species being discovered or recognised at a rate of several each year, and much new information concerning their biology and distribution being made available. A good deal of this work is centred on the various Recording Schemes organised from the Biological Records Centre at Abbots Ripton, and on the entomological societies. The national entomological societies are the Royal Entomological Society of London, the British Entomological and Natural History Society and the Amateur Entomologist's Society. The last-mentioned is particularly suited to the amateur with a newly awakened interest in beetles.

Anatomy

Bearing in mind the great number of different species and the diversity of their modes of life, the anatomy of beetles is relatively uniform. Like all insects, beetles have an exoskeleton (external skeleton), but in their case it is generally particularly hard and thick. Indeed, a horny cuticle may be regarded as typical in this group of insects. A soft exoskeleton, as in the families Cantharidae and Malachiidae, for example, is an exception (Fig. 1 and 2).

Also characteristic of beetles are the wing-cases (elytra), which usually completely cover the hind part of the body including the abdomen. They are actually the first pair of wings, but instead of being used for flying they protect the abdomen and the delicate membranous second pair of wings (alae). In some cases the elytra are abbreviated although they still generally provide full protection for the flight wings. This is the rule in the family Staphylinidae (Rove Beetles) and Pselaphidae, while in a few other families (Cerambycidae, Meloidae, Nitidulidae) the elytra are short in some species. Occasionally the elytra are fused down the midline and form a solid armour plate; in such cases the membranous wings are usually missing, and the beetles are unable to fly (e. g. some Carabidae, Curculionidae, etc.).

In a few beetle families adults are found which lack wing-cases as well as flight wings, and have the appearance of larvae. The best known example is the female glowworm (Lampyridae).

Before taking off, beetles usually raise their elytra at a sloping angle to enable them to unfold their alae for flight. We can see this most easily by watching a cockchafer or a stag beetle, although a keen observer can also see it in a ladybird or a Colorado Beetle. Rose chafers are exceptional in being able to extend their flight wings without lifting their elytra, and these are also kept closed during flight.

As with all insects, a beetle's body is divided into three main parts − the head, thorax and abdomen. In most beetles these divisions are quite distinct. In turn, these major divisions are themselves composed of various segments, some of which are more or less clearly discernible

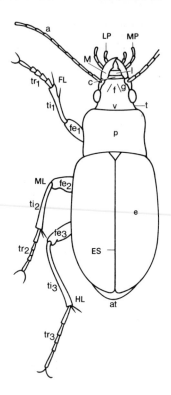

Fig. 1. Dorsal view of a beetle. a — antenna, LP — labial palp, M — mandible, MP — maxillary palp, l — upper lip (labrum), c — head-plate (clypeus), g — cheek (gena), t — temple, f — brow (frons), v — top of head (vertex), p — forepart of thorax (pronotum), e — wing-case (elytron), ES — elytral suture, at — anal tergite (pygidium), FL — foreleg, ML — middle leg, HL — hindleg, $fe_{1,2,3}$ — femora of the 3 pairs of legs, $ti_{1,2,3}$ — tarsi of the 3 pairs of legs.

(those in the abdomen and thorax), while the originally segmented structure of some parts (e.g. the head) can no longer be made out.

On the head we find most of the sensory organs and the mouthparts; the eyes are situated on the front of the head. In some, mostly subterranean, species the eyes have degenerated or completely disappeared. The eyes are of the compound type, that is to say, they are composed of a quantity of prismatic units known as ommatidia (Fig. 3). The structure of a compound eye is illustrated in Fig. 4. The compound eyes of beetles are rarely round (as are the camera-like eyes of mammals), and may be variously shaped. As a rule they curve kidney-wise round the base of the antennae, with one part on the upper surface of the head and the other part on the under surface. In whirligig beetles (Gyrinidae) the top and bottom halves of the eye are separate, so that the beetle actually has four eyes. Biologically, this is a very sensible arrangement; whirligig beetles live on the surface of the water and the 'upper eyes' can observe what is going on in the air above the water, while the 'lower eyes' can see what is happening in the water.

The antennae, which grow from the head, can be filiform (thread-like), claviform (club-shaped), flabellate (like a fan) or geniculate (bent in the middle) (see Fig. 5). They generally carry olfactory organs, but we know relatively little of their sensory functions.

12

The mouthparts are in principle always the same, but vary as regards details, according to the beetle's mode of life. The most important parts are the highly chitinized upper jaws (mandibles), which in plant-eating species are adapted for cutting off food and chewing it and in predacious species are usually sharp and pointed for catching and gripping prey. In a few cases they seem to serve no special purpose, like the huge antler-like mandibles of male stag beetles. The lower jaw (maxilla), which has several parts, is surmounted by multi-jointed maxillary palps. Further jointed (labial) palps are to be found on the lower lip or labium, which completes the lower mouth parts. These palps and their sensory organs are involved in tasting and selecting food. The upper mouthparts are completed by the upper lip or labrum.

The thorax consists of three segments (the pro-, meso- and metathorax), but the separation of the latter two parts cannot be seen from above owing to their fusion. They are also generally hidden by the wing-cases. On the under side of the body the segmentation is more clearly discernible, but it is also more confusing, because the segments are produced posteriorly and are covered by a complex arrangement of armoured plates. On each of the thoracic segments there is normally a pair of jointed legs, whose form can vary (Fig. 6), but which in general are used for locomotion (running, swimming, jumping) and are composed of a trochanter, a coxa, a femur, a tibia and multi-jointed tarsi. Two pairs of wings grow from the first two thoracic

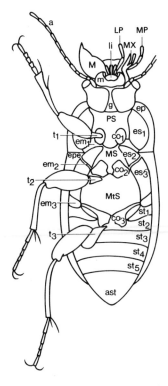

Fig. 2. Ventral view of a beetle. a — antenna, LP — labial palp, M — mandible, MX — maxilla, MP — maxillary palp, li — lower lip (labium), m — chin (mentum), g — throat (gula), ep — epipleuron of pronotum, epe — epipleura of elytra, $es_{1,2,3}$ — episterna of front, middle and hind part of thorax, $co_{1,2,3}$ — coxae, st_{1-5} — abdominal sternites, ast — anal sternite, $t_{1,2,3}$ — femoral rings (trochanters) of the 3 legs, PS, MS, MtS — pro —, meso — and metasternum, $em_{1,2,3}$ — epimera of the three parts of the thorax.

13

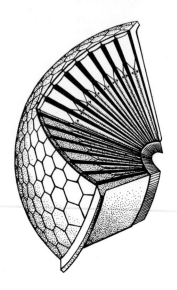

Fig. 3. Compound eye of a beetle, composed of a large number of prismatic units (ommatidia) seen on the surface as hexagons. A slice has been removed from the eye to reveal its internal structure.

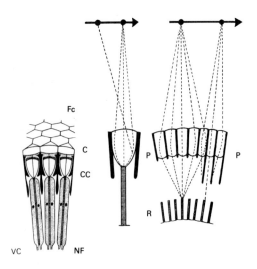

Fig. 4. Ommatidia, showing their structure and the pathway through them of rays of light, P — pigment cells, Fc — facets, C — corneal lens, CC — crystalline cone, NF — nerve fibre, R — rhabdom, VC — visual cell.

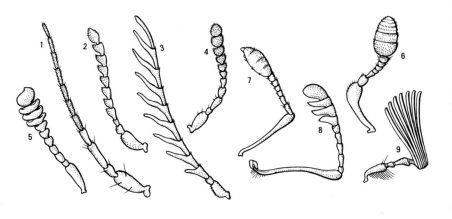

Fig. 5. Types of beetle antennae. 1 − ground beetle (Carabidae), 2 − click beetle (Elateridae), 3 − click beetle (Elateridae), 4 − leaf beetle (Chrysomelidae), 5 − carrion beetle (Silphidae), 6 − bark beetle (Scolytidae), 7 − weevil (Curculionidae), 8 − stag beetle (Lucanidae), 9 − cockchafer (Melolonthinae).

segments. The first pair are the wing cases (elytra) and the second pair the membranous wings (alae).

The abdomen consists of a number of segments (usually 8−9), each of which has a dorsal part (tergite) and a ventral part (sternite); these are more or less solid chitinous plates joined together by areas of thinner cuticle. The abdomen to a greater or lesser extent is thus flexible, unlike the head and thorax. The apical segments of the abdomen are often modified in a complex manner; they contain the sexual organs and as a rule they act as accessory organs in copulation.

In many cases the structure of the genitalia is a useful guide for the determination of a species. Some parts − especially in the males − are particularly well sclerified and of complicated structure. These often provide external criteria for identification. Very often, exact determination of a species is possible only on the basis of examination of the male genitalia.

We do not want to go into details on the internal anatomy of beetles here, but there are a few specific features which merit special attention.

The organs do not receive their oxygen supply via the blood stream, as they do in mammals, but directly through the tracheal system − a system of air-tubes growing inwards from spiracles (openings on the sides of the abdomen) and dividing into increasingly finer branches. 'Pumping' movements, which may be observed in the May-beetle, force the circulating air through the tracheal system, bringing fresh air into the body and thereby keeping the organs supplied with the necessary oxygen.

Beetles also have blood, but it contains no haemoglobin or any other oxygen-binding substance. It can be colourless, yellow, red or even green and it circulates in the body cavity instead of in blood vessels. The blood is pumped from the heart − a tubular organ with paired side-openings lying in the dorsal part of the abdomen.

Inside the ventral wall of the abdomen lies the abdominal part of the nerve-cord. This is swollen in every segment to form ganglia from which nerves run into the segments themselves.

15

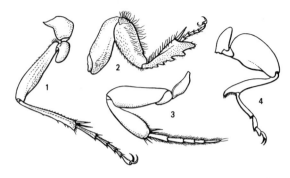

Fig. 6. Different types of beetle legs. 1 — for running (*Carabus*), 2 — for digging (*Geotrupes*), 3 — for swimming (*Dytiscus*), 4 — for jumping (*Psylliodes*).

The three thoracic segmental ganglia are fused, so that there is only a single large thoracic ganglion — the largest nerve cell complex in the beetle's body; the supra- and suboesophageal ganglia, which are situated in the head, are small by comparison.

Development — metamorphosis, hypermetamorphosis

Two contrasting types of development have evolved in insects. In one type, in which metamorphosis is said to be incomplete, the newly hatched larva bears a distinct resemblance to the adult insect or imago which it will become. Development in such hemimetabolous insects (e. g. grasshoppers and bugs) is characterized by successive moults as the larva grows steadily larger until, at the last moult, the fully-fledged adult appears. It is at this point that flying species acquire their wings.

A quite different type of development is characteristic of insects such as beetles, moths and butterflies, wasps and flies. Here, development progresses in a quite different way, and involves a radical transformation, or metamorphosis, before the adult stage is reached. In insects with a complete metamorphosis the newly hatched larva bears little resemblance to the imago. Although the larva generally moults several times, it merely increases in size and comes no nearer to resembling the adult insect. Between the larva and the imago there is an intermediate stage of development: this is the pupa, in which the organs undergo complete reconstruction. After a time the imago forces its way out of the pupal case and leaves it. There are thus at least four quite different stages in the developmental cycle: the egg, the larva, the pupa and the imago.

The eggs of beetles are generally minute and are likely to remain undetected unless they are laid in a clump and are brightly coloured, like the eggs of *Chrysomela populi,* which may be found on poplar leaves. The number of eggs laid by a single female beetle varies considerably according to the species, from a few dozen to a thousand or more. Beetles' eggs have received slight attention from researchers. Much of what is known about them is summarized in a recent book by H. E. Hinton (1981).

Beetle larvae display a great diversity of form (Fig. 7), but have likewise been relatively neglected and there is no comprehensive work for the identification of British species. The most useful general work for the specialist is that of Klausnitzer (1977). Beetle larvae live in and on all kinds of substrates, in water and on dry land. Predacious (e. g. ladybird, ground beetle, diving beetle) larvae and others living openly on plants (e. g. leaf beetle larvae) have well-formed limbs and are usually more or less efficient runners or swimmers. On the other hand beetle larvae which live in the substrate on which they feed (dung, decaying vegetation, wood, etc.), often have little need to move quickly or to move very far, so that during evolution their legs have degenerated or disappeared and in some cases have been replaced by thickened callosities for crawling.

Beetle pupae are often concealed from the eyes of possible predators (in the ground, under bark, or within plant tissues), but some (e. g. ladybird pupae) are suspended freely from plants. No beetle pupae are capable of locomotion, although there are some which are able to make defensive beating movements. In the pupa the larval organs are broken down and new adult structures formed. When this process is complete the contours of the adult beetle can often be detected through the pupal wall.

The imago which emerges from the pupa, i. e. the adult beetle, does not moult and therefore does not grow. The popular belief that a small beetle is just a young beetle which will grow bigger in time is a fallacy.

The metamorphosis described above applies in a general way to all beetles. In a few cases, however, not just one, but several different larval forms occur during the development of a species. This is known as hypermetamorphosis and may be illustrated by a particular example (Fig. 8).

In the spring a curious, rather shapeless beetle may sometimes be found crawling clumsily over a grassy field. The oil beetle *Meloe violaceus* is steely blue, violet or black and measures up to 3 cm or more. It lacks flight wings, and its short, stumpy elytra cover only a third or so of its bulky, swollen abdomen, especially in the female, which is a veritable egg-laying machine and lays large quantities of eggs in small holes in the ground. The newly hatched larva is about 3 mm long, is very active and exhibits a curious feature not found in any other insect: on each of its feet it has three claws. For this reason it is known as a triungulin. Actually it has only one true claw (in the middle) and two claw-like bristles, one on either side. After hatching, oil beetle larvae instinctively ascend the stems and leaves of the herbage amongst which the eggs are laid. Only those which reach a flower have any chance of developing further. Here the tiny larvae wait for a passing winged insect to settle, so that they can jump 'on board'. Again, only those larvae which obtain a ride on a burrowing-bee have any chance of further development;

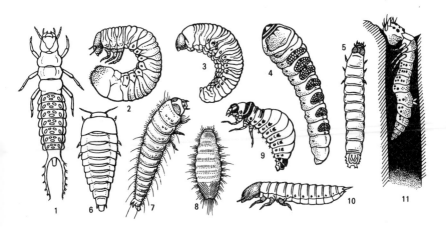

Fig. 7. Different types of beetle larvae. 1 — ground beetle, 2 — cockchafer, 3 — bark beetle (*Blastophagus*), 4 — longhorn beetle (*Cerambyx*), 5 — click beetle, 6 — carrion beetle, 7 — bacon beetle, 8 — museum beetle, 9 — Colorado Beetle, 10 — *Dascillus,* 11 — tiger beetle.

17

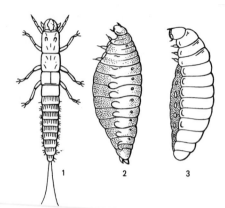

Fig. 8. Different larval stages of *Meloe* (hypermetamorphosis). 1 — first larval stage (triungulin), 2 — second larval stage, 3 — third larval stage.

the rest are doomed to death. Burrowing-bees are related to the Honey-bee, but live solitarily. They dig cells in the ground, which they fill with nectar, placing an egg in each before sealing the cell and going off to dig the next one. If a burrowing-bee carrying nectar returns to its brood cell with an oil beetle larva clinging to its coat, the larva dismounts. However, if the bee has not yet laid an egg on the nectar, the beetle larva will drown. Those lucky enough to land on a bee's egg feed on the egg while using it as a raft. A totally different secondary larva appears after the first moult. The new larva is blind, with a plump soft body and very short legs. Overall it resembles a tiny cockchafer grub. In this stage the oil beetle larva is able to swim in the nectar on which it feeds. It moults twice more, but without a marked further change of form. The third moult brings it to a resting phase which, however, is not the actual pupal stage. The pseudopupa has only vestiges of legs and head appendages and remains enclosed in the old larval skin; this is the state in which it spends the winter. After a fresh moult in the spring it once again resembles the active secondary larva. Without feeding, the new larva moults to the pupal stage, from which the beetle itself finally emerges.

Ecology

In the course of their evolutionary history beetles have become adapted to the most diverse ecosystems. As terrestrial animals breathing atmospheric air they occupy a multitude of ecological niches on dry land, some as extreme specialists, others as generalists. Whole groups of beetles, such as the families Dytiscidae and Hydrophilidae (predacious diving beetles and water scavenger beetles), have taken secondarily to the water — like seals among the mammals; it is there that the greater part of their development takes place and they have acquired many specific characteristics fitting them for a life in water.

Although to be found in brackish water, beetles almost completely avoid strongly salt water. There are, however, halophilic (i. e. salt-loving) species which live chiefly or solely on the seashore or in inland localities with salt deposits. Such specialized species are known as halobionts.

For each species, genus or family discussed in the illustrated part of this book the preferred type of habitat is noted. It would be repetitious to list all of these habitats here, as beetles are to be found in virtually all terrestrial ecosystems.

We should like to draw the reader's attention to a type of special relationship which is not uncommon and that is the role of beetles or beetle larvae as 'domestic animals' of other insects, especially those living in association with ants (i. e. myrmecophilous species). However, not all beetles or beetle larvae found in the company of ants are 'domestic animals', cared for by their hosts and doing them certain favours in return. An association between beetles and ants can have a quite different basis, such as parasitism. For example, the ants which act as hosts of the larvae of the leaf beetle genus *Clytra* receive no benefit from their guests. When a female beetle enters an ants' nest to lay its eggs it is immediately attacked by the occupants. However, the beetle is able to protect its more vulnerable parts (legs and antennae) by tucking them into grooves in its body; in addition, it lies absolutely still and 'plays possum'. The ants eventually abandon their futile attacks, leaving the beetle to acquire the odour of the nest and lay its eggs in peace. It takes care not to leave the eggs unprotected in the ants' nest and wraps each of them in a layer of dung to discourage any greedy inhabitants. When the larva hatches it cracks the dung capsule open down one side, but leaves its abdomen inside. During its development, which may take two years or even longer, the larva enlarges its capsule with more dung, soil and saliva so that, as it grows, it can always retreat right inside it. Finally, before pupating, the capsule is sealed. On the outside of the capsule there are special ribs enabling the ants to grip it and pick it up, since when the ants 'move house' they take the beetles' larvae with them, along with their own brood. *Clytra* larvae probably live mainly on dead insects brought into the nest by the ants, but no doubt also devour their hosts' brood, thereby doing them considerable harm.

The larva of *Potosia cuprea,* a member of the rose-chafer family (Cetoniidae), is also a myrmecophile, and lives in decaying fragments of wood in the deeper parts of the nests of the Wood Ant. It apparently does little or no harm to its hosts and in turn is left by them to its own devices. Although very local in Britain the species is common in much of Europe.

However, many beetles have a much closer relationship to their ant hosts, and are actually fed and tended by them. This is the case with *Lomechusoides strumosa,* a rove beetle measuring 5.5−6.5 mm, which is found in the nests of *Formica* species, and with three *Lomechusa* species (two in Britain) measuring 3.5−5 mm. At the sides of their first abdominal tergites these beetles have tufts of bristles (trichomes) from which the ants lick a special secretory substance. Similar trichomes are sometimes present at the apex of the femur and the tip of the abdomen. Although this secretion is clearly not an essential foodstuff the ants are very fond of it, and the beetles are repeatedly 'milked' by them. In turn, the beetles beg food from their hosts by tickling them with their antennae and are willigly fed by them. However, they repay this hospitality by devouring their hosts' brood and their larvae live entirely on the ants' offspring.

The extent to which these beetles have adapted themselves to living in the company of ants is amazing; indeed, they are no longer capable of living without them. Their adaptations are sometimes surprisingly intricate. For instance, when conditions in the nest deteriorate − e. g. during a long spell of bad weather, when the ants are unable to collect an adequate amount of food − the ants may resort to devouring their own brood. To combat the consequent danger to their own young the beetles have developed a special feature not found in any of their free-living relatives. They are either viviparous (giving birth to live larvae) or ovoviviparous (laying eggs from which the larvae hatch out as soon as they have been laid), with the result that both the length of time needed for development of the larvae and the danger of their being eaten are substantially reduced.

Ants' nests are sometimes attacked by beetles of this type on such a scale that the continued existence of the ant colony is put at risk.

Lomechusa species have yet another peculiarity − they switch hosts. From autumn to spring the adult beetles live with various *Myrmica* species, but in the spring the females lay their eggs in the nests of *Formica* species, and here the offspring complete their whole development. In all *Lomechusa* species there is considerable variation in colour and in the form of the pronotum, the different varieties of one species preferring to make their home with different kinds of ant.

The family Pselaphidae includes many species which inhabit ants' nests, in a like manner to the rove beetles described above. In some cases the bond between host and guest is a loose one, while in others it is very strong. These beetles are all very small and none exceed 3 mm in length. They include the species *Claviger testaceus,* which measures 2.1−2.3 mm and lives chiefly in the nests of the Yellow Ant (*Lasius flavus*). Completely blind, eyeless and lacking some of the usual segments from feelers and legs, these insects would be helpless outside the ants' nest. The few joints left on the feelers are adapted for use by the ants as handles when transporting their domestic animals.

Species of *Claviger*, like those of *Lomechusa*, secrete a substance which the ants lick avidly from tufts of hair. The beetles beg food from the ants, but also devour their brood.

Physiology

As well as colonizing every type of environment, beetles have also learnt to obtain nourishment from every possible quarter and there is probably no organic matter which at least some of them do not eat; and even though they may not eat it, they also chew through inorganic materials, such as lead, for example. Because of their tremendous diversity of diet we are able to give only a few examples and to make a few general remarks.

Different species of beetles have very different bills of fare. Some are so highly specialized that they can eat only a specific type of food. A good example is the Colorado Beetle, which is found almost solely on potato plants, whose leaves are eaten by both the beetles and their larvae. It is not absolutely specialized (monophagous), however, since it also occurs on other *Solanum* species, and may therefore be considered as oligophagous. At the other end of the scale are the polyphagous species, among which *Stegobium* undoubtedly has one of the most wide-ranging diets. Between these omnivorous and polyphagous species and the specialized monophagous and oligophagous species there exists a wide range of intermediate types.

Many beetle families include primarily predacious species. Good examples are the ground beetles, rove beetles and predacious diving beetles. Worms, slugs and snails, other insects and even vertebrates like tadpoles and young fish − none are safe from attack. Many predacious beetles do not eat their prey piecemeal, but suck it dry. To be able to do this they first of all inject digestive juices into their prey, wait a while and then suck out the liquefied contents. Part of the digestive process thus takes place outside their body; this is known as extra-oral digestion. Some predatory species do not restrict themselves to animal food. For example, ground beetles are not infrequently to be seen on umbelliferous plants eating the milky young seeds. The ground beetle *Harpalus rufipes,* which is fairly common in cultivated areas, can be a scourge of strawberry growers, since it eats the acini (seeds) on the surface of fleshy strawberries, so damaging the fruit.

The number of beetles living on plants is extremely large. Some prefer a particular plant or part of a plant (for example asparagus leaves or *Antirrhinum* flowers); others are less choosy. All the parts of plants are eaten − flowers, leaves, fruits, stems and roots. Many species of beetles live in wood − some in the living tree, others in dead wood.

Decaying organic matter is a frequent food of various specialists. Two types of material play a specially important role. One is dung − consumed by dung (coprophagous) beetles and the other is dead animal matter − eaten by carrion (necrophagous) beetles.

Dung beetles are to a large extent responsible for the quick disappearance of waste matter; we shall return to this question again later in connection with the care of the brood. Without these scavengers it would not be long before dung − especially from cattle and other ruminants − collected in such masses that the growth of young vegetation would be endangered.

As well as food, beetles need water. If it is their natural medium (i. e. if they live in water) they must be able to find a new home should their immediate source dry up. Many water beetles are consequently expert and active fliers. Even under good conditions they may leave their homes to go in search of a new one. Predacious diving beetles are active after dark and then, in the moonlight, they are apt to mistake a greenhouse or a tarry road for a sheet of water, sometimes with dire results.

The dependence of beetles on water is very variable. Many species are hygrophilous, that is like or need considerable moisture; they are to be found mainly beside water, in marshy ground and in bogs, and are unable to survive droughts *in situ*. Other species occur chiefly in dry places, e.g. on heaths or on sunny, dry and warm (xerothermic) slopes. In reality such species are generally quite tolerant of moisture, but are bound to warm, dry localities because of their need of warmth.

Deserts represent the extreme of a dry environment, but even there we can find many species, especially darkling beetles (Tenebrionidae), which require very little moisture and have adapted their mode of life to desert conditions. They shelter from the burning heat of the day at the roots of plants or in some other protected, shady spot and come out only at night, when it is cooler and there may possibly be a dew. Such desert species are generally omnivorous, living on fragments of plant or animal waste, from which they obtain some of the necessary moisture.

Habitats which, from the beetle's point of view, are as extreme as a desert are also to be found in Europe. The species which develop in dry wood provide a good example; included here are members of a large number of families, in particular Anobiidae, Cerambycidae and Scolytidae. The woodworm, as the larva of the Furniture Beetle, *Anobium punctatum,* is known, goes through the whole of its development in completely dry wood with not a drop of water. The only reason it can survive and develop in such an environment is that it can produce water by breaking down the fat in its own body. Other species are able to live in dry wood by means of similar chemical processes.

Apart from food and water, beetles, of course, need air, particularly oxygen. This presents no difficulty for the majority of beetles and their larvae, since they are surrounded by air, which is taken up by their tracheal system through spiracles on the sides of their abdomen. Aquatic species have a greater problem. In adapting themselves to a new element (water) they have developed various ways of dealing with this in the course of their evolution.

The simplest solution for water beetles — and the one the majority have adopted — is to take their air supply with them. Predacious diving beetles carry air in the space between the upper surface of their abdomen and their elytra (in the subelytral cavity). Since the space is water-tight, air can be stored there with perfect safety. The disadvantage is that the air makes the beetle buoyant. To dive it has to take very powerful strokes and it therefore spends much of its time near the surface, clinging to plants. That is one of the reasons why these beetles chiefly inhabit water with abundant vegetation.

Water scavenger beetles (Hydrophilidae) have adopted a different technique. They carry air trapped between the hairs which clothe the under side of their body. Small beetles of other families also carry their air supply in a similar way.

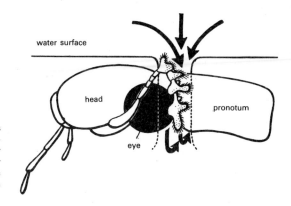

Fig. 9. How silver water beetles collect air. The antennae are constructed and used in such a way that air can pass via the hairy segments from the surface of the water to the reservoir under the beetle's body.

Used air contains hardly any oxygen, or none at all, so from time to time the air supply must be renewed. This is also done in a variety of ways. If we sit down beside a pond or a pool inhabited by predacious diving beetles we shall not have long to wait before they float to the surface. For a time they hang there head downwards, and then dive into deeper water again. While they are at the surface the old, used-up air under their elytra is replaced by new air rich in oxygen.

Some small water beetle species do not possess a subelytral cavity, but carry their air supply in the form of a small air bubble at the tip of their abdomen. This must likewise be replaced from time to time by the beetle hanging upside down at the surface.

Big water scavenger beetles change their air in a less conspicuous manner. They generally surface among a tangle of plants and are therefore virtually invisible. Unlike predacious diving beetles they surface head first and their antennae play an important role in the exchange of air, since they provide a means of channelling the atmospheric air to the air reservoir below the abdomen (Fig. 9).

Some water beetles have yet another way of obtaining air; this time it is not atmospheric air, but the oxygen given off by aquatic plants. The most striking examples are leaf beetles of the genera *Macroplea, Donacia* and *Plateumaris*. Adults of the two British *Macroplea* species live under water, while those of the roughly 20 species of the other two genera are to be found on plants growing in or beside water. The larvae of these beetles are extremely well adapted to underwater conditions. The eggs are laid under water where they are inserted into the tissues of aquatic plants. The larvae either feed from within the plant, obtaining their oxygen from the air channels of their host, or they feed externally, in which case they tap the plant's air supply by means of a hook-like structure at the tip of their abdomen. Most beetles which live in water pupate on land, but *Donacia* larvae are an exception. When pupating a *Donacia* larva ensures that the pupal cuticle retains a connection with the plant's air supply. On emerging, the young adult beetle crawls out of the water and takes up atmospheric air in the normal way.

Reproduction

Many species of beetle have a long larval period and it is not uncommon for it to last several years; adults have an extremely variable life span, some living for several years while others, such as the cockchafer, survive for no more than a few weeks. The main function of the adult stage is to reproduce, thus ensuring the survival of the species. To be able to fulfil this important biological task, both male and female beetles possess a number of morphological peculiarities. They also display much intricate, sometimes seemingly bizarre behaviour in connection with courtship and mating.

As in other insect groups a certain number of beetle species reproduce by parthenogenesis: individuals in populations consisting solely of females produce female offspring without their eggs being fertilized by males. However, most beetle species are bisexual, and the first step towards reproduction is naturally that males and females should locate each other. The ways in which this is achieved are many and varied and here we can give only a few brief descriptions as examples. In most cases the sense of smell probably plays an important role, since, using this faculty, a beetle can 'recognize' a potential partner from a considerable distance and so undertake an active search for it. Usually it is the male which 'scents' and tracks down the female. Insects' organs of smell are in general far superior to those of vertebrates; indeed, they are so sensitive that they are able to detect a single molecule of scent. The tips of a male cockchafer's antennae are covered with tens of thousands of small olfactory organs, all tightly packed together and enabling the cockchafer to 'scent' females from great distances.

Vision is often of only very minor significance or not used at all in the search for a partner. Where vision is employed to detect signals exchanged between the two sexes it is generally when potential mates are already at close quarters. In many cases there is no need for the use of attractants or long-range signals, because males and females automatically come together anyway, usually at a feeding site, and can find a mate by trial and error, as it were. For example, the metallic wood-borers of the genus *Anthaxia* have (like many other beetles) a special predilection for yellow flowers (some species obtain their food solely from such flowers). This not only makes matters much simpler for the beetle collector, but greatly increases the beetles' chances of finding a partner. If, in the small space of a flowerhead, a beetle is still unable to find a member of the same species and the opposite sex by smell or by vision, there is nothing left for it but to put matters directly to the test. For this reason, it is by no means uncommon, especially among beetles frequenting flowers, to see copulating couples of completely different genera. The male is usually the more active sex when it comes to seeking out a mate, but there are cases in which the female plays the leading role. A few years ago we observed a very interesting case of this kind.

The scarabaeid beetle *Hoplia coerulea* displays particularly marked sexual dimorphism. The male is bright sky blue from above and gleaming silver on the under side, while the less vividly coloured female has a brown back and a yellowish under side. The females are apparently very rare, however, and the ratio of this sex to males even in large collections is about 1 : 1,000. There is a biological explanation of this purely illusory bias towards the male sex. During the swarming period (June) the males sit in the warm sunshine on all kinds of plants, gripping them tightly with their fore- and hindlegs. The hindlegs are hooked and are particularly strong; like the rest of the body they are held fully extended, so that the beetle projects from the plant at an angle of 90 degrees. It can stay for hours in this unusual position, in which it may be detected from a great distance. The dull-looking female apparently spends most of its time in the soil, comming out only when ready to mate. It then climbs up a plant (we have observed females climbing sedges, grasses, tamarisks and thistles, etc.). If, on its upward journey, it encounters a male of the same species, the two pair immediately. Pairing lasts only a few (on an average 10−20) seconds, and immediately afterwards the female either drops to the ground or crawls down the plant and once more buries itself in the soil. If it reaches the top of the plant without meeting a potential mate, it drops to the ground and climbs another plant. There is no sign that the partners 'scent' each other and the accidental nature of encounters between the sexes is indicated by the behaviour of males when they happen to come together. At first they attempt to pair but when repeated efforts prove unsuccessful they engage in a kind of wrestling match, hooking their powerful hindlegs together and pushing each other about, until one of them finally gives up and the 'victor' returns to its typical waiting position.

Conflicts between individual beetles are not uncommon, and can assume the character of violent duels. They usually take place between members of the same sex (mostly males, but sometimes females). The mention of fighting automatically brings to mind stag beetles. The males are undoubtedly among the most impressive of our native beetles and their huge mandibles appear well suited for use as weapons. Appearances are deceptive, however, and these overgrown appendages are capable of only a gentle nip. The females, which have small mandibles, have a much more vicious bite. The males are attracted to sweet fermenting sap as it flows out of trees and feed on this until they fall from the tree, in an apparently drunken stupor. If several males arrive to feed at one site they may compete for the sap but this can scarcely be regarded as a battle. A stag beetle with holes in its elytra is far more likely to have been injured by a bird's beak than by a rival beetle. However, violent battles between members of the same species and sex take place in sexton beetles, about whose biology we shall have more to say later on. If several of these beetles settle on a cadaver, struggles ensue until one male and one female are left victorious, ensuring that reproduction is carried on by the strongest and fittest.

The most usual basis for a combat is the defence of territory. We observed behaviour of this type in males of the longhorn beetle *Acanthocinus aedilis,* which are to be found chiefly on pine tree stumps. They conceal themselves in cracks in the bark, with their feelers tucked in lengthwise, and are thus very hard to see, since they are similar in colour to the bark. Even their exceedingly long antennae, which in the male may be five times the length of the body, are difficult to make out since they are disruptively coloured, with alternating bands of light and dark. If there is a large *Acanthocinus* population in a given area, it is noticeable that the males are distributed fairly regularly over the tree stumps. One spring, in a freshly felled pine plantation in South Tyrol, we found one male specimen of *Acanthocinus aedilis* to every stump, the only exception being especially large stumps, on which there might be two or three. We were also able to observe how this distribution came about − through combats. Rivals stand face to face, with their antennae by their sides, each trying to force the other backwards by

23

pushing with its forehead, for all the world like little billy-goats. The loser abandons the field of battle and goes in search of another tree stump. There are several reasons why such duels are seldom seen. One is that the beetles are effectively camouflaged by their colouring. Secondly, their populations are rarely large enough to allow frequent encounters between two males, and thirdly, size differences (males range from 12−20 mm in length) are often so pronounced that many an encounter is virtually decided before it starts.

Pairing in beetles is sometimes of short duration, but may last for several hours. In some species the union is loose and the partners fall apart at the slightest disturbance, but in others it is so firm that the insects can hardly be separated without injuring them. During pairing sperm cells are transferred to the female's body, where the eggs are fertilized.

The eggs are sometimes laid soon after pairing, but in some cases there is a considerable delay. The sperm cells may be stored for some time in the female's body, in a special organ known as the spermatheca, before they actually reach the eggs.

The female rarely lays the fertilized eggs at random. Provision is generally made to ensure that larvae, once they are hatched, find themselves in suitable circumstances.

Parental care

The care of the brood is one of the most fascinating aspects of beetle biology. The steps nature has taken to minimise the loss of progeny are so varied and intricate that very few theoretical possibilities fail to have been realised. However, our knowledge of these mechanisms is all too incomplete and many exciting discoveries no doubt remain to be made.

The simplest way in which a female beetle can provide for its brood is to lay its eggs on the plants on which the larvae live. The Colorado Beetle lays its eggs on potato plants, Alder Leaf Beetle lays them on alders and the Poplar Leaf Beetle on poplars, i. e. on the plants they eat themselves. When the beetle frequents flowers and lives on pollen and nectar, but lays its eggs on other, specific plants, as many longhorn and leaf beetles do, we have a more complicated pattern of behaviour. The purpose of this kind of forward planning is to ensure that the larvae have food at their disposal as soon as they leave the egg. This is of the greatest importance, since in most cases the tiny newly hatched larva would be unable to find the right plant by itself.

Many species, rather than lay the eggs on the outside of a plant, insert them within plant tissues. For this the female has a special organ known as an ovipositor with which it can penetrate the plant (or any other substrate) to lay its eggs. Larvae living internally on the tissues of a plant are often involved in complex relationships with their host.

The poplar beetle *Saperda populnea* cares for its brood in a very striking and interesting manner (Fig. 10). In depositing each egg the female displays a complicated series of actions. First of all it makes a cut in the form of an upturned horseshoe in the bark of a small aspen branch, thereby cutting off the flow of sap at that particular spot, so that the bark becomes soft. The female accelerates decay by gnawing further cross-furrows inside the horseshoe. Lastly, it cuts a hollow in the bark at the bottom of the horseshoe and lays an egg in it. The tree reacts to this ill-treatment by producing a gall-like excrescence, on which the larva feeds. The first stage of this relationship is a race for time between the larva and the plant − and for the former it is a matter of life or death. The excrescence over the larva continues to grow and threatens to crush it to death, but the larva eats it as fast as it grows, so keeping a free space round itself. However, if there is a long spell of damp, chilly weather after the eggs have been laid or the larvae hatched, the swelling grows very quickly and the larva may then be unable to keep pace with it. The larva of *Saperda populnea* spends only the first part of its life inside the gall; later on it tunnels its way into the twig itself and feeds there. It later pupates inside the twig and when the adult emerges in due course it chews its way out into the open air. The whole of this developmental cycle takes two years. Examples of parental care such as these galls may escape the notice of an otherwise observant student of nature, but there are other instances which are likely to bring themselves directly to our attention. Not every hazelnut shell contains a perfect kernel; sometimes a shell is filled with crumbly brown mass. What is this mealy substance and

Fig. 10. *Saperda populnea* — brood care. Left: the female cuts a horseshoe incision in the bark. Middle: the completed cut. Right: the female laying an egg in the cavity.

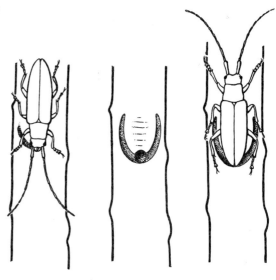

where does it come from? When the hazelnut is still green and soft and the kernel is just beginning to develop, the female of the species *Curculio nucum* comes along. This member of the Curculionidae (weevil family) has an extremely long 'snout' — an extension of the head with the mouth parts at the tip. With this the beetle drills a hole in the growing nut, disengages, turns round, feels for the hole with the tip of its abdomen and lays an egg in it. It then turns round once more and seals the hole with a drop of secretion from its mouth to prevent the egg from dropping out or falling prey to predators. When the larva hatches it begins to feed on the kernel, continuing until all of it has been consumed and only larval excrement is left behind. By the time the kernel has been eaten the larva is fully grown; it then bores its way out through the now hard nutshell, drops to the ground, buries itself in the soil and pupates.

Curculio glandium, a close relative of *Curculio nucum,* has a similar biology, but lays its eggs in young acorns, whose kernels are likewise eaten by the larvae. In the British Isles there are further species of the same genus whose larvae live in acorns and various galls.

Predacious diving beetles (Dytiscidae) also provide for their brood in a very interesting manner. With its sharp-edged ovipositor the female cuts a hole in the leaf of an aquatic plant (plants like *Sagittaria,* sweet flag, yellow flag, water plantain and pondweed, which have a high assimilation rate, are preferred) and then enlarges it until there is enough room for the unusually large egg (7 mm long in large *Dytiscus* species). The female *Dytiscus* takes 2–3 months to lay all of its 1,000 eggs in this way. The larvae do not eat plant tissue, however, but live predaciously in the water, so the only reason for the eggs being deposited in this way is to protect them and, more importantly, especially to provide them with oxygen. If the eggs are not inserted into plants they immediately sink to the bottom and go mouldy.

Instinctive behaviour of a complex nature is required from females which construct some kind of a shelter for the eggs before laying them. Those built by rove beetles of the genus *Bledius* are relatively simple. These beetles inhabit burrows in wet sand or mud where they live on algae. The female digs egg chambers off its burrow with the chambers lying one above the other at up to 6–7 levels. After the eggs have been laid the chambers are sealed off. In addition, to counter the danger of their being flooded out or at least made damp, each of the eggs is placed on a mud platform which projects obliquely into the chamber and prevents the egg from coming into contact with the floor. Many *Bledius* species provision larval burrows with food and it has been demonstrated that in one species the female lays its egg on a small mat of algae so that newly hatched larvae have a supply of food conveniently to hand.

Dung-eating Scarabaeidae care for their brood in a similar manner (Fig. 11). In the genus *Aphodius* parental care is of a simple type. Most of the 85 species living in central Europe live in the dung of various mammals, while a few live in rich garden soil or rotting vegetation. The female *Aphodius* lays its eggs directly in the substrate on which its developing larvae will feed. The essential feature of care for the new generation is a hunt for the right material, but there are indications that parental care extends further. After laying the eggs females survive to witness the hatching of the new generation and for some time afterwards remain in the dung together with the brood. The males, on the other hand, die soon after mating.

The dung-eating members of the genus *Onthophagus* exhibit a higher level of parental care. Mated pairs co-operate to build special burrows, of a characteristic pattern for each species. In the soil under a pile of dung they tunnel branched passages — usually a main passage with side-arms leading off it. Brood chambers are hollowed out in or at the end of these passages. The chambers are then provisioned with dung and an egg is laid in each. Most of the work entailed in construction of the burrow devolves on the female, while the male merely clears away the excavated earth and brings dung in. The burrow extends to a depth of 5−20 cm (small species do not burrow far into the ground; large species go deeper). The larvae take about 30 days to complete their development and then construct a cocoon of dung in which to pupate; the pupal period lasts about 14 days. Those dung beetles of the genus *Geotrupes* which feed mainly on the dung of herbivorous mammals make similar burrows. In the ground below the dung a mated pair of *Geotrupes* dig a tunnel, usually at a depth of 40−60 cm; this has 4−6 side-arms, each of which widens at the end into a chamber, in which an egg is laid. The beetles

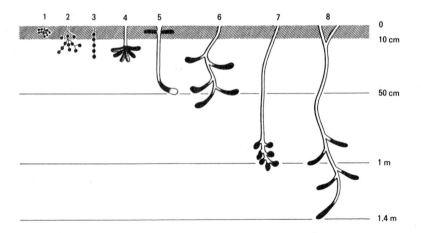

Fig. 11. Brood-burrow systems of dung-feeding scarabaeoid beetles. 1−3: *Onthophagus* species, 4−6: *Geotrupes* species, 7: *Lethrus apterus,* 8: *Typhaeus typhoeus.*

then drag dung down into the burrow and plug the chambers with it. As the growing larvae feed, their parents keep them regularly supplied with fresh dung, so that at the end there is always some left over, and there it remains until the young beetles of the new generation eventually emerge from the burrow. Since the larvae usually take 12−13 months to complete their development, the whole cycle takes two years. In addition to brood chambers, *Geotrupes* also build 'store-rooms'. These do not lie so deep as the brood chambers and they contain sufficient dung to keep the adults supplied with food for 4−5 days.

Among British dung beetles the deepest burrows are those of *Typhaeus typhoeus*. The pronotum of a male *Typhaeus* bears three forwardly projecting spines and cannot be mistaken for that of any other beetle. The species has a predilection for sandy heaths and open pinewoods, where it is sometimes fairly common. The burrow has a main passage with side-arms and lies at a depth of 1−1.5 metres. The brood chambers are provisioned with rabbit dung by preference, although sheep and red deer dung are also sometimes used. The female does not lay the eggs directly on the dung, as other dung beetles do, but some way away, in the soil, so that the larvae have to make an effort to reach their first meal.

Lethrus apterus, like some *Geotrupes* species, does not provision its brood burrows with dung. The female of this 'dung' beetle excavates tunnels with side-arms at a depth of almost half a metre and carries fresh leaves and shoots into them; here the plant matter ferments and it is on this that the larvae live. The adult beetles are very fond of vine shoots and can do considerable damage in vineyards.

For centuries man has been acquainted with the activities of scarab beetles. The manner in which they care for their brood was already known in ancient Egypt, but as the Egyptians were not aware of the purpose to which their dung-gathering activities were put they wove a myth round these insects. Today we know that their activities, although neither sacred nor mythical, are − from our point of view −extremely useful. Scarabs remove large quantities of dung and are thus very valuable scavengers. They bury dung to feed their brood but, unlike *Onthophagus* and *Geotrupes,* first transport it to a different spot. When their sense of smell leads them to a pile of dung, they take a portion and roll it into a ball with their powerful, shovel-like forelegs and their unusually long hindlegs. When the dung-ball is fully formed they begin to roll it away with their hindlegs, so that they appear to be retreating backwards. Nothing can stop them, although the ball is usually considerably (and often several times) heavier than the beetle itself. The female either follows the retreating male, face to face, or clings to the dung and takes a free ride. Scarab beetles have a wonderful sense of smell and can scent dung from long distances. As the male beetles push their supply of dung along they may be attacked by others, but while they are busy squabbling a third may come along and steal the dung from under their noses. If there are only two antagonists, the loser (usually it is the would-be thief) indicates its submission by lying quite still, while the victor continues on its way with the dung. Violent disputes can also occur between females. When the male has gone a given distance (usually several metres) with the ball of dung and accompanying female, it stops to examine the ground. If the soil is suitable (many examinations may be needed and in between the dung is rolled from one place to another), the work of burying the 'pill' begins. The dung, with the female on it, is set aside and the male digs a pit in the ground; it then crawls down inside it, turns round, and pushes the soil − which is usually sandy − away with its forehead as if it were working a bulldozer. This process is repeated until the ball of dung, together with the female, either rolls into the hole by itself or is pushed down into it by the male. The male beetle then continues to excavate the soil below the dung, pushing the earth aside, so that the ball sinks deeper and deeper until it finally disappears from sight. All this happens surprisingly quickly. Once the dung is safely underground, the female takes over. At first it constructs a brood chamber, where the dung is not merely buried, but is surrounded by a space. It then kneads the ball of dung so that it is pear-shaped and lays an egg in a small cavity at its tip; the larva lives on the dung until it pupates. Many species of the genus *Scarabaeus* are to be found in the countries bordering the Mediterranean, but there are none in central Europe. However, another dung-rolling species of a different genus − *Sisyphus schaefferi,* which measures 6.5−12 mm, has exceedingly long hindlegs and lives on chalky ground − does occur, albeit patchily, in the southern part of central Europe. *Gymnopleurus geoffroyi,* another dung-roller, is essentially a south European insect, but in the last century it was found several times in south-western Germany (in Baden-Württemberg, western Bavaria and the southern Rhineland). This species makes its 'pills' out of cow dung. Two other *Gymnopleurus* species — *mopsus* and *sturmi* — likewise occasionally venture into the south-western and south-eastern parts of central Europe, but none of these southern dung-rolling species are to be found in the British Isles.

A quite different and very interesting form of care is practised by the leaf-rolling weevils (Curculionidae).

The best-known and most widely distributed of these leaf-rollers is *Deporaus betulae,* which measures only 3—4 mm in length and is to be seen only in the spring (May), its breeding season. The leaf-rolls which it prepares before laying its eggs are more conspicuous than the actual beetle and may be spotted by any reasonably observant person. On birch trees we can often see large numbers of leaves that have been rolled up to form small funnels. Only the base of the leaf is left intact; the rest, curled up and wilting, droops from the midrib. These are the egg chambers of *Deporaus betulae.* Their construction requires a rather complicated pattern of behaviour on the part of the female weevil. Near the stalk of a birch leaf, and starting from the outer edge, it makes an upright S-shaped cut. It then incises the midrib and makes a similar cut in the other half of the leaf. The sides of the wilting leaf are folded over to form a funnel and the leaf-roll is 'stitched' together by the female with well-placed stabs from its snout. As it rolls the leaf up, the beetle makes tiny incisions in its wilting surface and in each of them it lays an egg. One roll may contain anything from 2 to 5 eggs. The female takes about one hour to complete the whole structure. The larvae live on the tissue of the wilting leaf, one birch leaf providing more than enough food for the (up to 5) larvae. Pupation takes place in the ground. Fig. 12 illustrates the way in which *Deporaus betulae* cuts and rolls the leaf. Similar leaf-rollers are to be found on beech, alder and hazel.

Deporaus tristis is a closely related species, but is much rarer in central Europe and not found in Britain. It is bluer in colour than *D. betulae* and confines its attentions to maples. It also cuts the leaves in a different manner. Just above the leaf-stalk it bites through a maple leaf from one edge to the midrib, severs the midrib and continues the cut to the middle of the other half of the leaf. In the upper surface of this half of the leaf, towards its apex, the female gnaws almost

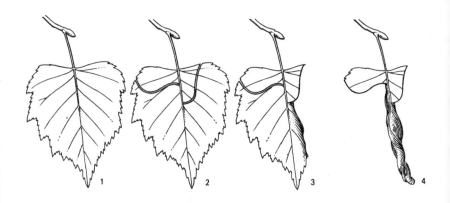

Fig. 12. How the weevil *Deporaus betulae* rolls a birch leaf to make a container for its eggs. 1 — intact leaf, 2 — cuts made by the beetle in the leaf, 3 — one half of the leaf almost rolled up, 4 — both halves rolled up, and the leaf-roll completed.

perfectly round holes in a series extending from the edge to the midrib. This perforated 'seam' marks the limit of the rolled part of the leaf. The roll is made fast with a secretion from the beetle's anus. Up to 4 eggs are deposited in each roll where they lie loose rather than in individual pockets.

Byctiscus betulae, another leaf-roller, is a pretty metallic green colour and measures 8−9 mm. Its rolls can be seen on various deciduous trees, but its favourite plants are grape-vines. The female does not incise the leaf itself to make it wither, but attacks the leaf-stalk. The withered leaf is rolled up cigar-wise and is stuck together with anal secretion; in it the female lays 4−6 eggs (though sometimes there may be as many as 15). *Byctiscus betulae* sometimes rolls up just one leaf, sometimes several together, although this does not seem to depend on the size of the leaves used. Apparently more are needed if the leaves are tough; in the case of a pliant vine leaf, for instance, a single one is sufficient. Although rare in Britain, this species is distributed over the whole of central Europe. Occasionally it occurs in abundance and in such years can do serious damage in vineyards, because if too many leaves are rolled up the bunches of grapes go dry at their base.

The above species all roll leaves up lengthwise, but there are also some which roll them crosswise. The best-known species of this type in central Europe is *Attelabus nitens.* The beetle is black, with bright red elytra, and measures 4−6 mm. It can be seen in the spring, on young oak leaves which have just unfolded. The female cuts across both sides of an oak leaf from the edges to the midrib, which it punctures, together with the veins, to cause the leaf to wither and make it more pliant. The two halves of the leaf are then brought together, so that the upper and under surface are in contact. The beetle then rolls up the leaf, working from the apex towards the base, tucking in the outer edges as it goes. To prevent the roll from coming undone, from time to time the beetle 'stitches' the two surfaces together with its snout, meanwhile laying 1−7 eggs in the roll. The larvae feed on the withered leaf-roll, which soon falls to the ground, and there the larvae spend the winter before pupating in the soil the following spring.

In connection with *Attelabus nitens* we must mention another species, whose care of its offspring, although unusual among beetles, has parallels among birds. It is well known that the Cuckoo neither makes a nest nor rears its own young, but delegates the task to foster-parents by laying its eggs in other birds' nests. A similar phenomenon is found in several insect groups, including beetles. The weevil *Rhynchites sericeus* looks for leaves rolled by *Attelabus nitens* and adds its eggs to the original contents. It can either do this while the other beetle is still at work, or later, after the roll has been completed, it punches a hole and lays its eggs through that. If we open a roll we can tell at once if it has been parasitized, since the parasite egg is white and is larger than that of the host. This is genuine brood parasitism and as a consequence this *Rhynchites* is known in Germany as the 'Cuckoo Weevil'.

Apoderus coryli is another species which rolls up the leaves crosswise. Like *Attelabus nitens* it has red elytra, but has black rather than red legs. It incises the leaves from one edge only, but continues the cut across the midrib, and rolls up the leaf from the tip. The development of this species is very rapid and there are two generations in a year. *Apoderus coryli* prefers hazel leaves, but also uses alder, beech, poplar and oak leaves.

Although leaf-rolling beetles (with a few exceptions) do only very minor damage to the plants on which their larvae feed, there are other weevils which do far more harm by laying their eggs in other parts of the plant (shoots, buds and blossoms), from which they cut off the sap supply.

One of the best-known of such species is the Apple Blossom Weevil (*Anthonomus pomorum*), measuring 3.5−4.5 mm. The adult beetles mostly spend the winter among dead leaves on the ground at the edge of woods, but in the spring (in March, as a rule) they seek out apple-trees. The female lays its eggs in young apple-blossom buds, one to a bud. The bud at first continues growing, but after hatching the larva feeds on the anthers, the stigma and the base (receptacle) of the flower. As a consequence, the petals do not develop fully, although they still provide the larva with shelter; they wilt and go brown, so that the bud resembles one affected by frost. However, such buds remain for some time on the tree, and although a fruit is not formed as a rule, if the larva leaves a sufficient part of the receptacle intact, it may still produce an apple. *Anthonomus pomorum* occasionally occurs in large numbers and can then devastate orchards; it attacks pear- as well as apple-trees.

Pear- and apple-trees are frequented by *Anthonomus cinctus,* a close relative of the preceding species, which lays its eggs in much younger buds from the end of September until December. The larvae eat out the interior of the buds, so that they never blossom, and a fruit tree extensively attacked by this species retains its bare winter appearance even in the spring.

Another *Anthonomus* species − *A. rubi* − is not uncommon in gardens. This small black species has a covering of grey scales and measures only 2−3 mm, but has a fairly long snout. In the spring, the female lays its eggs in the buds of various plants belonging to the family Rosaceae, particularly raspberries, blackberries and strawberries. The beetle further cares for its brood by making a cut in the stalk of the bud in which it has laid an egg. In due course the bud withers, the larva eating it away from inside, and soon drops to the ground. The larva pupates in the soil and the adult beetle emerges in June or July to survive until the following spring. If, under such plants, we find buds looking as though they had been cut off, we can be sure that *Anthonomus rubi* was responsible. Another species, *Anthonomus varians,* which has very distinctive red elytra, has specialized in conifers. The eggs are laid in the male flowers of pine-trees, where the larvae live on pollen and eventually pupate.

Many weevils of the genus *Rhynchites* provide for their brood in a similar manner. *Rhynchites cupreus* mainly attacks plums. When the green, unripe plums measure about 1−1.5 cm in diameter, the female weevil bores a deep hole in the flesh, lays an egg in it and then gnaws the fruit-stalk, so that the unripe plum falls from the tree. The larva lives on the decaying flesh and pupates in the ground. These weevil larvae should not be confused with the 'maggots' (which are actually caterpillars) found in ripe plums. *Rhynchites cupreus* also attacks other plum-like fruits such as cherries. Related species (*Rhynchites aequatus, auratus, bacchus*) have similar habits.

Rhynchites coeruleus attacks the young, green shoots of fruit trees, but otherwise works on the same principle as the other species. The female lays an egg near the tip of a young shoot and then gnaws the base of the shoot, which withers, snaps off and falls to the ground. The larva feeds on the fallen shoot and pupates in the soil.

Rhynchites interpunctatus also occurs on fruit trees. At the point where the leaf-stalk joins the leaf, the female of this species gnaws a hole in the midrib and lays its eggs (usually two to a leaf). *Rhynchites aeneovirens* lays its eggs in oak buds; these are partly cut through at the base so that they are unable to develop and an egg is laid in the part above the incision.

As we have seen, beetles which roll leaves and insert their eggs in buds provide the eggs and larvae with protection as well as food. Protective casings of other types are also constructed by beetles. We have already noted one example − the dung capsule in which leaf beetles of the genus *Clytra* wrap their eggs.

Water scavenger beetles (Hydrophilidae) and the related Hydraenidae have adopted a different manner of providing for their brood. Most of these beetles live in water, but need to protect their eggs from getting too wet. At the tip of its abdomen the female has special glands which secrete a substance which the vaginal palps weave into a kind of web. These beetles thus possess a spinning apparatus similar to that of spiders, but instead of being used for catching prey the spun threads are used for the protection of the offspring (incidentally, spiders also wrap their eggs in silk).

The simplest egg cocoon web is woven by small beetles of the family Hydraenidae and by the genera *Sphaeridium* and *Cercyon* (Hydrophilidae). The female constructs a loose silk covering for single eggs or groups of eggs, which offers little protection in itself, but fixes them to the substrate. A web is then spun round and round the eggs until they are completely encased in it. The species of the genus *Helophorus* (Hydrophilidae) spin bottle-shaped cocoons, the species of the genus *Laccobius* (Hydrophilidae) make round cocoons and the species of the genus *Enochrus* (likewise Hydrophilidae) construct bowl-shaped containers for their eggs.

This type of care of the brood is most highly developed in the largest silver water beetles, such as *Hydrophilus piceus,* measuring up to 5 cm in length. These beetles place their eggs on tiny rafts which float on the water surface. The base of each raft is composed of a single sheet of silk. The eggs are deposited singly in silken tubes lying on this platform which in turn are provided with a loosely woven cover; this ensures that the raft will not capsize. At one end of the raft the female constructs a long funnel, which probably ensures a supply of air if the raft should become wedged among vegetation and partly submerged (Fig. 13).

Those cases in which the eggs are laid under conditions involving some provision for the

Fig. 13. Floating 'egg cocoon' of the Great Silver
Water Beetle (*Hydrophilus piceus*).

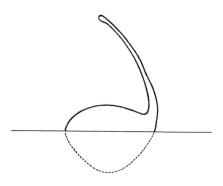

larvae qualify as instances of parental care, even though the parents do not tend their offspring themselves and, in fact, never even see them. There are, however, cases in which the parents play an active part in looking after both the eggs and the larvae, so that a direct parent-offspring relationship exists.

In the simplest cases the female (or the male) carries the eggs around with it, ensuring a greater degree of protection than if the eggs were merely deposited somewhere and left to the mercy of predators. *Helochares lividus*, a water scavenger beetle measuring 4–6 mm, is to be found in ponds and ditches in most parts of Britain, as well as in a number of European countries. Before laying its eggs the female covers the under side of its abdomen with a silken web. The eggs are arranged on this in a definite pattern and finally are covered with another layer of woven silk. They are then carried about on the under side of the female's abdomen in this bag until the larvae hatch.

Spercheus emarginatus lives in stagnant water rich in nutrients; it is rare in central Europe and possibly extinct in Britain. Since their larvae differ markedly in structure from those of other Hydrophilidae, the genus *Spercheus* is sometimes placed in a separate family, Spercheidae. The female cares for the brood in much the same way as *Helochares lividus*. In a cocoon attached to the under side of its abdomen it carries some 60 eggs about with it until the larvae are hatched. In situations of possible danger the female can clearly be seen to force the bag upwards with its femora until it is covered (and hence protected) by the elytra.

The Horned Dung Beetle (*Copris lunaris*), which measures 16–24 mm in length, practises a different kind of care. This beetle was once widely distributed in southern England as well as throughout central Europe, but is now generally rare except in the southern part of its range. The male and female beetles co-operate to excavate brood chambers immediately under a pat of dung (usually of cattle) and provision these with the dung. This is kneaded into pear-shaped 'cakes' until there are seven or eight (occasionally more) to a chamber, each cake with an egg lying in a depression at its tip. Although it plays no further part in providing food for the larvae, the female remains in the brood chambers until the new generation emerges, when it leaves with the young beetles.

Wood-inhabiting beetles such as bark beetles of the family Scolytidae also provide well for their brood. The Lineate Bark Beetle (*Xyloterus lineatus*), measuring 3–4 mm in length, may serve as an example. Although rare in Britain, this species occurs all over central Europe, sometimes in large numbers, living in the wood of conifers. The female gnaws two brood passages leading in opposite directions, 5–6 cm deep into the wood, and lays the eggs in niches on either side. From each side of the maternal passages the larvae make their own tunnels. They do not live on the wood itself, however, but on an ambrosia fungus grown in the passages by the female. The female carries the spores in its gut, but they are not digested there, even

31

when the beetle goes without food for months. The association between fungus and beetle is so close that the spores are evidently not able to germinate unless they have been in the beetle's alimentary tract. The female transfers some of the spores to the walls of the passages, which are soon coated with the fungus. To prevent these 'mushroom beds' from being overrun by other fungi, yeasts and bacteria, the female beetle keeps them regularly 'weeded' and also keeps the passages clear of larval excrement and powdered wood. On the other hand, it keeps some tunnels blocked, so regulating the humidity levels in the system as a whole. Although the female *Xyloterus* does not care for the brood directly, these efforts ensure that its larvae have a healthy environment and a good food supply. The importance of the female beetle's work is revealed when it is unable to perform its normal house-keeping functions; in such a situation the 'mushroom beds' are soon overrun by bacteria, yeasts and other fungi and the larvae starve to death.

The many such fungus-growing bark beetle species live mainly in conifers, but some attack deciduous trees, such as oaks, beeches and birches. The method by which they provide for their offspring is in principle always the same, although the way various tasks are divided between the sexes varies considerably. Like the males of most species, those of the Lineate Bark Beetle play almost no part in the care of the brood, but in some species the male helps to keep the passages clear of dung and unwanted fragments of wood.

Burying (or sexton) beetles practise a particularly advanced form of brood care. In the case of most beetles the sexes live separately, except during the short mating season, but there are a few species or groups of species where the partners remain together for an extended period in a kind of seasonal 'marriage'. This is the case with the completely black or black- and orange-patterned burying beetles belonging to the genus *Nicrophorus*. They are normally little seen, but are relatively easy to catch with bait. If we partly bury a tin containing a dead animal (mouse or small bird), or even a piece of meat, at the edge of a wood, leave it there uncovered and return again in two or three days, we are quite likely to find that some burying beetles have been trapped. These beetles fly by night, looking for carrion which, as they have an excellent sense of smell, they can probably detect from a considerable distance. Large numbers of burying beetles may collect round a single dead animal in the course of a night. They immediately begin to scrape away the soil from under the corpse, which in time gradually sinks into the ground. If there are several beetles working together, conflicts arise, eventually leaving only one couple in possession to complete the interment. Meanwhile the corpse has been neatly rolled up into a kind of ball, which in 3−10 hours is safely hidden away in a grave 5−10 cm below the surface of the soil. When this work has been completed, the pair of beetles mate, after which the male is driven away. The female excavates a short passage leading out from the side of the grave and lays a dozen or more eggs there. In the five days before the larvae hatch, the female does not remain idle. It gnaws a hole in the surface of the cadaver, filling this with a substance secreted by its own alimentary tract. As these digestive juices gradually dissolve the corpse, the hole widens like a crater. On the fifth day after the eggs have been laid the female adopts a new pattern of behaviour. Making a squeaking sound, it runs round and round the carrion, tempting the newly hatched larvae to come and feed. The larvae respond to the female's call, finding their way to the ball of carrion where they collect in the crater. As they gather round the female, they are fed by it, in the manner of a mother bird with nestlings, drops of liquid food being passed from mouth to mouth. Such feeding by the mother occurs only during the first hours after hatching and, once again, immediately after the first moult. Otherwise the larvae are able to fend for themselves. Boring their way into the carrion, they develop extraordinarily quickly, and are full-grown at seven days when they retire into the soil to pupate. Throughout this period (i. e. up to the time that the larvae pupate), the female remains with the buried corpse and defends its brood against all intruders such as carrion-eating or predacious insects. If the brood chamber is damaged, the female immediately repairs it. There is thus a direct mother-offspring relationship among sexton beetles (a very rare phenomenon among non-social insects) and the care of the brood ceases only when the larvae pupate.

Disguise and defence

Beetles have developed many ways of protecting their brood, the general rule being: the better the protection for the offspring, the smaller the number of eggs required. Where the beetles do not look after their brood they may need to lay a large number of eggs to compensate for losses and ensure the survival of the species. But what about the beetles themselves? Have they any protection against predators? Although adult beetles may be short-lived they need to survive long enough to achieve the essential task of reproduction. In some cases mating takes place very soon after emergence from the pupa. The male may die immediately after pairing and the female after laying the eggs. However, if a species overwinters in the imago stage the adults are likely to live for several months. Some beetles live for several years and reproduce several times.

Beetles have developed the most diverse forms of defence, some passive, some active, irrespective of how long they live. A simple form of protection is what is known as cryptic coloration. For example, many leaf beetles (Chrysomelidae) and weevils (Curculionidae) are green and are therefore difficult to detect on vegetation. The most extreme examples in this respect are the tortoise beetles (Cassidinae), which are not only often green, but also have an unusually flat body. Their pronotum and elytra together form a tortoise-like carapace. Their larvae are also unusual, in that they live openly on the plant, like the beetle itself. The body of the larva bristles with spines and at the tip of the abdomen there are two long processes which

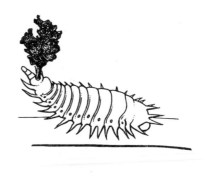

Fig. 14. Tortoise beetle (*Cassida*) larva. Left: larva with faecal shield, right: side view showing recurved tip of abdomen and faecal shield held well over the larva's back.

33

can be recurved over the back. The larvae impale their excrement on these processes and hold them over their body like an umbrella. The 'umbrella' would seem to be intended as protection, partly against the sun (the larvae are very delicately built) and partly against predators, which may be deterred by the coating of dung (Fig. 14). However, certain observations place some doubt on the role of faecal masks in providing protection. Those larvae which live in the shade appear to have particularly large masks and the masks tend to be shed at a time when the larvae are especially vulnerable to predators (prior to pupation).

The whole question of camouflage remains open to debate. It may be noted that many of a beetle's enemies (particularly parasites) locate their victims not by sight, but by smell, in which case visual disguise will provide no protection.

Coloration may also be involved in advertisement rather than concealment. Among longhorn beetles there are many species resembling wasps – some because their membranous wings lie uncovered on their abdomen and others because of their striking black and yellow markings. The beetles thus evidently imitate wasps – a phenomenon which comes under the heading of mimicry. Those who stress the biological significance of mimicry claim that genuine Hymenoptera are largely avoided by birds and other predators and that the appearance of their harmless imitators gives these the same protection. Sceptics, on the other hand, rightly point out that even wasps are not infrequently caught and eaten by birds.

Now let us take a look at another curiosity, that of warning coloration. Here again, the principle is that the animal does not wish to disguise itself, but to make itself conspicuous. Animals which do this are mostly poisonous or at least unpalatable to potential predators. Let us cite an example from among the vertebrates. Among amphibians we have a Yellow-bellied Toad and a Fire-bellied Toad, whose skin, in both cases, contains poison glands. If the toads feel themselves to be in danger they turn the brilliant yellow-and-black (or red-and-black) parts of their body towards the enemy, as if to say: 'Beware! I am poisonous!'. And this same yellow-and-black or red-and-black colouring recurs time and time again among insects, usually in evil-tasting species (Burnet moths) or species containing poison (Colorado Beetles). One predator's poison may still be another's meat, however; for instance, pheasants adore Colorado Beetles.

If the real biological significance of features which seem to perform a defensive function were as easy to establish as it may appear, differences of opinion would have been cleared up long ago. It may be that small advantages afforded by camouflage, mimicry or warning colouring in the past have been sufficient to promote the development of such phenomena in the course of the ages.

Similar problems arise when we come to the beetles' possibilities of active defence. As an example, let us take the large ground beetles of the genus *Carabus,* which are known to most nature lovers. When picking up these beetles one must beware of their powerful mandibles, since they defend themselves most vigorously and sometimes even puncture human skin. In addition, they are able to squirt their digestive juices at an enemy; the fluid is highly corrosive and care should be taken not to get any in the eyes. That is not all, however. Carabid beetles often possess pygidial glands secreting a musky substance. If a *Carabus* is held in the hand for only a short time, it may be hours before we can get rid of the smell. From the human point of view one is bound to admit that such species are particularly well protected against their foes, since they bite and squirt and stink into the bargain. What is (for us) surprising, however, is that *Carabus* beetles are an important component of the diets of birds of prey and owls – more important than other large beetles (e. g. dung beetles) which would appear to be less well protected. This has been demonstrated by examining birds' crop contents. Furthermore, foxes, hedgehogs and toads are very fond of these beetles.

Among the ground beetles there is a small group which practises a most unusual form of defence, known as crepitation. These are the bombardier beetles. In central Europe, the species *Brachinus crepitans* and *explodens* occur on chalky ground; the former is also to be found in southern England. A larger bombardier beetle – *Aptinus bombardius* – occurs in the southeastern parts of central Europe. At their anal orifice, these beetles have an intricately constructed paired apparatus which, when they are disturbed, receives a volatile substance from special glands and ejects it under high pressure. On contact with the air (i. e. with oxygen) the substance explodes with a distinct cracking sound and a puff of smoke smelling of nitrous acid.

Poisonous or distasteful secretions are by no means rare among beetles. We have all held a ladybird in our hand at one time or another. If we let it run about on our hand, nothing happens, but if we hold it in our closed fist we are soon reminded of its presence by the appearance of a sticky yellow fluid with a disagreeable smell. Good powers of observation are needed to find out how this fluid is produced. In fact, it is their blood and when they are disturbed this is squeezed by a reflex through small pores in the membranes between the femur and the tibia, i. e. in the knee. The drops of blood are very large compared with the size of the beetle and a ladybird can 'bleed' only a few times in succession, while the protection which this 'bleeding' and the subsequent feigning of death are supposed to afford is very dubious. Apart from their many parasites, ladybirds are eaten by a whole series of other animals, many of which are very partial to them. Their enemies include blackbirds, cuckoos, garden warblers, sparrows, frogs and toads and other insects such as tiger beetles, carrion beetles, soldier beetles, dragon-flies, assassin bugs and robber-flies. However, there are no doubt many other animals which do not like the taste of ladybirds and avoid them — to the benefit of these beetles and their survival.

Ladybirds are not the only creatures which expel blood in this way and it has long been known that the habit is shared by oil beetles of the genus *Meloe* (family Meloidae). The blood of oil beetles is very rich in cantharidin, and the occurrence of this substance has also been demonstrated in other beetle families. For many animals it is a deadly poison (for a human being as little as 0.03 g is a lethal dose). On the other hand, hedgehogs, bats and many birds, such as chickens, ducks, turkeys and swallows, are known not only to tolerate cantharidin, but even to have a predilection for beetles containing it.

The bright green Spanish Fly (*Lytta vesicatoria*) is not in fact a fly but, like the oil beetles, is a member of the family Meloidae and also contains a large amount of cantharidin. It lives mainly in the Mediterranean region, but is to be found sporadically, sometimes in large numbers, further north, occasionally as far north as England. In central Europe, it was much commoner in the last century than it is today; for instance, in a newspaper printed in 1870 we can read that Spanish Flies were then sold by the pound in the weekly market in Stuttgart. In the Middle Ages dried and powdered Spanish Fly was widely used as an aphrodisiac. In even earlier times physicians such as Hippocrates and Galen made frequent use of cantharidin, since in small amounts and at low concentrations it may well have been of some use in the treatment of certain diseases. Today it is still used — though on only a small scale — in the preparation of blistering plasters. Attempts to produce it synthetically seem so far to have failed.

Production of sounds and light

If we think of sound production in insects, grasshoppers, whose chirping fills meadows and fields in the summer and autumn, or field and house crickets, are likely to be the first examples to come to mind. Those who have visited Mediterranean countries will no doubt also recall the shrill chirping of the cicadas on the pines. Many beetles also produce sounds but, as these are by no means loud, the fact is not widely appreciated. However, in most cases, beetle sounds, like those of grasshoppers and crickets, are made by stridulation, i. e. by rubbing hard cuticular structures together.

Stridulation achieved by rubbing the posterior edge of the pronotum against the anterior part of the hind-body is quite common in beetles and characteristic of a fairly large group of leaf beetles. As the pronotum is moved up and down, areas of cuticle which bear fine ridges are rubbed together. The resultant sounds are clearly audible, especially if we pick the insects up in our fingers and hold them to our ear. Smaller species naturally make less noise than large ones. The same type of sound production (using the posterior margin of the pronotum) is also common among longhorn beetles, which chirp primarily when they are excited — and if they are held in a human hand they get very excited indeed.

Other species move the anterior part of their abdomen up and down, causing friction against ridges on the edge of the elytra; they include the dor beetles (dung beetles of the genus *Geotrupes*). Beetles may also have sound-producing organs on many other parts of their body — between the vertex of the head and the leading edge of the pronotum (ground beetles, darkling beetles, leaf beetles), between the throat and prothorax (Nosodendridae, Anobiidae, darkling beetles, bark beetles) and between the posterior part of the abdomen and the elytra (Curculionidae, etc.); the legs (chiefly the femur and the coxa) and the elytra can also be rubbed against various parts of the body to produce sounds.

There is one group of beetles with a curious and unusual way of producing sounds. The Death-watch Beetle, *Xestobium rufovillosum,* a member of the family Anobiidae, lives in dry wood, furniture and buildings, etc. The male and the female remain in their dark, labyrinthine passages, deep down in the wood, until it is time to pair. To be able to find each other they have evolved an unusual type of 'mating call'. They tap their head and pronotum on the walls of their tunnels, employing a series of single beats in fairly rapid succession. The tone and the strength of the sound depend on the acoustic properties of the wood but to the human ear it often resembles the ticking of a clock.

Light production (or bioluminescence) is known in diverse animal groups, from the unicellular to the highly developed. In the glowworms (Lampyridae), only a few species of which are known in central Europe, and only one is at all frequently seen in Britain, it is particularly impressive. Many of us will have seen the tiny flashes made by the flying beetles, or their intense glow in the grass on a warm summer's evening. The flying beetles are the males, which 'switch' their 'lamp' on and off according to a specific rhythm. Study of some of the many species of Lampyridae which are to be found in the tropics has revealed that each species has its own characteristic signal. Females of the common European glowworm are unable to fly and lack both wings and elytra. They crouch glowing in the grass, signalling to the males that they are waiting for a partner. The light-producing organs are situated on the ventral surface of the last abdominal segment. The light-producing layer, which is composed of light-coloured cells, lies on the surface with a layer of dark cells beneath acting as a reflector. The light produced is a truly cold light, unlike most forms of illumination created by man, which give out a good deal of heat and only a small percentage of light. The luminescence of glowworms consumes very little energy, is composed of almost 100 % light and produces no heat. It involves a chemical reaction with a luminescent substance like luciferin or pyrophorin being activated by a catalyst, such as luciferase. The reaction also requires the presence of oxygen, and this is probably controlled through excitation of the nervous system. The secret of the beetles' luminescence is yet to be elucidated in full, although the organs of dead beetles can be made to glow again. However, the biological significance of the luminescence seems to be unequivocal. The flying male sees the female's signal and is guided by it to its partner. This explanation is supported by the fact that the luminescent females turn up the tip of their abdomen to reveal the light organs on the under side and make it easier for the males to find them. Why do the males also glow, then? And the pupa, and the larvae, and even the eggs? Some indication of the answer may be found in the finding that the females glow especially intensely after pairing, so that the degree of luminscence seems to reflect the beetle's level of excitation. At first it probably had no biological significance (and in the case of the eggs, the pupae, the larvae and the males it may still have none), but once light production had been 'invented' and become genetically fixed, it was roped into service (at least in the females) on behalf of reproduction.

Beetles and man

Relationships between insects and man are often direct, sometimes painfully so. Take, for example, wasps and bees, or the gnats and other biting flies which so often ruin a pleasant walk on a balmy summer evening. There are also the various parasites which have devoted themselves entirely to man, e.g. head and body lice, human fleas and bed-bugs. Even tiny thrips can cause the skin to itch unpleasantly. There are few such direct relationships between man and beetles, at least in temperate countries, unless we count the occasions when a minute rove beetle or some other species gets into our eye.

However, beetles affect man indirectly in a myriad ways. There have been beetles on our planet for over 200 million years and they have established themselves virtually everywhere, in every kind of ecosystem. Seeing that it is only a few million years since man took possession of the Earth, it is not surprising that his 'spheres of interest' overlap those of beetles at many points. Beetles were here long before man, but man, from his egocentric standpoint, regards any of them with which he has come to compete for resources as 'pests'. Many species to be found in the house and garden, or in the fields and woods, are so designated. Since these are species that we are particularly likely to come up against, we should like to discuss in some detail the life history of a few of the more important. We hope the reader will think not only of the damage which (from his point of view) these beetles do, but will also appreciate the wonders of adaptation to special ways of life that the various species represent.

Indoor pests

There are a number of beetle species which may be found going about their secret business in our houses. A particularly troublesome co-tenant is the House Longhorn (*Hylotrupes bajulus*), which in central and northern Europe is rarely to be seen out-of-doors, but often frequents the woodwork of our houses. With its telescopic ovipositor stretched full-length, the female lays about 120 eggs in cracks in processed pine or other soft wood, which the larvae later burrow into. On the surface they leave a paper-thin layer intact, so that outwardly there is no trace of their activities. They eat only the sap-wood and do not touch the heart-wood, the reason being that they need the minute traces of protein present in the former. The protein is their sole nourishment and is necessary for growth as well as providing them with energy. They are unable to digest the woody matter (lignin) themselves and in their alimentary tract there are no fungi or bacteria to do it for them, as is the case with many other insects. The duration of their development varies and depends chiefly on the age of the wood. Under favourable conditions it takes only 3 or 4 years, but in older wood with a very low protein content it may take 6, 10, 15 years or even longer. If protein intake is only just sufficient to cover energy requirements, the larva continues to feed, but without growing, and if the amount of protein falls below this level it dies. In a large-scale attack the rafters of a house can be eaten away to a depth of several centimetres, leaving only the thin surface layer untouched. If we press such a spot with a pencil, the pencil sinks deep into the powdered wood. The strength of the rafters is naturally affected, the extent of the damage depending on the degree to which they have been eaten. The larvae pupate in the wood and when the beetles emerge they bite their way out through oval holes measuring about 3×5 mm. Fortunately, although a serious pest in parts of Surrey, the House Longhorn is generally of very restricted occurrence in Britain. However, in areas where the species is well established a householder needs to exercise considerable vigilance. We should not wait until we see the beetles or their exit holes, but should examine the rafters at regular intervals. We can do this either by tapping the woodwork or by putting our ear to the wood and listening, keeping very still. If a rafter has been attacked, we may hear the larvae gnawing away at the wood. Recently, there has been a large increase in the incidence of this beetle in central Europe, for which man himself is mainly to blame. At one time all timber used for the construction of roofs consisted of heart-wood, but today sap-wood is also used — a change which has made things easier for the House Longhorn. Not infrequently the House Longhorn disappears as suddenly as it came, since even this beetle has other enemies (e.g. parasitic ichneumon wasps) as well as man.

In an attic, or a wood-panelled room, we may occasionally encounter other longhorn beetles, such as the shining blue *Callidium violaceum* or the variably coloured *Phymatodes testaceus*. *Callidium violaceum* attacks dry wood of both conifers and deciduous trees. The females lay their eggs in old, dead wood in the open, but if this wood is then processed, this will not prevent the emergence of adult beetles in due course. If we come across this beetle in our house, there is no need for alarm, since the females hardly ever lay their eggs in worked timber as the House Longhorn does, and the same applies to *Phymatodes testaceus*. The larva of the latter species develops only beneath the bark of various deciduous trees (chiefly oaks), but before pupating it bores a curved passage 3—6 cm deep into the wood. If the timber is meanwhile processed, the beetle may emerge from the newly finished product the following spring. It is thus implicit in their biology that *Callidium* and *Phymatodes* can emerge only from newly processed wood and apart from their pupation holes the damage they do is not very serious, because the next generation does not lay its eggs in wood which has already been worked. Neither species is of common occurrence in Britain.

Warehouses and flour-mills, and any part of the home where grain or flour is stored, house another important pest species. The Grain Weevil (*Sitophilus granarius*), a member of the weevil (Curculionidae) family, measures only 3—4 mm and is unable to fly. However, although it originally came from the east, today it is truly cosmopolitan in distribution. The female bores a hole in a grain of corn, lays an egg there and then removes almost all traces of its activities by sealing the hole with a secretory substance. The larva devours the contents of the grain, the husk being left intact until the adult beetle eventually bites its way out. Two beetles can develop in a single grain of wheat or rye, which are the preferred cereals. Barley and maize are also eaten, but oats are attacked only if they have been de-husked, as the awns are too hard for the beetles to bite through. These long-lived beetles also attack flour and flour products, such as noodles and macaroni. The female Grain Weevil lays an average of 150 eggs. The only thing which can hold up the development is cold weather and since there are normally 3 or 4 generations in a year, a single female, under ideal conditions, could produce over 5 million progeny by the third generation. Grain Weevils can thus proliferate very easily and very quickly. Considerable damage may result from their activities. Economic losses stem not only from the loss of grain actually eaten, but also from inhibition of germination in seed-corn. A severe attack also leads to increased humidity, which in turn promotes the growth of moulds and bacteria, so that the grain becomes swollen, over-heated and begins to ferment.

The closely related *Sitophilus oryzae,* the Rice Weevil, principally attacks rice, but also feeds on noodles and similar products. Its biology resembles that of the Grain Weevil, but, unlike that species, it is able to fly and can therefore attack rice growing in the fields. It requires a great deal of warmth, however, and in temperate countries its development is slow, the generations are therefore much further apart, and the danger of a serious infestation is correspondingly smaller. The only place where it can be a real danger is in warehouses. In the warmer parts of the world it is one of the most serious pests of stored products, attacking maize, many other types of cereal, chickpeas and cottonseed. The beetle itself has an even wider dietary range and will nibble fruit (e.g. peaches, grapes, apples), edible chestnuts and processed tobacco.

Two main groups of pests are of significance in the living-rooms and bedrooms of a house. One group attacks wood and the other fabrics (carpets, furs, and all kinds of textiles). In the section on sound production we briefly made the acquaintance of the Death-watch Beetle, a representative of the family Anobiidae. Anobiid beetles bore holes in old wood and we are all familiar with the round holes they make, or the powdered wood which dribbles out of them. The commonest and most widely distributed of these species is the Furniture Beetle (*Anobium punctatum*), which bores holes in all kinds of timber (from both coniferous and deciduous trees) and attacks furniture, wooden works of art, or virtually anything made of wood. Like many other members of the family, the Furniture Beetle taps the wood with its head to attract a potential mate, but the sounds are not audible to the human ear. The Furniture Beetle's other name, Woodworm, is apt, since the larva riddles the wood on which it feeds with holes. This species is not confined to houses, however, but is also to be found in dry conifer and hardwood timber (including ivy) in the open (Fig. 15).

In addition to the Furniture Beetle (Woodworm), houses can be invaded by a whole series of beetles from the same family. *Ernobius mollis* is found in building timber with the bark still on it and occasionally attacks furniture. *Oligomerus ptilinoides* is to be found chiefly in southern, southwestern and western Europe, where it is known in building timber and furniture; it has also been reported in the southern part of central Europe, but may be only an accidental guest there. *Anobium rufipes* is closely related to the Furniture Beetle and occurs all over central Europe, but is much rarer than its cousin: it was formerly also regarded as a furniture pest. *Anobium pertinax,* the third species of this genus, is found throughout the whole of central Europe; it occurs mostly in the open, but is occasionally found in houses, and while it prefers timber from coniferous trees it will sometimes make do with hardwoods. This beetle apparently used to be commoner than it is today. *Priobium carpini* is also known to feed on processed wood in central Europe, but cannot be described as a common species. *Ptilinus pectinicornis,* a species in which the male has long pectinate antennae, occurs from May to July in hardwoods, especially beech. It has recently displayed a tendency to attack processed wood,

Fig. 15. Damage to wood from the foot of a cupboard by the Woodworm, the larva of the furniture beetle *Anobium punctatum*.

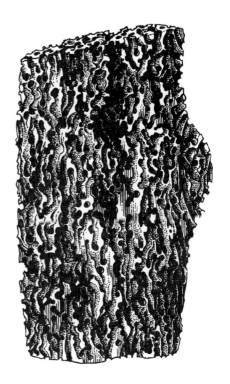

in which, together with the Woodworm, it can do serious damage. The related species *Ptilinus fuscus* has similar habits. Of these various anobiid beetles only *Ernobius mollis* and *Ptilinus pectinicornis* are found in Britain. We have noted a number of Anobiidae which may be found in dwellings, but the majority of the members of this wood-boring family live in the open and even those which also occur indoors are often much more prevalent in the wild. In natural circumstances they are often responsible for initiating the recycling of dead wood. Not only do they eat a large amount of it themselves, but they also make it available to other organisms such as fungi and bacteria, accelerate its decomposition and are thus of some importance in the economy of nature. However, if in accordance with their natural habits they venture to attack what human beings consider to be their own valuable property, the are swiftly condemned.

There is another small longhorn beetle whose larvae bore in wood and which may make an appearance in the house. The larvae of *Gracilia minuta* tunnel in the wood of various plants such as oaks, beeches, spindle-trees, hawthorns and rose- and blackberry-bushes, where they first of all live beneath the bark of small branches and twigs and then burrow more deeply in the wood. This species lives chiefly in the Mediterranean region and further north is seldom found in the open. However, since it attacks osiers it is frequently imported in wicker-work articles. A report from Holland dated 1932 tells how 12,000 wicker baskets had to be destroyed there because of the damage caused by this beetle. Also, particularly in France, it is known to attack wine cask hoops made of sweet chestnut wood.

It is not exactly comforting to know that we share our homes with insects which eat our rafters, furniture and other woodwork, even if woodworm holes are considered to be an intrinsic part of old wooden carvings. But who is going to wear a valuable fur coat full of holes, who would wish to leave a carpet with holes in it on their floor, or wear an insect-damaged woollen dress or jacket? The best-known miscreant in this respect is naturally the clothes-moth, whose caterpillars devour woollen fabrics and furs. However, there are also a number of beetles which feed on materials of animal origin. One of them is *Attagenus pellio,* a not uncommon member of the carpet beetle (Dermestidae) family, which measures 4−5 mm and has a white streak in the middle of each elytron. The beetle is to be seen in the open from March to May on various flowers, on whitethorn, blackthorn, fruit trees and garden shrubs, eating pollen. Adult beetles which have emerged from pupation in the house can be seen at this time striving to get out of the windows so that they can obtain a meal of pollen. In this state the beetles exhibit positive phototaxis, that is to say, they fly towards light. Conversely, the fertilized females become negatively phototactic and look for some dark retreat, so that they are liable to fly into the house through open windows. They also retire to hollow trees and other dark places, such as the nests of birds where the larvae live on feathers, hair and other material containing keratin. These were, in general, the original habitats of what are now synanthropic species, i. e. species living in the company of man. In the house, *Attagenus pellio* deposits its eggs on furs, woollen goods, carpets and other textiles. The yellow larvae are very agile and can easily be identified by the tuft of long hairs at the tip of their abdomen. *Attagenus piceus,* a close relative of the above species, has no white streaks on its elytra: it has similar habits, but exhibits a greater tendency to attack flour and other vegetable material.

Both out-of-doors on flowers and indoors we can find together with *Attagenus pellio* a small, round, rather brightly coloured beetle measuring 3−4.5 mm belonging to the same family (Dermestidae). This is *Anthrenus scrophulariae,* one of the carpet beetles, whose name tells us where it, or its larva, is most likely to be found. It has a similar way of life to *Attagenus pellio,* but two ecological variants seem to have evolved − an outdoor race which lives in birds' nests, and never comes indoors, and an indoor variant, which never leaves the house. The two have

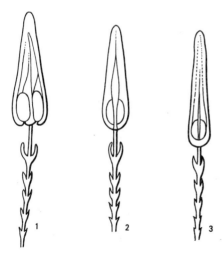

Fig. 16. Barbed hairs of *Anthrenus* larvae. 1 − *Anthrenus museorum,* 2 − *Anthrenus verbasci,* 3 − *Anthrenus fuscus.*

apparently already developed different colouring, the outdoor insects being light yellow in colour along the elytral suture, whereas the indoor variant is red. *Anthrenus* larvae have one curious feature. Among their normal body hairs are barbed hairs (Fig. 16), often growing in tufts, which can be pointed in all directions and spread out fan-wise. If a larva is attacked by a predator, batteries of these hairs are directed towards it: if the predator bites, it finds its mouth parts full of barbed hairs, as these break off easily, and before it can get rid of them the agile larva has had time to make itself scarce.

Anthrenus verbasci, the commonest species of this genus, is somewhat smaller and less brightly coloured. It has similar habits to *A. scrophulariae,* but the larvae are especially fond of dead insects as food. Outdoors the beetles are frequently to be found on flowers, eating pollen. The larvae mostly wander from place to place, since the remains of dead insects are to be found everywhere, but are particularly abundant in birds' nests. As well as feeding on carpets and woollen goods indoors the larvae can cause great damage to insect collections. Almost every amateur entomologist has had experience of these pests which, if left to their own devices, can completely destroy a collection. Regular check-ups are not enough and the collections must be sprayed with poison over and over again if the beetles are to be deterred. It is only quite recently that we have come to know the biology of the members of this genus in detail and have discovered just how dangerous they really are. A single young larva is not only able to squeeze itself through the tiniest of cracks and find its way into a closed entomological drawer or store-box, but can even bore through a millimetre-thick plastic container. In central Europe, *Anthrenus verbasci* is the commonest species in zoological collections. In Britain another species, *Anthrenus sarnicus,* threatens to become an even greater pest. Two other species, the Museum Beetle (*Anthrenus museorum*) and *A. pimpinellae* have similar habits but are less serious pests. The other members of the genus, all with a generally similar way of life (in central Europe alone there are 16 species), are either rare or of localized occurrence, so that they are usually of no commercial significance.

Niptus hololeucus is another small beetle which can be a nuisance in our homes. It is yellow, and somewhat resembles a small spider covered with hairs. In the middle of the nineteenth century it is known to have been brought to Europe from Asia Minor in pigs' bristles and from southern Russia in rhubarb roots. It became established in central and northern Europe and in the 1920's, when large infestations were first reported, the newspapers were full of hair-raising accounts: 'Wherever this beetle settles, there is no escape. In Europe it continues the work of destruction which in Asia has already made it the scourge of both natives and Europeans. It devours whole houses!' That is rubbish, of course. *Niptus hololeucus* actually multiplies on a large scale only in buildings where chaff has been used as insulation between floor and ceiling. This is because its larvae require food with a high starch content and are thus largely dependent on cereals and cereal products. Chaff contains quite a large amount of crushed grain and the beetles can reproduce in it undisturbed until they begin to well out from behind the skirting-boards and overrun houses and stores. For pupation the larvae seek out material of more substance; rotting wood suits their requirements particularly well. The adult beetle will attack textiles, upholstered furniture, woollen blankets, carpets and clothing, but although it may do some damage it is a nuisance rather than a serious pest. If its breeding places are cleared out it will give no more trouble.

Ptinus fur is another member of the family Ptinidae. In this spider beetle the sexes are dimorphic, i. e. the male and the female differ in form. Both adults and larvae are highly polyphagous and eat material of animal and vegetable origin, including textiles, furs, leather, cereals, flour and bakery products. Even pharmaceutical products are not immune and seeds, roots and herbs are attacked. In the open the beetle is to be found in trees and birds' nests, but it mostly occurs in houses, where it is a nuisance rather than a serious pest. In central Europe there are over 20 species of this genus, and *Ptinus fur* is by no means the only one to exhibit synanthropic tendencies. However, other *Ptinus* species which are found indoors are often rather hard to identify, especially in the case of the females. *Ptinus raptor* is seldom seen in the open; in buildings it is found on dry waste materials, pharmaceutical powders and flour. *Ptinus pusillus* may be found beneath rotting bark, but is also commoner in houses. It has the same habits as *Ptinus fur* and not infrequently the two are found together. *Ptinus latro* is widely distributed, although usually uncommon. It occurs on old trees, on flowering shrubs and in timber yards, but is occasionally found in dwellings in the company of related species. *Ptinus villiger* occurs in northern and eastern Germany and in Austria and is completely synanthropic; it has also settled in North America. *Ptinus tectus* was originally imported to Europe from Australia, but is now a regular member of the European fauna. Although it may be found in birds' nests and on flowering pines, it is more often reported in houses and museums; in Britain it is probably the commonest species of spider beetle indoors.

One of the best-known pests in warehouses and stores is *Tenebrio molitor,* which pursues its activities by night. The larvae, known as 'mealworms', live in flour, bran, oat-flakes, flaked potatoes and other foodstuffs. The eggs are hard to see, as they are disguised by dust and flour particles which adhere to their sticky surface. Young larvae are also difficult to detect and it is not until they are bigger that they become easier to find. In the kitchen they can be got rid of by sieving the flour, but in flour-mills and food-stores matters are less simple. The beetle's development takes 1−2 years (less in warm surroundings). Since they are easy to rear, mealworms are often specially bred and sold as live food for caged birds. The finding of a beetle in the house does not necessarily mean that it spent its larval period there; it may just as well have flown in through an open window, since the species also occurs in the open and is attracted by light. Larvae living out-of-doors are to be found in saw-dust, beneath loose bark on old trees and in birds' nests. *Tenebrio obscurus* has similar habits, but is seldom seen in the open; it is to be found mostly in cellars and farm buildings and it likewise attacks flour, flour products and grain.

This family (darkling beetles − Tenebrionidae) includes a whole series of species which attack foodstuffs. The members of the genus *Tribolium* are tiny flour beetles measuring only 3−5 mm. Their minute eggs are laid in flour and bakery products and, since they are covered with a sticky secretion, they are well disguised by adhering particles of flour or dust. Under favourable conditions development takes barely 1 1/2 months. These beetles do not attack intact grain, but only that which has been damaged or ground into flour. Especially suitable as larvae food are any kind of flour, grits, semolina, oat flakes and bran. The beetles do not confine themselves to cereals, however, but attack many other stored products, such as peanuts, dried beans and peas, baking powder, ginger, powdered paprika, snuff and cocoa beans. The larvae also eat other insects and, at high densities, may indulge in cannibalism. The highest levels of infestation by this beetle occur in ground rice, in which densities of almost half a million beetles per hectolitre have been recorded. Apart from what they actually consume, these insects cause considerable losses by affecting the overall quality of flour which they infest. This becomes musty, its viscosity is affected and in consequence it is often unsuitable for making dough. The two commonest species, *Tribolium castaneum* and *confusum* measure 3−3.5 mm. They are both cosmopolitan species and in central Europe are strictly synanthropic. *Tribolium madens,* which is likewise distributed over practically the whole of the globe, occurs both in stores and in the open (e. g. in the woodmould of old trees). *Tribolium destructor,* measuring 5−5.5 mm, is distinctly larger. It probably came originally from South America, but today it is a very common beetle in northern and central Europe, in all kinds of stores. It is very catholic in its tastes and in addition to cereals and a wide variety of seeds it eats flour, bran, dog-biscuits and the like.

Two other darkling beetles (Tenebrionidae) similar in appearance to *Tribolium* species also occur in stores. These are the widely distributed and fairly common *Alphitobius diaperinus* and the rarer *Alphitobius laevigatus.* Neither can be regarded as a serious pest, however, since their larvae are definitely known to eat only spoilt goods. Neither species has so far been found in the open.

Palorus, another genus of the family Tenebrionidae, is represented by three species in central Europe. The beetles, which measure 3 mm, are sometimes found in the open, but also occur in grain or flour, occasionally in large numbers. *Palorus subdepressus* lives in the Mediterranean region, but is regularly imported to central Europe. It is to be found in the open, chiefly beneath decaying bark on old deciduous trees, but it also occasionally occurs in granaries. *Palorus ratzeburgi* mainly infests grain, flour and bran, often in large numbers; although seldom encountered in the open, it can sometimes be found beneath the bark of old deciduous trees, especially beeches.

Latheticus orizae is very similar in appearance to *Palorus* species. The beetles, which measure only 2.5 mm, today occur throughout the warmer regions of the world, although they probably originally came from India. They are frequently imported to European countries with cargoes such as rice, but the species has not become firmly established there. The larvae develop in wheat, rye, barley, maize and flour as well as in rice.

Before continuing, one more tenebrionid beetle, noted for the unusually large jaws of the male, rather like a miniature stag beetle, is deserving of mention. This is *Gnatocerus cornutus,* which measures 3.5−4 mm and occurs in central Europe only in association with food-stores and dwellings. It crops up from time to time in mills and granaries and has been found in barley flakes, bread, ship's biscuits, maize, wheat, rice and beans.

There are many other beetles which live on cereals or cereal products, but are of little significance in central and northern Europe as their true home is in warmer parts of the world. They are occasionally imported, but do not become established in temperate regions.

Two more species from two families whose acquaintance we have already made as fur and wood feeders should also be mentioned, as they exhibit atypical feeding preferences when compared with their relatives.

The genus *Trogoderma,* belonging to the family Dermestidae, includes four species living in central Europe. The beetles may occasionally be found in the open and they have sometimes been known to damage insect collections. One species is notable for the fact that its larvae need a temperature of 17 °C for their development: this is the Khapra Beetle (*Trogoderma granarium*), which measures 1.7−3 mm and comes originally from India, where it lives on stored wheat, barley, maize and legumes. It is regularly imported to Europe, but because of its need for heat the only places where it can prosper are the stores of malt kept in breweries, where the necessary warmth is always available.

Lasioderma serricorne, the Cigarette Beetle, is a small and rather flat anobiid measuring some 2−2.5 mm in length. This beetle has a predilection for cured tobacco leaves, and is frequently imported to Europe. However, because of its need for high temperatures it has not become truly naturalized. The larvae by no means confine their attentions to tobacco, and will feed on a variety of other vegetable and animal products. The female beetle will lay its eggs on processed tobacco, as well as on a tobacco leaf, and is said to have an excellent taste in cigars. An expert (on beetles as well as on good cigars) was heard to remark that after looking forward to a good cigar it was not exactly a pleasure to smoke a burning *Lasioderma* larva − the effect was disagreeably like one's very first smoke.

As we have seen, the number of beetles which feed on cereals and cereal products is very large, but relatively few of these restrict their attentions to the seeds of cereal crops, and most will also attack other foodstuffs. However, the species of one family of beetles − Bruchidae − feed only on seeds, and virtually restrict their attentions to one kind of seed − pulses. Such pulses (e. g. lentils, butter beans and dried peas) are to be found in every kitchen and it is not surprising that it is there, at least on occasion, that we find these pests.

Bruchus pisorum, which measures 4−5 mm, is a major pest as far as peas are concerned, but it should be noted that this species has no connection with the maggots found in fresh green peas, as these are actually caterpillars. The female of *Bruchus pisorum* appears in pea fields when the plants are in flower and lays its eggs on very young pods into which the larvae burrow and bore their way into the seeds (one larva to one pea). The larva eats part of the pea, which nevertheless continues to grow, although if the larva eats the germ, the seed is naturally unable to germinate. In warm countries the adult beetle leaves the pea in the autumn and hibernates, but this seldom happens in central Europe, where the beetles generally remain in the pea until the following spring or even later (up to 14 months). Dried peas can therefore contain live beetles without this being readily detectable. If beetles are found in pease-pudding, however, not everybody is prepared to take it calmly and if the peas used are relatively fresh, their larvae may also be present as an added delicacy! Stories are told of field kitchens where the pea soup met with special praise for its flavoursome little pieces of bacon, the little bits of 'bacon' being none other than the larvae of *Bruchus pisorum.* If peas which have been attacked are not eaten until the following year, the beetles are likely to emerge in the meantime, making small round exit holes. Although this may cause some consternation in the kitchen the exodus of adult beetles means that the danger is past. The remaining peas will be free from both beetles and their larvae and cannot be attacked again, as eggs are laid only on the young pods of growing plants. In reality this bruchid is a pest of crops rather than stored products. By the time the peas are ripe there is no longer any point in attempting to combat bruchid attack, as by then any affected peas are already unsuitable as food.

Bruchus rufimanus, a close relative of *Bruchus pisorum,* has generally similar habits, but mainly attacks haricot beans (occasionally other beans or peas). Several beetles may develop in a single bean. *Bruchus rufimanus* females lay their eggs on young beans growing in the open, never on old beans. One little difference compared with *Bruchus pisorum* is that the adults emerge from the beans in the autumn.

Bruchus lentis, which lays its eggs in the open flowers of lentil plants, is not a native of central Europe. However, it has similar habits to the two preceding species and is quite often imported in consignments of dried lentils. There is always one larva to one lentil, but a single lentil is not sufficient for the larva's whole development, so it needs to transfer from one seed to another at some point. It may even leave the original plant and crawl to another. The larvae pupate in September and the beetles do not emerge until the following spring, so that there is always a danger of our finding the black-coloured adults floating in our lentil soup.

Bruchus is a large genus and most of its species develop in papilionaceous plants. It would be possible to draw up a long list of *Bruchus* species which are pests in one way or another. Not all of them attack beans, peas, lentils and similar foodstuffs: seeds of clover and vetch, mimosa and acacia as well as peanuts and cottonseed are also eaten.

Another bean weevil, *Acanthoscelides obtectus,* until fairly recently was found solely in imported beans, often in large numbers. A haricot bean may contain up to 30 beetles, but what distinguishes this species from those of *Bruchus* is that its female will lay its eggs in old beans, so that *Acanthoscelides obtectus* is also a true stored products pest. Unfortunately, in central Europe this species has now taken to feeding on young bean plants in fields and gardens. It will also develop in other legumes as well as beans. The number of generations is controlled by temperature and under favourable conditions 4−5 generations may be produced in one year.

A number of species of bean weevil are found only out-of-doors. A few, such as *Bruchidius fasciatus* and *cisti* develop in the seeds of broom and may be found sitting in the flowers. Vetches and sweet peas also have their own particular bean weevils: *Bruchus atomarius,* for instance, has specialized in vetch seeds.

Compared with the number of pest species associated with wood and foodstuffs of vegetable origin, the number of beetles to be found in products of animal origin in the home is very small. The most important belong to the genus *Dermestes,* from which the whole family (Dermestidae) takes its name. By far the commonest is the cosmopolitan Bacon Beetle (*Dermestes lardarius*), which occurs all over central Europe. It resembles *Attagenus pellio* in form, but is larger and has a wide grey band across the anterior part of its elytra. Like all its relatives, in the open it lives on carrion and that is probably its natural food. Today, however, bacon beetles are mostly to be found in houses and stores. The larvae attack bacon, sausages, ham and smoked meat, dried and smoked fish, furs, skins, bristles, hairs, horns, hooves, feathers and stuffed animals. Since the larvae strip bones of even the minutest of meat fibres, they are used by zoologists to clean vertebrate skeletons: if an animal cadaver is placed in a container with specially bred *Dermestes* larvae, its bones are picked absolutely clean in next to no time.

Other *Dermestes* species have similar habits. *Dermestes vulpinus* has been found among tanned cattle skins and gut, and *Dermestes cadaverinus* attacks leather, silk and woollen fabrics. *Dermestes carnivorus* is repeatedly imported from South and North America, while *Dermestes peruvianus* is likewise brought to Europe in skins and gut from the New World. *Dermestes frischii* is found in dried gut and dried fish and *Dermestes bicolor* is to be found in dwellings and in pigeon-houses, where it may attack the live fledglings: it is also said to attack freshly hatched chicks and ducklings.

The list of beetle pests of households is so long that to sensitive minds it may appear rather horrifying. There is little need for concern, however, since our property is generally left unmolested. It is easier for the female beetles to lay their eggs on materials which are not shut away in cupboards, boxes, tins, bottles and the like. Furthermore, to be able to develop they need quite a long period of undisturbed peace. We thus do not need to stand in fear of beetles − not even of the species with which we conclude this section on beetles in the home. However, this beetle is an altogether special case. We have already seen that many species are quite catholic as regards their choice of food, but in this respect *Stegobium paniceum* is in a class of its own. This tiny beetle, measuring only 2−4 mm, belongs to the family Anobiidae.

It exhibits a degree of preference for bread and other bakery products, but will breed in every conceivable type of vegetable and animal product, including the hottest spices and the most poisonous drugs, such as the roots of deadly nightshade, from which belladonna is made. It has even been observed to eat its way through lead and tinfoil. According to experts, the only materials which are safe from attack are cast-iron and other hard metals, glass, chinaware and stone. The newly hatched larvae are only 0.5 mm long and 0.12 mm wide, so that they can squeeze through the narrowest cracks. They are long-legged, very agile and have an extremely keen sense of smell, so that they are well equipped to search for food. Furthermore, they are able to go for up to eight days without nourishment. *Stegobium paniceum* is certainly a major pest, and in the home may be the beetle we most often meet with.

Garden pests

Beetles which are garden pests will not be discussed here in as much detail as those found indoors. There are so many of them that they would need a book to themselves, and we shall therefore describe just a few of the more important ones.

The majority of the many species of ground beetles (Carabidae) found in central Europe are predators. Their presence in gardens is generally welcome, since they live chiefly on other insects, many of which are harmful to garden flowers and vegetables. Some feed on slugs and snails. One species, *Harpalus rufipes,* sometimes known as the Strawberry Seed Beetle, has developed — for a ground beetle — a curious taste in food, since it eats the little seeds (acini) on the surface of ripe strawberries. This does not destroy the fruit, but spoils their appearance and can also damage the flesh. If a large number of the beetles is present in a garden or strawberry field the crop can be severely affected.

Beetles whose adult and/or larval stages eat plants are a more serious problem. Let us begin with *Lilioceris lilii,* a species of leaf beetle (Chrysomelidae) which attacks ornamental plants. The red-bodied, black-legged beetle appears in the spring, when lilies start to shoot. The adults can be seen (and heard, as they stridulate audibly) on garden lilies from April to June. The female lays its eggs on various lilies, and larval development takes place entirely on these plants, which are not infrequently stripped bare by their guests. The larvae of this and related species of leaf-beetle have a habit of coating their backs with their own excrement. When full-grown they descend to the ground and pupate. The adults of *Lilioceris lilii* emerge in September and spend the winter in hibernation.

Lilioceris merdigera, a close relative of the preceding species, is easily distinguishable from it by its redder legs. Otherwise the two are very similar both in appearance and in habits. *Lilioceris merdigera* is to be found, sometimes in numbers, on lilies-of-the-valley, Solomon's Seal and various *Lilium* species. It also favours onions and leeks, etc. (*Allium* species) and can do considerable damage in onion beds.

Species of the related genus *Crioceris* are similar in form to those of *Lilioceris.* They are smaller, however, and all have brightly patterned elytra — sometimes striped and sometimes spotted, although the colour pattern within each species is extremely variable. Two species in particular are common and widely distributed in central Europe. These are *Crioceris asparagi* and *Crioceris duodecimpunctata,* both of which measure 5—6.5 mm and may be seen from April to October in asparagus beds. Both adults and larvae eat asparagus leaves and the species are regarded by asparagus growers as serious pests. Two other species occurring in the eastern and southeastern parts of central Europe also feed on asparagus, but the occurrence of *Crioceris quinquepunctata* and *Crioceris quatuordecimpunctata* is generally sporadic, and these beetles are rarely to be seen in gardens.

Before passing on to other garden pests mention may be made of the group of weevils already discussed in connection with parental care, those which lay their eggs in blossoms, berries, fruits, shoots and leaves and are responsible for considerable damage to strawberry, raspberry and blackberry plants, rose-bushes and fruit trees (plums, apples, pears).

While the damage done by the beetles discussed above can be kept within bounds, there is one group of leaf beetles which can truly wreak havoc in the garden. These are the flea-beetles (Halticinae), small, uniformly brown or striped beetles mostly measuring only 2—4 mm and easily identified by their thick hind femora. They can jump astoundingly well with their hindlegs and their vernacular name is certainly apt. Leaps of 50−60 cm (height and distance) by individuals measuring no more than 2.5 mm in length have been recorded. In central Europe there are 23 genera of flea-beetles, with hundreds of species. The beetles and their larvae live chiefly on plants of the family Cruciferae and thus attack cabbages, turnips, radishes and cress, etc. Flea-beetles generally overwinter as adults, coming out of hiding in the spring, and feed on seedlings or young plants, sometimes devouring them completely. The larvae continue the work of destruction on older plants, where they feed on roots from the outside, or mine the roots, stems and leaves. Not all flea-beetles have specialized in cultivated plants, of course, and many are of very localized occurrence. The most important genus in gardens is *Phyllotreta*, whose two dozen species are all very small and are either uniformly metallic black or have yellow stripes running down their elytra; almost all of them live entirely on Cruciferae. Two of the yellow-striped species − *Phyllotreta undulata* and *Phyllotreta vittula* ⸺ are distributed over the whole of central Europe and are very common. No less common are the two unicoloured species *Phyllotreta atra*, which is black, and *Phyllotreta cruciferae*, which has a metallic green colour; these two species often do considerable damage to cruciferous crops. Further members of the genus which the gardener is likely to meet are *Phyllotreta nemorum, nigripes* and *armoraciae,* the last of which is very partial to horseradish (*Armoracia rusticana*).

If our young lettuce plants vanish over-night without leaving a trace, if older lettuces wither or other plants display similar signs, we should dig in the soil beneath and the miscreants − wireworms − will no doubt come to light. Wireworms, so-called because of their long cylindrical bodies and hard cuticle, are the larvae of click beetles (Elateridae). In general they are predacious, but some species are completely vegetarian, with a special predilection for lettuce and potatoes; not content with eating the roots of the potatoes, the larvae also attack the tubers and riddle them with their tunnels. However, if wireworms appear in the garden in large numbers, there is one easy way in which most of them can be caught. If we make a small pile of cut grass or clover and examine it after a 3−4 day interval, we are likely to find that a number of the larvae have been attracted to the heap, where they may be readily collected and disposed of.

One of the most unpopular of garden insects in Continental Europe is the Colorado Beetle (*Leptinotarsa decemlineata),* which originally came from America, found its way into Europe at the beginning of the present century and is now completely acclimatized there. As far as central Europe is concerned every possible step was taken to combat this species, which posed a considerable threat to potato crops, but to no avail. Nothing has been able to prevent the beetle's eastward march. The history of its spread and its remorseless advance shows just how helpless man can be, despite all the means at his disposal, against an insect whose only weapon is its great prolificity.

The Colorado Beetle was first discovered in the state of Colorado (USA) in 1824, where the beetles and their larvae lived on a wild member of the genus *Solanum* (which includes potatoes, tomatoes and nightshades). After 1850, when the potato (*Solanum tuberosum*) began to be cultivated in their native region, something unpredictable happened − *Leptinotarsa decemlineata* abandoned its original host plant − *Solanum rostratum* − and switched over to the potato. That in itself would not have been sufficient to make the beetle the supreme pest it afterwards became, nor was the abundance of food made available to both beetles and larvae in the form of potato monocultures the crucial factor. What really decided the issue was that, in adapting to the potato as a host, the beetle's rate of reproduction was greatly increased. This in turn provided the basis for a rapid expansion of the species' range. It was not long before the first reports of damage to crops came in, and not only from Colorado (in 1859 the beetle was found infesting fields in Nebraska). In 15 years the beetle traversed the whole of North America from west to east and by 1874, it had reached the Atlantic coast. With extensive traffic across the Atlantic this now meant that there was considerable danger of Europe being invaded. Indeed, only two years later beetles were discovered on a steamer and even in a warehouse in Bremen in Germany. The following year (1877), finds were not only reported in Liverpool and Rotterdam, but infested fields were discovered in two inland areas of Germany. One of these, near Mühlheim on the Rhine, was discovered in June 1877 in time (with the beetles still in their first generation), and was dealt with without too much difficulty.

The situation in Schildau near Torgau (Saxony), where 16 foci of infestation, evidently already comprising second generation insects, were found, was much more serious. Here it cost a great deal of time and money to get rid of the pests. One question which will never be answered, though, is how the beetles got into these areas in the first place. It is doubtful whether all the beetles near Torgau were destroyed, since 10 years later, in 1887, the Colorado Beetle reappeared there and was also found in the Meppen district in north-west Germany. Every possible method was tried in continued attempts to deal with the pest. The elimination of a focus near Stade on the Lower Elbe in 1914 cost 60,000 gold marks even in those days. Then came the First World War and with it confusion and slackening of precautions and preventive measures. There is no question that American troop-ships brought more of the beetles to Bordeaux and that from there they set out on their final relentless march eastwards. And when the aftermath of war had died away, people woke up to the realization that the Colorado Beetle had got the better of them.

In 1922, some 250 square kilometres round Bordeaux were infested. In 1934 a fresh focus discovered near Stade was again eliminated, but in 1936 the Colorado Beetle crossed the Franco-German border on a broad front and invaded Germany; this time its advance eastwards could not be stopped. In the ensuing 25 years, despite continuing attempts to check its spread, the beetle occupied the whole of south-western and central Europe. Although it has not succeeded in establishing itself in the British Isles, since then it has advanced into Scandinavia and the Balkan Peninsula and has penetrated deep into the USSR. It will no doubt not be long before it brings its triumphant progress round the northern hemisphere full circle and arrives back at its starting point.

After hibernating, the adult beetles reappear in the spring and immediately make for the potato tops. The female, which may live for over two years, lays its eggs on the leaves. A single female can lay over 2,000 eggs and since two generations mature in a year, the number of offspring produced under favourable conditions is astronomical. The Colorado Beetle is undoubtedly a major pest, although no longer such a threat to potato crops. In the first place, there are now efficient means of keeping it in check, and secondly, it evidently does not find suitable conditions for its development in every part of Europe. For example, it avoids high altitudes, which remain virtually free from this pest without any preventive measures having to be taken.

Pests of agriculture

Almost all of the pests of kitchen gardens and flower beds also affect field crops. For example, Colorado Beetles and wireworms attack potato fields. However, it is often additional species which cause the most serious damage to crops cultivated on a large scale.

We have already seen that ground beetles may be at least partly vegetarian, but the species of *Zabrus,* relatively large ground beetles measuring 11−20 mm, are completely phytophagous. *Zabrus tenebrioides,* the commonest species, is today rather scarce in central Europe as well as the British Isles and, like the other two central European species of the genus, is more prevalent towards the east and south-east. It can be a serious pest of cereals. Adults climb various cereal plants to eat the seeds while they are still soft. In this way they certainly damage crops, but as the period during which the grain is suitable as food is comparatively short, losses are not too severe. When no seeds are available the adults feed on cereal leaves. If they do this in the spring, when the corn is still young and tender, and if the beetles appear in large numbers, the damage to the crop can be considerable. However, the activities of the larvae have a more serious effect. They live in the fields, in vertical burrows which they dig 20−30 cm deep into the ground, drag cereal leaves down into these shafts and consume them there. In recent years there have been reports of whole fields of wheat and rye having been stripped bare by these beetles and their larvae and having to be re-sown.

In central Europe there is also a group of leaf beetles (Chrysomelidae) which attack cereals. These are the six species of the genera *Lema* and *Oulema,* which measure 3−5 mm; some of them are a uniform shining blue or green while others are blue and red. The adults, all of which are able to stridulate audibly, hibernate (sometimes indoors), and seek out cereal plants in the spring. The beetles and their larvae eat the tissue between the veins of leaves, the resulting damage forming a characteristic pattern of longitudinal stripes. The larvae, which somewhat resemble tiny slugs, have a gleaming, slime-covered back, on which they carry their own excreta. *Lema lichenis* and *Oulema melanopa* are fairly common in central Europe, but it is doubtful whether they really do as much damage to cereals as is often claimed, since they are not absolutely dependent on cereals for their existence and also feed on various grasses.

Wireworms, the larvae of click beetles a few species of which prefer cereals to lettuce and potatoes, are quite a different proposition. The greatest damage is probably done by the species *Agriotes lineatus* and *obscurus* and *Selatosomus aeneus,* whose larvae live in the ground and eat roots − mainly of cereals. Being predators, they also devour cockchafer grubs, maggots and other pests, so that in this respect they can be classified as useful insects. However, such benefits are small in comparison with the damage they do by eating roots.

We must return here for a moment to the flea-beetles, since some are pests of agricultural crops which we are unlikely to meet with in gardens. The species of the genus *Aphthona* live mostly on spurges (*Euphorbia* spp.), but despite its name, *Aphthona euphorbiae* is actually an important pest of flax. This beetle is fairly common all over Europe and from March to October can be found on flax (*Linum usitatissimum*), which is also attacked by another flea-beetle, *Longitarsus parvulus.* A further flea-beetle, *Crepidodera ferruginea,* which measures about 3 mm, is sometimes a cereal pest; it occurs throughout the whole of Europe and can be found from the end of May till October.

One last genus of flea-beetles deserving mention is *Psylliodes,* some 30 species of which live in central Europe. The beetles frequent various plants, but particularly favour Cruciferae. *Psylliodes attenuata* and *Psylliodes chrysocephala* in particular are known as serious agricultural pests, the latter mainly for the damage it does to oil-seed rape and turnip crops. This species has quite different habits from the majority of leaf beetles, which hibernate as adults, come out of hiding in the spring, mate and then lay their eggs. Female *Psylliodes chrysocephala* lay their eggs in the autumn and then die; the young larvae spend the winter in the stems or roots of their host plant (rape, turnip) and the following spring pupate in the soil. When the adult beetles first emerge, they move to hedgerows or the margins of woods, but return later in the year to rape fields, where they nibble the leaves of young plants. Lastly, to bring the cycle full circle, the female lays the eggs. In years of abundance this species may wreak havoc in rape fields, but in severe winters most of the young larvae die inside the plants.

Meligethes aeneus, which measures only 2−2.5 mm, is another rape pest but from a quite different family − the Nitidulidae. It occurs all over central Europe and sometimes appears in unusually large numbers. Both adults and larvae feed on the flowers of various cruciferous plants, but prefer rape and turnips. The adults mainly eat pollen and seldom touch the pistil or the ovary. Normally the female lays one egg to a flower-bud. The larva bites its way into the bud and eats the anthers, after which it may move on to another bud. When full-grown, the larva leaves the plant to pupate in the soil. The rape crop suffers only if *Meligethes* are present when the plants are in bud. If the flowers are already open, the beetle and larvae eat only the pollen. However, damage to the developing fruit by bud-feeding larvae may result in crop losses of up to 25 per cent.

A few species of the large weevil genus *Ceutorhynchus* may occur together with *Meligethes aeneus. Ceutorhynchus quadridens* lays its eggs on *Brassica* species − especially rape − in May and June. The larvae eat out the inside of leaf-stalks, leaf ribs and stems. The damage they make is not visible externally, but the plant wilts as a result and young plants may die. Large scale infestation by this weevil can cause severe losses.

Ceutorhynchus napi appears in rape fields as early as the middle of March. The female lays its eggs on the stems in which the larvae feed − usually until the stem is quite hollow. This leads to the formation of galls, deformation and sometimes collapse of the stems, but losses nevertheless remain within reasonable limits. This species does more serious damage in cabbage fields, where young plants are often destroyed completely and seedlings develop twisted hearts.

A third species of this genus, *Ceutorhynchus assimilis,* overwinters in the adult stage in hedgerows and at the edge of woods. In the spring the beetles move onto cruciferous plants, on which they feed to promote maturation of the eggs. The new generation of adults appear by the end of June and they also feed on cruciferous plants, but do far less damage than the larvae. The female lays its eggs in young pods and the larvae devour the developing seeds, so that in years of abundance they can cause severe losses. The larvae pupate in the soil.

Most central European species of Silphidae, such as the burying beetles (*Nicrophorus* spp.), live on carrion and are thus necrophagous, but a few are predators and eat living animals such as caterpillars, slugs and worms. One species lives on decaying vegetable matter and there is one genus whose two species atypically for this family prove a headache to farmers by eating fresh plants, especially beets; these are *Blitophaga opaca* and *undata*. For hibernation the beetles choose warm, sunny spots at the edges of woods, where they hide away in the litter. In the spring they re-emerge, appear in the fields and eat the leaves of young beet plants. Their eggs are laid in the soil and the larvae — which resemble woodlice — also attack young plants (mangolds and sugar-beet). The beetles occur in large numbers only in exceptionally warm years, following a warm, dry winter which allows most of the hibernating adults to survive. Fields in the vicinity of woods, naturally enough, tend to be the most severely attacked. The above species both occur as far to the north and west as the British Isles, but they are of markedly less frequent occurrence the further west we go. For instance, there are many reports from the GDR of damage done by these beetles, while in the FRG they are rare.

The most familiar beetle to most people in central Europe is still the May-beetle or Cockchafer, despite a great decrease in its numbers in recent decades because of the measures taken to combat it. The Cockchafer has been celebrated in verse and in song, but in fact, the German name of *Maikäfer* covers three different species which can readily be differentiated by the shape of their pygidium (the tip of their abdomen) (Fig. 17). The commonest of these, and the only one found in southern Britain, is the Common Cockchafer (*Melolontha melolontha*). In central Europe it is not to be found at altitudes of over 1,000 m. *Melolontha hippocastani* has a preference for sandy heaths and wooded regions, and is found, although not commonly, in northern Britain as well as over much of Continental Europe. *Melolontha pectoralis* does not occur in the British Isles and now occurs only in the southwestern part of central Europe. The beetles of all three species appear in May to feed on the leaves of deciduous trees. The females oviposit in the soil, where the grubs live on small roots — their development taking 3−5 years. In a given area, only every third, fourth or fifth year is normally one when large numbers of cockchafers can be seen on the wing; in the intervening years they are hardly to be seen at all.

To give the reader who has never seen these insects in massed flight some idea of their numbers, we should like to cite a few statistics. In one area in the Rhineland-Pfalz region of Germany, 22 million cockchafers were caught in 1911 and 14 million in 1915. In 1939, some 15 tons, corresponding to about 18 million beetles, were caught on a mountain road near Heppenheim and the number of cockchafers washed up by a single tide on the Baltic coast in 1938 was estimated at 26 million. In years of abundance the adult beetles hang in tight clusters from deciduous trees, which are soon stripped bare, and if nothing else is then available they will even switch their attentions to conifers. However, the damage done by the beetles to trees is not so great as that done by the grubs to the roots of crop plants. As well as eating humus, the grubs attack all types of roots and are capable of destroying whole meadows, cornfields and potato crops. In years of particular abundance they consume virtually all the vegetable matter they can find in the soil, completely eating out a space about one centimetre deep, over which the yellowed grass can be rolled up like a carpet. The damage caused by cockchafers until as recently as two or three decades ago was enormous, and estimated to be worth 100 million gold marks in Germany, between 250 and 1,000 million gold marks in France and 20 million gold crowns in Austria. In the 1950's and 1960's attempts to control cockchafer

Fig. 17. Pygidium of the three cockchafer species found in central Europe. 1 − *Melolontha melolontha* (the Common Cockchafer), 2 − *Melolontha hippocastani* (the Northern Cockchafer), 3 − *Melolontha pectoralis* (not found in the British Isles).

49

populations were organized on a massive scale. Helicopters were widely used to spray insecticides in areas of cockchafer abundance, and vast numbers of them perished. Today – no doubt largely as a result of these operations – the May-beetle is something of a rarity and it is said that in Germany a single specimen will fetch as much as $0.5 - 1$ DM (about $12 - 25$ pence). Every now and again, however, one hears of new outbreaks (in southwest Germany, for example) – and the voice of profit is raised, demanding that the beetles be exterminated by aerial bombardment with pesticides.

Woodland and forest pests

In this context let us first of all make further reference to the May-beetle, which is able to defoliate whole deciduous trees. Opinions concerning the effect of the adult beetle's ravages vary. However, even if the tree is completely denuded (this always happens in May), it puts out new shoots in midsummer of the same year. That means a smaller growth of wood and a narrower annual ring, but, on the other hand, stronger wood. At all events, the May-beetle does less damage in the sphere of forestry than it does to agriculture.

Forest pests – and there can be a great many of them – give notice of their presence in various ways. Many attack and damage or even kill living trees. Other species attack felled timber and spoil it by tunnelling deep passages. Such wood is virtually useless for construction purposes or furniture making. Since the damage done by a given species cannot always be clearly distinguished, the various species are discussed below in a systematic sequence, together with a short account of their biology.

In central Europe there are only three species of the family Lymexylidae, all of which attack timber. One of them (*Hylecoetus flabellicornis*) does not occur in Britain and is probably no longer to be found in Germany. *Lymexylon navale* was first described in 1746 by Linnaeus, who found it on a pile of oak wood on a wharf at Göteborg in Sweden. This species is rare in central Europe, especially in the western part, but lately its numbers seem to have increased. *Hylecoetus dermestoides,* whose life and habits are largely similar to those of the other two species, is far commoner. However, the adults are not often seen as they live only a few days. After pairing, the female lays its eggs in cracks and crevices in felled timber or on standing dead or diseased trees: healthy trees are seldom attacked. The young larvae bore their way into the wood: the tunnels are at first very narrow, but as the larva grows they steadily widen. Since they penetrate the wood to a depth of $20 - 25$ cm whole trunks half a metre in diameter are affected, making them fit only for firewood. The larvae do not eat the wood, but live on a fungus (*Endomyces hylecoeti*), which grows on the walls of their tunnels. The fungus requires oxygen for its growth and the passages must therefore be kept clear of powdered wood. To enable it to do this, i. e. to eject the waste from the narrow tunnel entrance, the larva has a long-tipped, tapering abdomen. Extensively attacked trunks can thus be recognized from the amount of powdered wood strewn round them. It is interesting to note the way in which the fungus is transferred from one beetle generation to the next. Attached to its ovipositor the female has a pocket (mycangium) filled with fungal spores and as the eggs are laid spores are smeared over them. After hatching, the larvae remain with the egg-shell for a time. Spores, which adhere to their body, are later carried into their tunnels, where they germinate.

As far as is known, *Lymexylon navale* larvae live on the wood gnawed away in the course of making their tunnels, since no white fungus has been found coating their tunnels. Also, unlike those of *Hylecoetus,* the larvae do not eject powdered wood from their burrows.

The large family of metallic wood-borers or jewel beetles (Buprestidae) is poorly represented in Britain and represented in central Europe by species of relatively modest size. The adult beetles are found mostly on flowers, especially yellow ones, but many of their larvae live in wood where, however, they do comparatively little damage. Some species chiefly attack rotting wood or stumps, while a great many do not penetrate the wood proper, but tunnel between the bark and wood. Admittedly, this may have some effect on the tree's water supply, but metallic wood-borers chiefly attack diseased or otherwise weakened trees and seldom occur in numbers. A few small *Agrilus* species are unpopular with foresters because of the damage they do to young plants. *Agrilus viridis* chiefly attacks young beeches, but can also be seen on willows and has been reported on birches, alders, candleberry bushes, maples and poplars. The larvae of *Agrilus angustulus* live mainly in oaks, but also in beeches, hornbeams and hazels, while *Agrilus biguttatus* larvae are to be found in various types of oak.

When discussing household pests we made the acquaintance of the House Longhorn. Longhorn beetles (Cerambycidae) are highly prized by collectors, since they include some of the most handsome of our native species. However, they also include a number of serious pests, particularly in the field of forestry.

The three *Tetropium* species which inhabit central Europe are the most serious longhorn forest pests. They attack the trunks of standing conifers, especially if they are diseased or weakened. If a stand has already been damaged by high winds, bark beetles, caterpillars (of *Lymantria monacha*), and *Tetropium* beetles can complete its destruction within three years. Conifer stands on poor soil are also susceptible to attack and in years when they are particularly abundant the beetles will even attack healthy trees. The incidence of *Tetropium* species in central Europe has decreased during the past few decades, as forest 'hygiene' has made life extremely difficult for many wood-eating insects. Populations of many once abundant forest species have dwindled almost to the point of disappearing, while a number of the longhorn beetles coveted by collectors are verging on extinction.

Of the three *Tetropium* species, two are now so rare in central Europe that they no longer have any significance as pests; these are *Tetropium gabrieli,* which lives on larches, and *Tetropium fuscum,* which occurs on firs and pines. The third species, *Tetropium castaneum,* is to be found on old coniferous trees from May to July. The females lay their eggs in cracks and crevices in the bark. The young larvae make burrows between the bark and sap-wood, and these cut across the vascular bundles so affecting the tree's water supply. If the larval burrows are sufficiently extensive no more water reaches the crown, and the tree dies. Diseased and weakened trees are particularly vulnerable. The damage done by this species to timber is compounded by the full-grown larvae, which bore curved passages into the wood itself. The outer wood of a tree damaged in this way has no commercial value. Because of their similar mode of life, the two *Criocephalus* species, *rusticus* and *tristis,* together with *Asemum striatum,* may also be regarded as pests of pine and occasionally of other conifers; sometimes the adults emerge from already processed wood. However, these species also attack stumps and rotting wood of no commercial value, and are often rare so that they present little threat to timber production.

Compared with other species of the family, these longhorn species have relatively short feelers. One of the most impressive longhorns of central Europe is *Cerambyx cerdo,* which can measure up to 5 cm. The female's sturdy feelers are the same length as its body, but the male's are much longer. The beetles, which are to be found from May to August, are active in the evening and at night. The female lays its eggs on oaks (occasionally other deciduous trees), generally selecting old, and disease-weakened trees. At first the larvae burrow in the bark, but later turn their attention to the wood itself in which they tunnel in all directions. Since larval development takes 3−5 years and the tunnels are wide enough to admit a finger, timber from trees attacked by *Cerambyx cerdo* is good for very little. In view of the high commercial value of mature oak, the damage caused by *Cerambyx cerdo* can understandably be very serious. The physiological damage caused is practically nil, and oak trees survive and continue to grow for years, while successive generations of these beetles develop inside them; on the other hand, as timber the wood is ruined. However, today *Cerambyx cerdo* is no longer a menace as this handsome beetle has been hunted down mercilessly. It had already disappeared from most parts of Europe many years ago and the last 'Cerambyx oaks' have now been deliberately felled in many of its last places of refuge. The time may not be far distant when we shall be able to see *Cerambyx cerdo* only in entomological collections.

Populations of several related species persist in southeast Europe (*Cerambyx velutinus, miles, nodulosus, carinatus),* and some of these also occur in the Mediterranean region and Asia Minor. However, it may not be long before these species suffer the fate met with by *Cerambyx cerdo* in the more densely populated lands of central Europe.

Cerambyx scopolii has a similar life-history to *Cerambyx cerdo,* but is only 17−28 mm in length and its development takes only two years. The larvae live in the wood of various deciduous trees, but since they favour stumps and branches they have so far escaped the fate of their bigger relatives. The beetles are to be found in central Europe from May to July, when they can still be quite abundant in some places on flowering shrubs and on timber. Nevertheless, they can be pests, especially in orchards.

There are a number of smaller longhorn beetles, none quite so serious a pest as *Cerambyx cerdo,* whose larvae live beneath bark and later burrow into the wood of various trees, so rendering them of little use as timber. These species may be seen, chiefly from May to July, on felled tree-trunks which have not yet been de-barked and on stumps, cord-wood and brushwood.

Although extremely local and rare in Britain *Pyrrhidium sanguineum,* a red longhorn beetle measuring 8−12 mm, is still fairly common in parts of central Europe. The larvae live in various deciduous trees, particularly oaks. The beetles can be seen from April to June, running about on felled trunks and tree stumps. Before pupating the larvae burrow up to 6 cm deep into the wood.

Phymatodes testaceus is often seen in timber yards and may be found emerging from stacks of firewood, but its larvae also burrow in timber awaiting processing. This species prefers oak, but will also attack the wood of other deciduous trees.

Many longhorn beetles have black and yellow stripes like those of wasps. Some of these spend the larval period beneath bark, finally going deep into the wood to pupate, and so damaging it. Most of the species of the genera *Chlorophorus, Clytus* and *Xylotrechus* are too rare to be regarded seriously as pests. *Plagionotus arcuatus* is an exception. Its length (6−20 mm) makes it one of the biggest members of this group, and although probably extinct in Britain it occurs over the whole of central Europe where it is quite abundant in places. The beetles can be seen from May to July on the surface of wood in which their larvae feed; the females lay their eggs on the bark of oak trunks and occasionally other deciduous trees. The larvae at first live immediately beneath the bark, but burrow their way into the wood when ready to pupate. Since their tunnels measure up to 7 cm they do considerable damage, especially in years when they are abundant.

The genus *Monochamus* is represented by four species in central Europe. These are notable for the length of their antennae, which in males are more than double the length of the body. All four species live on conifers and primarily inhabit mountain forests. The adult beetles gnaw the bark of young twigs and shoots, but do far less damage than the larvae. The female lays its eggs on tree trunks, where the larvae at first feed under the bark, but later tunnel into the wood. The biggest species, *sartor,* attacks pines, especially after they have been felled. *M. sutor* is smaller and is the commonest species of the genus; it attacks spruces and other conifers, as well as pines. *M. galloprovincialis* is rarer than *sutor,* its larvae living mainly in pines. The fourth species, *saltuarius,* occurs only in the southeastern part of central Europe, but its range extends far to the east, reaching right across Asia to Japan.

In the section dealing with parental care we made the acquaintance of the longhorn *Saperda populnea,* whose activities result in the formation of galls on aspens. In the relevant literature this beetle is described as an occasional pest, but this description fits its larger relative *Saperda carcharias* much better. The adult beetles of this species betray their presence by the large holes which they eat in poplar leaves from June to September. Larval development which takes two years takes place in the wood of poplars. Young trees up to 3 cm in trunk diameter die as a direct result of their depradations or are so severely damaged that a strong wind will snap them. Older and stronger poplars survive, even when eaten by *Saperda* larvae for years, but their timber has no value except as firewood.

Before continuing, there is one further instance of damage caused by longhorn beetles which is worthy of mention. Several species (e. g. *Leptura rubra*) have been reported as pests because of the holes made by them in telegraph poles. To the beetles such poles apparently resemble dead standing trunks or tree stumps. As telegraph poles serve a human purpose the normally useful activities of these particular insects in consuming dead wood made pests of them in this instance. This problem largely belongs to the past, however, since telegraph poles, at least in areas where they are most susceptible to beetle damage, are no longer made of wood.

In the section on parental care we encountered various species of weevils which damage the buds, blossoms, leaves and shoots of trees. Not surprisingly, as most of them are strict vegetarians, weevils are also of significance in forestry. The best-known and most unwelcome pest is the Pine Weevil (*Hylobius abietis*). This species has several peculiarities distinguishing it from other beetles. A particularly important characteristic is that it is the adult beetles and not their larvae which cause the damage. The larvae live in dying conifer roots, that is to say, mostly in root stumps, on which the eggs are also laid. The larvae tunnel between the inner bark and the sap-wood and burrow into the wood to pupate. Their developmental period is of variable length. The eggs are generally laid in April or May with the first young adults of the new generation often appearing as soon as August or September. However, the larvae may wait about a year before pupating. Adult pine weevils have a long life span, often living for as much as three years. The beetles feed on the bark and needles of conifers, causing the greatest damage in young plantations. The holes made by them penetrate deep into the inner bark or sap-wood; very often repeated attacks are made at one site, leading to permanent scarring of the wood. Forestry experts rank this beetle as a plantation pest of the first order, and as such it occupies the attention of foresters in central Europe perhaps more than any other forest insect. Man is largely to blame himself for this situation, however, as the practice of clear-felling whole tracts of forest particularly favours the Pine Weevil. The stumps provide accommodation for numerous larvae while young trees planted on the newly cleared ground provide adults with an abundant food-supply close at hand as they emerge. This is an ideal situation for the beetles, and one not usually found under natural conditions, as the Pine Weevil cannot fly and has to look for its breeding sites and food 'on foot'. Foresters therefore sometimes dig trenches to trap the beetles. These may be gold-mines for the entomologist, as all kinds of other insects are caught in them as well.

The weevil genus *Pissodes* includes a number of central European species. They are secondary forest pests, that is to say, they only attack trees which have already been weakened by the assaults of other insects. The habits of all the species are similar. The female lays its eggs on the bark of conifers, while the larvae eat meandering passages in the bark and sap-wood, later pupating deep in the wood, where they make a comfortable bed of chewed fragments of wood for themselves. The females lay most of their eggs in the spring, but oviposition continues throughout much of the year. Adults live 2−3 years and the three developmental stages are therefore often found together.

Pissodes castaneus, which is smaller than *Hylobius abietis,* is a pest of some importance. The adult beetles gnaw deep holes in the bark of the twigs and shoots of conifers, but the larvae do much more serious damage. They make winding burrows between the bark and sap-wood, and fill these with powdered waste, thereby cutting off the supply of sap. The pupal chamber encroaches on the wood. This species occurs chiefly in young pine plantations (of 3−15-year-old trees) and if on poor soil may seriously diminish the vigour of the young trees. If, in addition, the trees are gnawed by deer or damaged by storms or a fire, the beetles may kill off the whole stand. Trees attacked by *Pissodes castaneus* can be recognized in the summer by the drops of resin which appear on their bark and by their brown, withered needles.

Pissodes piniphilus, which also favours pines, is smaller than the last species, but resembles it in other respects, including its habits. This species occurs chiefly on 30- to 50-year-old trees and attacks the bark where it is smooth and relatively thin. Here the adult beetles feed and lay their eggs. This species can do considerable damage, since although it prefers diseased trees, healthy trees are also attacked when the beetle occurs at high densities. White drops of resin on the bark and wilting of the apical shoots betray the beetles' presence.

Of the other two *Pissodes* species which live on pines, *Pissodes pini* inhabits the crowns of old trees and *Pissodes validirostris* develops in the cones. Both are capable of doing damage, but are less harmful than the three preceding species.

Pissodes hercyniae lives on mature spruces which are over 50 years old. It is not found on healthy trees, however, but only on those already weakened by heavy snow, caterpillars or other means. It has a particular predilection for smoke-damaged trees. If the trees attacked still have plenty of sap, the larvae drown in the resin, so that healthy trees are in no danger, and this species is consequently only a secondary pest. When the winter is over the female makes holes in the bark on the upper half of the tree and lays its eggs in them. The larvae eat irregular tunnels in the inner bark, but pupate in the sap-wood; their developmental cycle takes one year. Not infrequently they occur together with another species − *Pissodes scabricollis* − whose biology is very similar.

Pissodes piceae lives in a similar manner to the above species, but occurs only on silver firs. It may represent one of the many factors contributing to the steady decline and disappearance of these trees.

Many weevils eat the leaves or needles of various trees and in years of abundance such species can do a certain amount of damage, though not to an extent which makes them all worth mentioning. We will confine ourselves to just one genus — *Rhynchaenus*. One of the commonest species, *Rhynchaenus fagi,* occurs only where there are beeches, on which the adult beetles feed, attacking leaves, leaf-stalks and female flowers. Adults overwinter in leaf litter and reappear in the spring when the leaf buds begin to shoot. The larvae feed in the full-grown leaves, doing considerably more damage than the adults. They first of all mine long tunnels and then excavate wide cavities in the leaves, which in these places turn brown, so that a severely infested tree looks as though its leaves were frost-bitten; the result is a smaller growth of wood and smaller production of beech-nuts. The related species *Rhynchaenus quercus* has similar habits, but attacks oaks; other *Rhynchaenus* species are to be found on birches, alders, willows and elms.

We cannot conclude this section without mentioning the bark beetles (Scolytidae), which probably play a more important role in forestry than any other insects. The great majority of the roughly 120 species of these beetles in central Europe may be regarded as forest pests. The damage they do is of two different kinds and is related to their different brood biologies.

The majority of species breed in bark. The adult beetles gnaw through the outer bark and in or beneath it tunnel passages for the eggs; the larvae afterwards make passages of their own. The patterns made by the passages are very variable. For instance, if the males are polygamous there are several maternal shafts leading from the mating chamber. Very often an individual species can be identified from the pattern of its burrows. What makes these bark beetles serious pests is that their tunnels often encroach on the sap-wood and so interrupt the tree's supplies of nutrients and water, etc. In cases of large-scale infestation, whole plantations or woods may die. Normally the beetles prefer diseased, weakened or damaged trees, but if breeding conditions are particularly favourable, e. g. after large-scale damage by snow and wind, the expanding populations of bark beetles have a catastrophic effect, as healthy trees are then also attacked, especially in conifer forests. In this situation man is again partly responsible for the damage; in natural mixed woodlands bark beetles do not find such ideal conditions, as the various species are more or less specialized for feeding on particular kinds of trees and very large populations can develop quickly only in commercially more profitable monocultures.

Bark beetles which breed in the wood itself do quite different damage, since their burrows affect the commercial value of the wood. They are therefore properly to be regarded as pests of timber rather than of the forest trees themselves. The larvae of such bark beetles live in tunnels bored in the wood by the adults but do not eat the wood itself. Their food is the fungi which develop from spores brought into the burrows by the adults. The damage done by both types of beetles, i. e. those which breed in bark and those which breed in wood, is compounded by the fungal and other diseases which they so often carry.

Here we have room to mention only the commonest and — for forestry — most dangerous of the many species of these beetles.

A large number of bark-breeding species occur on deciduous trees, but the damage they do is seldom very serious. However, Elm Bark Beetles (particularly *Scolytus scolytus* and *S. multistriatus)* are known to be the principal vectors of Dutch Elm Disease, and other species may be implicated in the spread of other serious fungal diseases.

Among the few species breeding in the actual wood of deciduous trees, the only one worth mentioning is *Xyleborus dispar,* which attacks practically all types of deciduous trees and occasionally pines as well. Sometimes it does serious damage to fruit trees, especially apples and plums. Trees already harmed by drought or frost, etc, are particularly at risk.

The damage done by bark- and wood-breeding species to conifers is immeasurably greater. One of the species most feared by foresters is *Dendroctonus micans,* which breeds in 20- to 40-year-old spruces and in firs. It is unusually large for a bark beetle and can be responsible for blocking the flow of resin. It thus poses a threat to healthy trees and is therefore classified as a primary pest. It is often succeeded in its attacks by other beetles (e. g. *Pissodes* species) or by fungi (e. g. honey fungus), which hasten the process of decay. The biology of *Dendroctonus micans* has a particularly interesting feature. The female does not excavate a brood burrow beneath the bark, but merely hollows out a small cavity in which it lays the eggs singly or in little piles. Some of the resulting larvae then begin burrowing into the wood, working side by side in phalanx formation, while a small group follows behind, removing powdered wood, excreta, exuviae and dead larvae to the rear where this waste material is compacted into a firm slab. After a time these larvae force their way forwards to the head of the phalanx and the work in the rear is taken over by others.

One of the best-known and most destructive of bark beetles is the Engraver Beetle, *Ips typographus,* which is found mostly in spruces, but sometimes also in larches and pines. Since the male is polygamous, the mating chamber in the bark can have up to seven maternal shafts leading from it, and since every female lays 20−100 eggs there may be 20−100 larval burrows leading from each maternal shaft. These are at first very narrow, but grow rapidly wider and are very tortuous. The tunnelling larvae cut off the supply of sap in the inner bark with the result that the trunk eventually dries up and dies. Population explosions of the Engraver Beetle are most likely to occur in monocultures situated, on unsuitable ground and after damage by snow and wind. There may be two generations in years with favourable weather. In years when they are particularly abundant, these beetles will also attack healthy trees.

Pityokteines curvidens, a close relative of the above species, lives chiefly on firs and less often on other conifers. The males are again polygamous, their mating chamber in which the larvae also pupate lying in the sap-wood, at depths of up to 1 cm. As a rule there are two generations in one year, but if conditions are favourable there may be three. It is thus not surprising that populations of this bark beetle also have a tendency to increase extremely rapidly. Stands of silver fir on unsuitable ground and trees weakened by drought are particularly vulnerable. Together with *Pissodes piceae, Pityokteines curvidens* may be a contributory factor in the gradual decline of the silver fir.

The biology of *Ips cembrae* resembles in general that of the two preceding species, but its host is the larch and seldom any other conifer. Its burrows and brood chambers lie mainly in the bark and cause the tree little harm. Far more serious is the damage done by the adult beetles to the tops of young larches and to young shoots.

Tomicus piniperda, a monogamous bark-breeding species, causes similar damage to pines (less often to spruces and larches). The depredations of the larvae, which burrow mainly in the bark, are of less commercial significance than the damage done by the adults, which eat the previous year's new shoots. After large-scale attack − when the ground under the tree may be strewn with broken twigs − the trees look as if they had been pruned.

Tomicus minor has similar habits to its larger relative, but whereas *piniperda* swarms early in the year and may occasionally be active as early as February, *minor* does not appear until the middle of March or April; it does much more damage, however, since its burrows go deep into the sap-wood, cutting off the supply of sap, resulting in the death of the crown if not of the whole tree.

Damage done by wood-breeding bark beetles is always the same type. Firstly, their activities lower the commercial value of the wood, and secondly, their burrows leave the way open for invasion by other pests (especially fungi) which accelerate the process of wood decay.

Xyloterus lineatus, the Lineate Bark Beetle, breeds in spruces and other conifers. Wood-breeders are generally less specialized than those which breed in the bark, evidently because the larvae eat fungi and not the wood itself. Of all the wood-breeding bark beetles *Xyloterus lineatus* displays the most pronounced tendency to proliferate suddenly. It will even attack de-barked logs stored in damp surroundings.

Gnathotrichus materiarius is a North American beetle which breeds in the wood of both conifers and deciduous trees. The first specimen to be found in Germany was caught in 1965 in the Black Forest and the beetle was caught in Holland in the same year. This 'imported' beetle, previously known only from pines and Douglas firs, has since spread throughout the Black Forest and now belongs to the native fauna.

Platypus cylindrus is the last forest pest on our list. It is the sole central European representative of the family Platypodidae. The adult beetle is much like a bark beetle in general appearance, but has a more elongate body. Its biology may be succinctly summarized by stating that it is a fungus-growing monogamous beetle which breeds in the wood of standing or freshly felled oaks. Occasionally it will attack beeches, ashes, chestnuts or limes. The beetles swarm in June and July. The sexes practise division of labour, with the female excavating the brood passages, while the male clears away the waste. Since the brood passages lie in the heart-wood, the damage is considerable. However, this beetle is rare in most parts of central Europe, as well as in Britain.

Beneficial species

The preceding sections showed that numerous species of beetle compete with man for resources and, from the human standpoint, are pests and to a greater or lesser extent cause damage in houses, gardens, woods and fields. It was also made clear in the foregoing sections, however, that the reason why beetles' spheres of activity so often overlap and intersect with our own is the endless multitude of their species and the fact that they have settled in practically every type of ecosystem.

If we insist on viewing beetles from the narrow standpoint of our immediate economic interest there is another group which we ought not to overlook, i. e. beetles which are useful to man. What would happen to our fruit and vegetables and where would most of our other vegetation be were it not for the insects which carry pollen? Though bees (and various other insects) transport pollen from flower to flower, beetles certainly do their fair share.

Among the predacious beetles there are many which feed on those other insects which man regards as pests. Many ground beetles assist the farmer and the forester in their fight against grubs, caterpillars and slugs. In this connection, *Calosoma sycophanta* deserves special mention. Both the beetles and the larvae live on trees where they hunt caterpillars and pupae of various moths including *Lymantria dispar, Lymantria monacha, Euproctis chrysorrhoea, Panolis flammea* and *Dendrolimus pini,* all of which do tremendous damage to trees. In the course of its development a *Calosoma sycophanta* larva eats some 40 large caterpillars, while one adult consumes about 400 in a year. A large *Calosoma sycophanta* population is thus one of the best ways of keeping a forest 'clean'. At the beginning of this century North American forests were ravaged by moths (*Lymantria dispar* and *Euproctis chrysorrhoea*) brought in from Europe; as a control measure 6,000 specimens of *Calosoma sycophanta* were imported, allowed to multiply and then released. The damage was successfully contained and today *Calosoma sycophanta* is completely at home in North America. As a sequel to this successful 'naturalization', *Calosoma sycophanta* was also imported into Java after the First World War, again to combat caterpillar pests.

Many other beetle families also include species welcomed by the farmer and the forester. Like *Calosoma sycophanta,* the carrion beetle *Dendroxena quadripunctata* climbs trees and bushes in search of looper and other caterpillars. The members of the carrion beetle genera *Ablattaria* and *Phosphuga* live on slugs, snails and worms. The chequered beetle *Thanasimus formicarius* is a very effective predator of bark beetles in coniferous forests.

Homes in central Europe (but not in Britain) are occasionally visited by a beetle whose activities are definitely to be encouraged. Both adults and larvae of *Opilo domesticus* — one of the chequered beetles — are predators of various wood-feeding pests. Their appetites are considerable and one adult was seen to eat five Death-watch Beetles in an hour. The larvae are fairly long, but very thin, and therefore able to enter the burrows of quite small wood-boring beetles as well as those of the House Longhorn.

Opilo mollis is of similar appearance to *Opilo domesticus,* but only seldom found in households, where it hunts down longhorn beetles developing in wicker baskets and bottles. It normally lives in the open, where it feeds on the brood of bark beetles and tree-infesting longhorn beetles and is therefore an asset to forestry.

Another chequered beetle, *Tillus elongatus,* has been recorded from all parts of Europe, but is nevertheless rare. The very characteristically coloured black or blue-black and red beetle occurs in woods, on beeches and other deciduous trees. Like those of *Opilo,* its whitish larvae hunt other beetle grubs, their chief victims being the larvae of longhorn and jewel beetles.

Ladybirds (Coccinellidae), 100 species of which live in central Europe, are one of the best-known groups of beetles. They are popular with everybody, especially children, but are useful as well as pretty. A few species feed on plants or moulds, but the majority are predators. Some species have a predilection for aphids and are thus a great help in the garden, since both the beetles and their larvae eat these pests. The best-known species — and the one usually reproduced in children's books, etc — is the Seven-spot Ladybird (*Coccinella septempunctata*). It is one of the most abundant ladybirds in central Europe, and is easy to recognize as its colour pattern scarcely varies at all. It can be seen catching aphids and other small insects almost anywhere on herbaceous plants and is especially plentiful where aphids are numerous.

Often even more abundant, and quite as familiar, is the Two-spot Ladybird (*Adalia bipunctata*), but its colouring is so variable that an inexperienced amateur is bound to think he has several species before him. Two main forms can actually be distinguished. In one, the elytra are orange, each with a black spot; it is from this form that the ladybird takes both its Latin (*bipunctata*) and its vernacular name. In the other form the elytra have four or six red spots on a black background. However, between these two main forms there are countless other variants. This diversity of colour-pattern has a genetic basis but is partly under environmental control. The Two-spot Ladybird is particularly familiar as a winter-guest in houses; in the spring it comes out of hiding and appears on window-panes, trying to get out. After pairing, the female lays 100−150 eggs. The larvae are highly rapacious and devour numerous aphids. In 10−15 days, in which time they will have eaten 350−400 aphids, they are fully grown and pupate. The ladybird emerges after a pupation period of 5−10 days; it survives until the following year and also feeds on aphids.

Man thus has a whole series of beetle allies which help him in controlling other insect pests in a very wide variety of situations.

How to collect beetles

Beetles are to be found everywhere and the methods of catching them are correspondingly diverse. In addition, every experienced beetle collector has his own special techniques and tricks. The hints given below are therefore intended only as a guide to beginners. Most collectors doubtless began by making a casual find. One may have seen a ground beetle run across the path in front of him, another may have caught sight of a longhorn beetle perched on a flower, or one evening a May-beetle may have whirred in through a window, attracted indoors by the light. Once he has started to collect beetles, however, it is not long before the collector begins to concentrate on the most profitable hunting grounds. These include flowers of every possible kind, since many beetles live on pollen or nectar. On flowers we find representatives of many different families; yellow flowers are especially popular, particularly with jewel beetles (Buprestidae), but longhorn beetles, leaf beetles, nitidulids and rose chafers are also frequent flower-visitors. A good technique on hills and mountains is to look under stones, where ground beetles, rove beetles and even various leaf beetles and weevils are to be found. Stones provide shelter, as do pieces of timber and rotting tree stumps; the latter are a favourite winter haunt of ground beetles, burying beetles, click beetles and others. Beetles can thus be caught in the depths of winter simply by examining such stumps.

The greatest numbers of species and individuals, however, can be obtained by using various collecting aids. The most popular item is the sweep net, which is made of strong fabric and is attached to a frame with a stick or handle (Fig. 18); a collapsible frame makes the net easier to carry about. After sweeping the vegetation a few times with the net, the contents can be examined and the desired beetles taken out. Since this apparatus can be used for sweeping flowers as well as grasses, herbaceous plants, bushes and trees, the catch is often large, but beetles frequenting thick twigs and branches are generally missed. To catch these one needs a beating tray (Fig. 18) (in an emergency an umbrella comes in useful). The tray is held under a branch or a bush which is vigorously beaten a few times − preferably with a soft rubber truncheon to avoid damaging the vegetation too much. A more recent innovation, the car net, can also boast considerable success. This consists of a bag made of strong fabric fixed by its frame to the roof of a car. With the net in place one can drive slowly through the countryside, stopping to check the contents and select out specimens at convenient intervals. Car-net catches often include species which cannot be (or are rarely) obtained in any other way. It is a method which produces particularly good results along the margins of woods and on forest roads, especially just before sundown. Thousands of beetles may land in the net in a very short time, although the majority usually belong to only one or a very few species which happened to be swarming. The car net is thus not suitable for beginners. These beetles should not all be killed, as that would be irresponsible, but only an experienced collector is able to pick out the most interesting from such a vast number. The car net is used to catch beetles in flight and the other two pieces of apparatus to catch insects on vegetation, but an apparatus for catching beetles frequenting humus, fallen leaves, flood debris, moss and litter, etc. is also needed. For

Fig. 18. Some equipment for catching beetles. Left: bag sifter, middle: round beating tray, right: sweep-net.

this purpose a sifter is employed (Fig. 18), consisting of a bag made of strong material which has a built-in wire mesh filter and is tied together tightly at the bottom. Moss, fallen leaves, etc. are tipped into the space above the filter and the bag is vigorously shaken. Coarse material remains on the filter and, after a brief examination, can be discarded. Finer material and living organisms pass through the filter and collect at the bottom of the bag. When sufficient material has been sieved, the bottom of the bag is unbound and the contents are spread out on a white cloth (oil-cloth is the best). Most beetles at first lie quite still, but bit by bit they revive and try to run away — and that is the time to catch them. Sifted material does not need to be checked in the open country; it can be brought home in the bags and examined there at leisure. Plastic bags should be used only with care as condensation gathers inside them. Linen bags are preferable and in these the specimens can be kept in a cool place for several days.

Many species of soil-dwelling beetles live in burrows in earth, sand or clay banks and the best way to catch them is to flood them out. If we repeatedly splash water onto the sandy or clayey bank of a stream or pond we can soon drive the beetles there out of their lairs. A similar result can be achieved by digging up a divot of turf or cutting away a sample from a clay bank and washing the beetles out in a bucket of water. Being lighter than water, the beetles float to the surface and can be easily collected.

To complete the picture, we must not forget beetles living in water. Some of them hide away under submerged stones, wood and the like and cannot be persuaded to emerge. There is thus nothing left for it but to remove such material and examine it carefully. Aquatic plants can be shaken over a sifter, while species living freely in or on the water (predacious diving beetles, water scavenger beetles, whirligig beetles) are best caught with a net. This resembles the sweep net described above in most respects, but should not be made of thick material, which would offer too much resistance when dragged wet through the water. However, although not too closely woven the material used should be strong. A fine kitchen sieve can sometimes also make quite a satisfactory net, especially when investigating small pools and ditches.

Many other beetles may be collected by examining their special habitats: carrion, dung, both fresh and decaying fungi, birds' nests, etc. Many species are also readily caught with bait. The commonest, easiest and most successful method is to bury old tins or plastic beakers in the ground up to their rim and then place bait in them, the simplest being a piece of raw meat, fish, cheese, or fermenting fruit. (Some beetle experts have their own 'secret' recipe, their 'infallible' bait.) Ground beetles, rove beetles and carrion beetles among others are attracted by the smell of the bait and fall into the container, from which they are usually unable to escape. The traps should therefore be checked as often as possible (generally in the morning, as most predacious and carrion beetles are active by night) to make sure that the captive insects do not injure or devour each other. The bottom of the tin should also be perforated to let rain-water through, so that the beetles do not drown. It is equally important to cover the bait tin from above − preferably with a stone or a piece of wood. The beetles will always find a way to get at the bait; the purpose of the 'lid' is to prevent other animals, such as mice, shrews, foxes and (in inhabited areas) dogs, from stealing it. When the traps are no longer wanted they should be removed. It is irresponsible to take from nature what we do not need.

Unbaited pitfalls (or barber traps) are often used for quantitative investigations. In general they are the same as the traps described above and may also be used with bait, but are provided with chemicals for killing and preserving their catch. They can therefore be left for much longer intervals, but since all the insects in them are killed, they and similar methods should be used only for essential investigations of a quantitative type.

In general, the hints in this book on how to catch beetles are − like the book itself − intended primarily for the layman. A much more detailed discussion of methods used to collect beetles is contained in 'A Coleopterist's Handbook' published by the Amateur Entomologist's Society. Methods for collecting and preserving all groups of insects are dealt with in the 'Handbook for Collectors' published by the British Museum (Natural History).

How to kill and prepare beetles

The close study required for identification of most beetles generally necessitates the use of a lens or binocular microscope. The insects first need to be killed, and for this ethyl acetate (also known as acetic ether) is recommended. Absorbent material (e.g. tissue paper or clean sawdust) is placed in the bottom of a wide-necked jar or specimen tube and moistened with a few drops of this chemical, after which the container is sealed with a tight-fitting stopper. Plain ether and chloroform are unsuitable as they leave specimens very stiff and unsuitable for preparation. Containers should be checked before use to ensure that they are not dissolved by ethyl acetate. Glass is the most reliable material.

When killing beetles with coloured scales (many weevils and Scarabaeidae) care must be taken to use only a small amount of ethyl acetate or, even better, a cyanide jar (as for butterflies) should be used.

When out collecting beetles, killing jars and vials of various sizes should be taken. It is advisable to collect small and very small beetles separately from larger species. Beetles from different localities and habitats should also be kept in separate containers. It is important to label the containers immediately so as to avoid confusion later. If labels are placed inside the container they should be written in pencil, as the ink from a fountain-pen or a ball-point pen will run if it meets with ethyl acetate vapour.

Some of the equipment needed to prepare beetles can be made at home, although some will have to be bought in special shops catering for entomologists. Special entomological pins (ordinary pins and other needles are unsuitable because they are too short and generally go rusty), mounting blocks, a water-soluble glue, dissecting needles, fine brushes and a setting surface (a sheet of plastic foam about 2−3 cm thick covered with white paper) will all be needed. Large beetles are dealt with by pinning them to the setting surface ventral side downwards with an entomological pin thrust vertically through the anterior third of the right elytron. Some two-thirds of the pin should project below the specimen. Using a dissecting needle (a needle with a slightly curved tip, fixed in a holder), the appendages are arranged in the required position — the antennae preferably recurved over the thorax and the elytra and pointing forwards or sideways only if they are short. The legs should be arranged symmetrically close to the sides of the body, the forelegs pointing forwards and the middle legs and hindlegs backwards. If the appendages are spread out too much they are in danger of getting broken off when they are dry and brittle. The limbs are kept in the required position during setting with extra pins. Once set, beetles must be left for a time to dry in the air. No further treatment is usually needed, with one exception — members of the genus *Meloe*. These beetles have such a bulky body and such a thin cuticle that they rot rather than dry out, so that before setting them we must open their abdomen, remove the viscera and fill the shell with cottonwool. However, most beetles are so small that they either cannot be pinned directly, or there is a real danger that parts important for their identification may be destroyed by the pin. Such beetles are mounted by gluing them on to a card. The beetle is turned on to its back, the appendages are manipulated into a suitable position, a tiny drop of a water-soluble glue is applied to the card and the beetle is fixed in place ventral side down; this still leaves time to make any necessary alterations to the position of the body, legs and antennae before the glue dries.

The best time for setting is the day the insect is caught. As soon as it is placed in the killing jar its muscles usually go into spasms and it takes some time before they relax. To keep the beetles supple it is customary to add a few extra drops of ethyl acetate to the jar after returning home. Most beetles can be left in such a jar some time before dealing with them. If, by chance, they have become too dry they must be moistened before setting; any non-rusting vessel which can be tightly closed will do. The beetles are left for 24 hours (or longer, if necessary) until they are once again pliant. Thymol or some similar substance can be added to prevent mildew from forming.

Beetles treated soon after they have been caught take anything from a few days to a couple of weeks to dry (i. e. until the setting pins can be taken out and the beetle removed from the setting surface), according to their size. The environmental temperature and degree of humidity also influence the drying time. Re-moistened beetles dry very quickly after preparation and only need to be left a short time on the setting-board.

When the beetle is removed from the setting surface it must be provided with a label. Attached to every beetle's pin there should be a label giving the place and date of collection and the name of the collector, e. g.:

England
Surrey: Barnes
18 July 1983
D.J.Goodman

S.W. GERMANY
nr GERLINGEN
16.III.1979
K.W. Harde

In addition to this general purpose label, on which grid references may also be written, other labels detailing the circumstances under which the find was made (the habitat is particularly important), can also be used.

How to start a collection

Today the amateur entomologist is likely to be faced with a very pertinent question: is making an insect collection a justifiable activity? In a situation where man has already done such damage to the natural world, is it right to gather specimens simply so as to put them in a collection? Concern about this question has led to the publication, in Britain, of 'A Code for Insect Collecting', — and this code is followed by most insect collectors. It is reproduced at the end of this section. Certainly, collecting just for the sake of collecting is hardly any different from collecting for the sake of killing. However, collecting for a special purpose, for example, in order to investigate the composition of a local fauna, is different. Such collections can later be of great use to broader studies. Since so little is known about our native beetles, amateur entomologists who build up local or other special collections can make a very useful contribution to science. No sensible beetle collector does any real harm to the natural world and it is certainly not the amateur entomologist who is responsible for the impoverishment of our insect fauna. The real culprits are the individuals and public bodies who participate in the destruction of whole ecosystems. Not only are innumerable beetles killed by pesticides and artificial fertilisers, but with the destruction of natural habitats whole species may be eliminated. Forest 'hygiene' can have a catastrophic effect on wood-dwelling species, the draining of fens and other 'wetlands' makes many others homeless and the reclamation of every scrap of previously uncultivated land speeds the final retreat of a once flourishing native fauna.

How is a collection started and how do we build it up? This will naturally depend on how much time and effort the collector is able and willing to put into his hobby. At all events, once prepared and labelled specimens must be properly arranged. The guide to families in this book (pp. 69−77) shows that almost 100 different beetle families are represented in both central Europe and Britain. In general it will be preferable to keep the members of one family together. In most cases the descriptive part of this book will be a sufficient guide but, in some cases, the help of an experienced colleague may be needed. Right at the outset it is advisable to prepare several store boxes, which can either be bought in a special shop or made at home. Any strong cardboard or wooden box deep enough to take an entomological pin with room to spare will do. To the floor of this box should be glued a sheet of material which will firmly hold the pins once the beetles have been set; plastic foam or cork are the most satisfactory. Families with a large number of species should each be allotted their own box.

The more beetles we collect, the more difficult the arrangement of a collection becomes. After a time a decision may have to be made. What do we really want − a collection of locally occurring species or a collection of wider geographical scope but perhaps restricted to one particular beetle group? There is one thing every beginner should realise: that his collection is at risk from the very first day. If it is exposed to damp it may become mildewed. Also, we must not forget dust-lice and Museum Beetles, which can ruin a whole collection in a relatively short time. Regular inspection is not sufficient; from time to time store boxes must be treated with chemicals especially in the spring, as it is then that the worst of them, the Museum Beetle, flies into the house from outside. Its voracious larvae are able to find their way into a collection through the tiniest of cracks. Eggs may also be present, undetected, in prepared beetles we have left to dry, or in specimens given to us by a colleague. We must therefore be extremely careful if we are to obtain continued pleasure from collecting beetles, a hobby which can help to give us a broader and deeper knowledge and understanding of nature.

A code for insect collecting

(Reproduced by kind permission of the Joint Committee for the Conservation of British Insects)

This Committee believes that with the ever-increasing loss of habitats resulting from forestry, agriculture, and industrial, urban and recreational development, the point has been reached where a code for collecting should be considered in the interests of conservation of the British insect fauna, particularly Macrolepidoptera. The Committee considers that in many areas this loss has gone so far that collecting, which at one time would have had a trivial effect, could now affect the survival in them of one or more species if continued without restraint.

The Committee also believes that by subscribing to a code of collecting, entomologists will show themselves to be a concerned and responsible body of naturalists who have a positive contribution to make to the cause of conservation. It asks all entomologists to accept the following Code in principle and to try to observe it in practice.

1. COLLECTING—GENERAL

1.1 No more specimens than are strictly required for any purpose should be killed.

1.2 Readily identified insects should not be killed if the object is to 'look them over' for aberrations or other purposes: insects should be examined while alive and then released where they were captured.

1.3 The same species should not be taken in numbers year after year from the same locality.

1.4 Supposed or actual predators and parasites of insects should not be destroyed.

1.5 When collecting leaf-mines, galls and seed heads never collect all that can be found; leave as many as possible to allow the population to recover.

1.6 Consideration should be given to photography as an alternative to collecting, particularly in the case of butterflies.

1.7 Specimens for exchange, or disposal to other collectors, should be taken sparingly or not at all.

1.8 For commercial purposes insects should be either bred or obtained from old collections. Insect specimens should not be used for the manufacture of 'jewellery'.

2. COLLECTING—RARE AND ENDANGERED SPECIES

2.1 Specimens of Macrolepidoptera listed by this Committee (and published in the entomological journals) should be collected with the greatest restraint. As a guide, the Committee suggests that a pair of specimens is sufficient, but that those species in the greatest danger should not be collected at all. The list may be amended from time to time if this proves to be necessary.

2.2 Specimens of distinct local forms of Macrolepidoptera, particularly butterflies, should likewise be collected with restraint.

2.3 Collectors should attempt to break new ground rather than collect a local or rare species from a well-known and perhaps over-worked locality.

2.4 Previously unknown localities for rare species should be brought to the attention of this Committee, which undertakes to inform other organisations as appropriate and only in the interests of conservation.

3. COLLECTING—LIGHTS AND LIGHT-TRAPS

3.1 The 'catch' at light, particularly in a trap, should not be killed casually for subsequent examination.

3.2 Live trapping, for instance in traps filled with egg-tray material, is the preferred method of collecting. Anaesthetics are harmful and should not be used.

3.3 After examination of the catch the insects should be kept in cool, shady conditions and released away from the trap site at dusk. If this is not possible the insects should be released in long grass or other cover and not on lawns or bare surfaces.

3.4 Unwanted insects should not be fed to fish or insectivorous birds and mammals.

3.5 If a trap used for scientific purposes is found to be catching rare or local species unnecessarily it should be re-sited.

3.6 Traps and lights should be sited with care so as not to annoy neighbours or cause confusion.

4. COLLECTING—PERMISSION AND CONDITIONS

4.1 Always seek permission from landowner or occupier when collecting on private land.

4.2 Always comply with any conditions laid down by the granting of permission to collect.

4.3 When collecting on nature reserves, or sites of known interest to conservationists, supply a list of species collected to the appropriate authority.

4.4 When collecting on nature reserves it is particularly important to observe the code suggested in section 5.

5. COLLECTING—DAMAGE TO THE ENVIRONMENT

5.1 Do as little damage to the environment as possible. Remember the interests of other naturalists; be careful of nesting birds and vegetation, particularly rare plants.

5.2 When 'beating' for lepidopterous larvae or other insects never thrash trees and bushes so that foliage and twigs are removed. A sharp jarring of branches is both less damaging and more effective.

5.3 Coleopterists and others working dead timber should replace removed bark and worked material to the best of their ability. Not all the dead wood in a locality should be worked.

5.4 Overturned stones and logs should be replaced in their original positions.

5.5 Water weed and moss which has been worked for insects should be replaced in its appropriate habitat. Plant material in litter heaps should be replaced and not scattered about.

5.6 Twigs, small branches and foliage required as foodplants or because they are galled, e.g. by clearwings, should be removed neatly with secateurs or scissors and not broken off.

5.7 'Sugar' should not be applied so that it renders tree-trunks and other vegetation unnecessarily unsightly.

5.8 Exercise particular care when working for rare species, e.g. by searching for larvae rather than beating for them.

5.9 Remember the Country Code!

6. BREEDING

6.1 Breeding from a fertilised female or pairing in captivity is preferable to taking a series of specimens in the field.

6.2 Never collect more larvae or other livestock than can be supported by the available supply of foodplant.

6.3 Unwanted insects that have been reared should be released in the original locality, not just anywhere.

6.4 Before attempting to establish new populations or 'reinforce' existing ones please consult this Committee.

Classification and scientific names

In modern scientific works the myriad species making up the order Coleoptera (beetles) are apportioned among 20 or so superfamilies which, in turn, are divided into some 170 families. About 100 of these families have representatives in central Europe. All but a handful are also represented by species in the British Isles. The arrangement of families and higher categories serves to provide a reference system, but the grouping of species and genera is not a simple pigeon-holing process. Increasingly, classifications of beetles aim to reflect the evolutionary (phyletic) relationships of the species, rather than merely provide a means of grouping together those which are (sometimes only superficially) similar. With increasing knowledge classifications change (hopefully for the better), so that the systems employed in any two works are rarely identical. For example, the family classification used in Joy's (1932) *Practical Handbook of British Beetles* differs radically from that in most general use in Britain today. Competing systems of classification may also be in use at the same time. This is exemplified by differences in current practice between Britain on the one hand and central European countries on the other.

In this book, for ease of comparison with the only up-to-date and comprehensive work for the identification of central and north European beetles, the system employed in *Die Käfer Mitteleuropas* has been adopted. However, the spelling of a few family names has been emended (e.g. Leiodidae instead of Liodidae) to conform with the rules of zoological nomenclature.

The currently accepted family classsification which serves as a standard for British coleopterists is that employed in the Coleoptera part of *A Check List of British Insects* (1977). A generally similar system is also used in Scandinavia, North America and elsewhere. The discrepancies between the 'British' and 'central European' systems of classification may present the reader with difficulties if further information is sought in modern, specialist British works. For this reason a list of the differences in usage is given below:

Family, sub-family and genus equivalents

Current British Check List	Die Käfer Mitteleuropas and this book
Noteridae (separate family)	Noterinae (subfamily of Dytiscidae)
Helophorinae (Hydrophilidae)	included in Hydraenidae
Hydrochinae (Hydrophilidae)	included in Hydraenidae
Spercheinae (Hydrophilidae)	Spercheidae (separate family)
Catopinae (Leiodidae)	Catopidae (separate family)
Coloninae (Leiodidae)	Colonidae (separate family)
Malachiinae (Melyridae)	Malachiidae (separate family)
Psephenidae (separate family)	Eubriinae (subfamily of Dascillidae)
Elmidae (separate family)	Elminthinae (subfamily of Dryopidae)
Georissinae (Hydrophilidae)	Georissidae (separate family)
Limnichidae (separate family)	Limnichinae (subfamily of Byrrhidae)
Trogossitidae (separate family)	included in Peltidae
Silvanidae (separate family)	included in Cucujidae
Monotominae (Rhizophagidae)	included in Cucujidae
Hypocopridae (separate family)	included in Cucujidae

66

Biphyllidae (separate family)	included in Erotylidae
Merophysiidae (separate family)	included in Lathridiidae
Cerylonidae (separate family)	Cerylinae (subfamily of Colydiidae)
Aspidiphorus (Sphindidae)	Aspidiphoridae (separate family)
Salpingidae (separate family)	Salpinginae (subfamily of Pythidae)
Mycteridae (separate family)	Mycterinae (subfamily of Pythidae)
Anaspis (Scraptiidae)	Anaspidinae (subfamily of Mordellidae)
Tetratomidae (separate family)	included in Melandryidae
Lagriinae (Tenebrionidae)	Lagriidae (separate family)
Alleculinae (Tenebrionidae)	Alleculidae (separate family)
Geotrupidae (separate family)	Geotrupinae (subfamily of Scarabaeidae)
Trogidae (separate family)	Troginae (subfamily of Scarabaeidae)
Nemonychidae (separate family)	Rhinomacerinae (subfamily of Curculionidae)
Attelabidae (separate family)	Rhynchitinae, Attelabinae & Apoderinae (subfamilies of Curculionidae)
Apionidae (separate family)	Apioninae (subfamily of Curculionidae)

Note: family names have the ending -idae; sub-family names have the ending -inae; italicised names denote genera.

English vernacular names exist for many kinds of beetle (e.g. ladybird, glowworm, weevil), but such names are generally applicable to whole families or large groups of species. Only a few beetles (for example Spanish Fly, Nut Weevil) have common English names which apply to a single species. Common names also have other shortcomings. There are problems inherent in translating the vernacular from one language to another, and common names tend to vary from region to region, even within a single country. Sometimes the same name is applied to different species in different places. For example, the species generally known as the Death-watch Beetle in Britain is that which bears the scientific name *Xestobium rufovillosum* (p. 210 : 6). However, in central Europe the equivalent name in German is applied to another species of the same family − *Anobium pertinax* (p. 212 : 6).

The scientific names of species are intended to be universally applicable. An important aim of scientific nomenclature is that one particular name should be applied consistently to the same species. It is also axiomatic that no two species should bear the same name. The *Code of Zoological Nomenclature* exists to regulate the ways in which scientific names for beetles and other animals are formed and used. However, the Code has no legal status as such, and its enforcement depends on the voluntary agreement of zoologists to observe its provisions. Not surprisingly, differences of usage arise, and the same species may be referred to by different names in different works. This may simply reflect differences of opinion concerning relationships between species, so that one author refers a particular species to one genus, while another refers it to a second. In such questions of scientific judgment the Code has no say.

A lack of uniformity in scientific names is particularly evident in the case of well-known and common European beetles. In this book the scientific names used for the various species are those of the *Check List of British Insects* (1977). The reader should note that, ignoring minor differences of spelling, almost one-tenth of the species illustrated are listed under different names in the standard central European works.

Guide to families

Most insect handbooks include dichotomous keys for determination of at least the higher systematic groups (orders, families and genera). These have been dispensed with here, since a full key for the identification of families would be excessively long and would involve a very large number of detailed drawings. In addition, successful use of such a key would entail a good knowledge of beetle morphology and the possession of a binocular microscope.

Instead, on the following pages we have illustrated in outline a typical example of each of the beetle families represented in central Europe. The drawings used have been taken from '*Die Käfer Mitteleuropas*', the standard work (in 11 volumes) on central European beetles, by Freude, Harde and Lohse. The numbers immediately below the drawings are the same as those used by Freude *et al.* to codify the various genera and species. For example, in the family Carabidae the illustrated example is given the code number 66 : 8, which translates as:

66: genus *Chlaenius,* and

8: species *vestitus.*

Below the drawings the reader will also find the name of the family and the number of species known in central Europe. The figures in brackets denote the number of species found in the British Isles. The final line refers to the pages in the systematic part of this book which concern the relevant family.

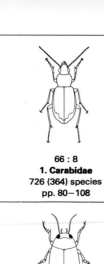

66 : 8
1. Carabidae
726 (364) species
pp. 80—108

1 : 1
2. Hygrobiidae
1 (1) species
—

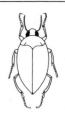

3 : 5
3. Haliplidae
20 (19) species
p. 110

23 : 9
4. Dytiscidae
154 (111) species
pp. 110—114

2 : 6
5. Gyrinidae
13 (12) species
p. 114

1 : 5
6. Rhysodidae
2 (0) species
—

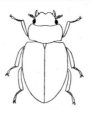

1 : 19
7. Hydraenidae
93 (55) species
p. 116

1 : 1
8. Spercheidae
1 (1) species
—

17 : 1
9. Hydrophilidae
72 (64) species
pp. 116—118

29 : 1
10. Histeridae
94 (50) species
pp. 120—122

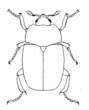

1 : 1
11. Sphaeritidae
1 (1) species
—

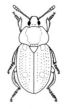

6 : 1
12. Silphidae
30 (20) species
pp. 124—126

2 : 1
13. Leptinidae
3 (1) species
p. 126

5 : 1
14. Catopidae
63 (32) species
p. 126

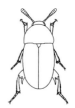

1 : 12
15. Colonidae
20 (9) species
p. 128

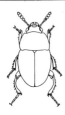

3 : 20
16. Leiodidae
82 (52) species
p. 128

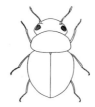

2 : 9
17. Clambidae
13 (9) species
p. 128

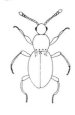

8 : 1
18. Scydmaenidae
84 (30) species
p. 130

8 : 3
19. Corylophidae
20 (10) species
p. 130

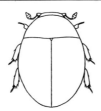

1 : 1
20. Sphaeriidae
1 (1) species
p. 132

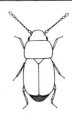

13 : 1
21. Ptiliidae
87 (72) species
pp. 132–134

2 : 1
22. Scaphidiidae
11 (5) species
p. 134

99 : 1
23. Staphylinidae
about 2,000
(994) species
pp. 136–158

25 : 1
24. Pselaphidae
131 (50) species
pp. 160–162

1 : 1
25. Lycidae
8 (4) species
p. 164

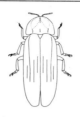

2 : 1 ♂
26. Lampyridae
3 (2) species
p. 164

2 : 5
27. Cantharidae
103 (41) species
p. 166

1 : 1a ♂
28. Drilidae
2 (1) species
p. 168

6 : 7
29. Malachiidae
50 (15) species
p. 168

5 : 6
30. Melyridae
(includes Phloiophilidae)
29 (8) species
p. 164

9 : 1
31. Cleridae
27 (9) species
p. 170

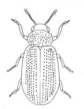

2 : 1
32. Derodontidae
2 (1) species
p. 170

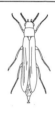

1 : 1
33. Lymexylidae
3 (2) species
p. 170

16 : 2
34. Elateridae
168 (69) species
pp. 172–176

1 : 1
35. Cerophytidae
1 (0) species
p. 176

3 : 1
36. Eucnemidae
25 (6) species
p. 176

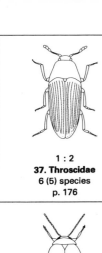

1 : 2
37. Throscidae
6 (5) species
p. 176

12 : 2
38. Buprestidae
118 (12) species
pp. 178–182

1 : 1
39. Dascillidae
(includes Psepehenidae)
1 (1) species
p. 184

6 : 1
40. Scirtidae
25 (19) species
p. 184

1 : 1
41. Eucinetidae
3 (1) species
—

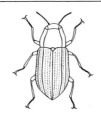

7 : 1
42. Dryopidae
42 (21) species
p. 184

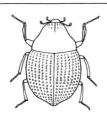

1 : 1
43. Georissidae
5 (1) species
—

2 : 6
44. Heteroceridae
15 (8) species
p. 186

1 : 17
45. Dermestidae
48 (30) species
p. 186

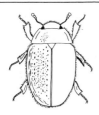

1 : 1
46. Nosodendridae
1 (0) species
p. 186

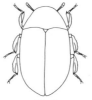

11 : 2
47. Byrrhidae
(includes Limnichidae)
39 (12) species
p. 186

3 : 1
48. Trogossitidae
(includes Peltidae)
10 (4) species
p. 188

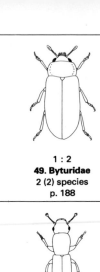

1 : 2
49. Byturidae
2 (2) species
p. 188

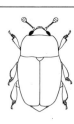

8 : 26
50. Nitidulidae
146 (95) species
pp. 188–190

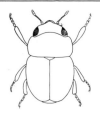

1 : 4
51. Cybocephalidae
5 (0) species
p. 192

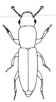

1 : 8
52. Rhizophagidae
14 (12) species
p. 192

7 : 2
53. Cucujidae (includes Hypocopridae)
49 (34) species
p. 192

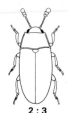

2 : 3
54. Erotylidae (includes Biphyllidae)
19 (7) species
p. 194

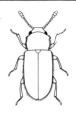

8 : 40
55. Cryptophagidae
134 (100) species
p. 194

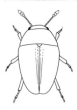

2 : 11
56. Phalacridae
22 (16) species
p. 196

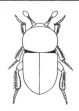

1 : 1
57. Thorictidae
2 (0) species
—

5 : 1
58. Lathridiidae
67 (51) species
p. 196

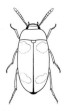

4 : 1
59. Mycetophagidae
14 (11) species
p. 198

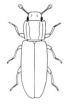

16 : 1
60. Colydiidae
39 (16) species
p. 198

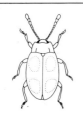

13 : 1
61. Endomychidae
23 (6) species
p. 198

25 : 3
62. Coccinellidae
88 (43) species
pp. 200–204

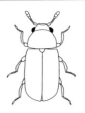

1 : 1
63. Sphindidae
1 (1) species
p. 206

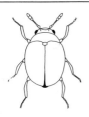

1 : 1
64. Aspidiphoridae
2 (1) species
p. 206

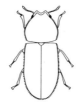

7 : 2
65. Cisidae
45 (22) species
p. 206

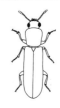

2 : 1
66. Lyctidae
4 (5) species
p. 208

8 : 1
67. Bostrychidae
18 (3) species
p. 208

12 : 12
68. Anobiidae
76 (28) species
pp. 210–214

5 : 1
69. Ptinidae
23 (21) species
p. 216

6 : 1
70. Oedemeridae
30 (9) species
p. 218

7 : 3
71. Pythidae
18 (12) species
p. 218

1 : 2
72. Pyrochroidae
3 (3) species
p. 220

1 : 1
73. Scraptiidae
2 (3) species
p. 220

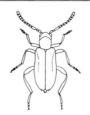

2 : 1
74. Aderidae
9 (3) species
p. 220

3 : 1
75. Anthicidae
32 (13) species
p. 220

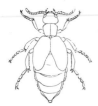

7 : 6
76. Meloidae
33 (9) species
p. 222

3 : 1
77. Rhipiphoridae
5 (1) species
p. 222

2 : 1
78. Mordellidae
118 (24) species
p. 222

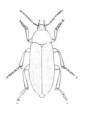

16 : 1
79. Melandryidae
41 (18) species
p. 224

1 : 1
80. Lagriidae
3 (2) species
p. 224

3 : 1
81. Alleculidae
33 (8) species
p. 224

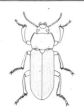

33 : 3
82. Tenebrionidae
74 (34) species
pp. 226–228

1 : 1
83. Boridae
1 (0) species

33 : 2
84. Scarabaeidae
218 (89) species
pp. 230–242

1 : 1 ♂
85. Lucanidae
7 (3) species
p. 244

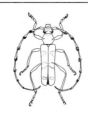

46 : 1
86. Cerambycidae
231 (63) species
pp. 246–270

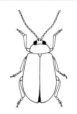

46 : 1
87. Chrysomelidae
574 (256) species
pp. 272–282

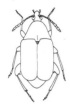

6 : 1
88. Bruchidae
35 (13) species
pp. 284–286

3 : 1
89. Anthribidae
22 (8) species
p. 286

30 : 1
90. Scolytidae
119 (57) species
pp. 312–316

1 : 1
91. Platypodidae
1 (1) species
p. 316

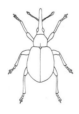

13 : 67
92. Curculionidae
about 1,200 (416) species
pp. 286–312

Guide to species

The precise identification of northern and central European beetles can present formidable problems to the beginner, even when armed with the appropriate specialist literature and a good microscope. This is especially true of small species belonging to such families as Ptiliidae, Cryptophagidae, Nitidulidae and Staphylinidae. However, even some of the larger beetles may sometimes be difficult to distinguish from their close relatives. For example, there are about ten central European species of *Ampedus* click beetle with red wing-cases; several of these might be confused with the two illustrated on page 172 (*Ampedus sanguineus* and *A. pomorum*).

Nevertheless, the coloured illustrations in the section which follows should enable the more distinctive British and central European beetles to be identified to species. At the same time, a large selection of other species, including representatives of the majority of northern and central European beetle genera, are also figured. Using the illustrations, an approximate identification, usually at least to genus, will be possible for all but the most 'difficult' groups, such as some Staphylinidae, some Ptiliidae, etc.. To enable the reader to judge whether the correct species has indeed been located, after looking through the illustrations, relevant information is included in the text. For each genus the number of species by which it is represented in central Europe is indicated, and the number of species (if any) found in the British Isles is also noted. If the species illustrated is not the only member of its genus to be found in the relevant region, identification to species may well be impracticable. However, some such species have very distinctive features which enable them to be distinguished from all of their relatives, and in these cases the recognition features receive mention. As an example of how this might work in practice let us consider the carrion beetles illustrated on page 124. If the beetle which we wish to identify has the distinctive colouring and other features of *Oiceoptoma thoracica* (fig. 5) we may by sure of our identification. The text makes it clear that this species is the only member of its genus found in central and northern Europe, and that it resembles no species of any other genus. If, by its abbreviated elytra and other features, we conclude that the beetle before us is a member of the genus *Nicrophorus* the position is rather different. If our specimen is uniformly black it will be compared with the illustration of *N. humator* (fig. 1) which, the text informs us, is the only British *Nicrophorus* of this colour. If, on the other hand, the specimen has elytra which are patterned orange-red and black, more or less resembling *N. vespillo* (fig. 2), we cannot be sure which species we have. The text tells us that *Nicrophorus* is represented in Britain, but mentions no features by which *N. vespillo* can be distinguished from the others (except the plain black *N. humator*). This is because the five orange-red and black British species of the genus are not easy to tell apart.

In the following section each species entry includes a scientific name which, for species found in the British Isles, conforms to current British usage. Where a different scientific name is applied to the species in the standard central European work of Freude, Harde & Lohse, or has been widely used in other literature, this is indicated in the text. Common English names are included where these are well-known and widely used. The species name is followed by an indication of body length, measured from the front of the head to the tip of the abdomen, ignoring the legs and antennae. Careful attention should be paid to the measurements, as illustrations are not all to the same scale.

Also accompanying each name, and at the right of the page, are two numbers. These are to enable the species to be located in the standard work of Freude *et al,* so that a provisional identification using the coloured plates may be followed up by consulting the keys and figures in that more exhaustive work. For example, the number 25 : 3 in the family Coccinellidae shows that we are dealing with coccinellid genus no. 25 (*Coccinella*), and species no. 3 of that genus (*septempunctata*) — the Seven-spot Ladybird. Species known to occur in the British Isles are indicated by an asterisk.

As noted above, the text provides information concerning diagnostic features and the number of related and similar species. It also attempts to summarise the more salient points with regard to the species' general biology.

Family Carabidae — ground beetles

This exceedingly large family is represented in central Europe by 89 genera and 726 species; 364 are found in the British Isles. It has frequently been subdivided into smaller families (the extreme being 25), but the present consensus is to regard all ground beetles, with the not infrequent exception of the tiger beetles, as belonging to a single family. The Rhysodidae are also frequently placed as a sub-group of the Carabidae. Ground beetles are mostly predacious, although a good number of species are omnivorous or vegetarian.

1 *Cicindela sylvatica, 14—20 mm   (1 : 2)

Eleven species of the genus *Cicindela* live in central Europe (5 in the British Isles) and this group of ground beetles, known as tiger beetles, are often regarded as a separate family, or at least a separate subfamily. All the species have a similar body form. They are the only ground beetles which instantly fly away when disturbed. Both beetles and larvae (which lie in wait for their prey at the mouths of their burrows) are exclusively predacious. *C. sylvatica* can be distinguished from all other species of the genus by its black labrum, which has a sharp ridge down the centre. This species occurs mainly in the northern and eastern part of central Europe. In Britain it is restricted to the southern counties of England. The beetles are to be found from April to August on sandy ground, especially heathland, but are generally local and rare.

2 *Cicindela germanica, 7.5—10.5 mm   (1 : 8)

This tiny, dark green to bluish green species is distributed from western Europe to Asia, but is of very local occurrence in central Europe. In Britain it is known to occur in only a few southern counties of England. The beetles are to be found from May to September; unlike most other tiger beetles they do not readily take to the wing.

3 *Cicindela hybrida, 11.5—15.5 mm   (1 : 5)

The variability of the dorsal markings of this species has led to the description of several subspecies, varieties and aberrations. *C. hybrida* is one of the commonest tiger beetles in most parts of Europe but very local in Britain. The beetles can be observed from April to October, particularly in sandy places near the sea, but also inland, even up to 2,000 m in the mountains of central Europe.

4 *Cicindela campestris* — Field Tiger Beetle, 10.5—14.5 mm   (1 : 7)

This beetle, which is usually green with a pale spot on each elytron, is the best known and commonest member of the genus in the British Isles and much of Europe. The beetles can be seen from April to September.

5 Cicindela silvicola, 12—16 mm   (1 : 3)

This species may occasionally be confused with *C. hybrida,* but it always has a light-coloured labrum (upper lip). It is a montane central European species with a range extending to central Italy. From April to August the beetles can be seen on dry, sandy paths in mountain forests. The species is absent in flat country.

6 *Cicindela maritima, 10—13 mm   (1 : 6)

Long regarded as only a subspecies of *C. hybrida,* but clearly a species in its own right. It can be distinguished from *C. hybrida* by the central spot on its elytra, which turn backward at a sharper angle. This species is widespread in Europe and Asia. In northern Europe it is to be found from April to September, but only on open sandy ground beside the Baltic, the North Sea and the Irish Sea.

7 Calosoma sycophanta, 17.5—28 mm   (2 : 2)

In central Europe there are five species of the genus *Calosoma.* Both the beetles and the larvae of most species climb trees where they prey on other insects; the adult beetles can also fly very well. The larval period is usually only a few weeks, but the beetles live 2—4 years. *Calosoma sycophanta* was imported into North America to combat caterpillar pests and was soon completely acclimatized. It is absent from the British Isles and rare in the western part of central Europe, but fairly common in the south and the east.

8 *Calosoma inquisitor, 13.5—20 mm   (2 : 1)

This species — the commonest of the genus in central Europe and the only species found in Britain — inhabits oakwoods, and where caterpillar pests are present it is not infrequently very common. Its elytra are usually brassy-green but may also be blue or black.

9 Calosoma auropunctatum, 20—30 mm

The most characteristic features of this beetle, which mainly inhabits the Mediterranean region and is rare in central Europe, are the gold-green dimples in its elytra.

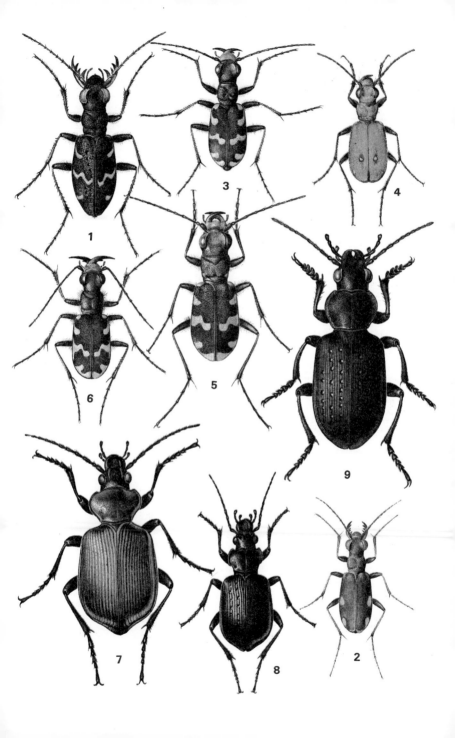

1 *Procerus gigas,* 40−60 mm (3 : 1)

Of the various species of the genus *Procerus* which occur in south-eastern Europe and the Near East, this is the only one with a distribution extending to central Europe, where it is found in Styria and Carinthia (Austria). The beetle resembles the more widespread and common *Carabus coriaceus,* but is much larger. It stalks its prey (mainly edible snails) by night, but occasionally in the daytime as well. It may live for three years or more.

2 *Carabus coriaceus,* 30−40 mm (4 : 1)

In central Europe there are 33 species of the genus *Carabus,* large and flightless ground beetles whose membranous hindwings have in most cases regressed; 11 species occur in the British Isles. They are primarily predators, but also eat fruit. *Carabus* species have an abdominal gland from which they can release or actively squirt a malodorous defensive secretion. The males can be identified by the wide tarsal segments of their first pair of legs. Although not found in the British Isles, *Carabus coriaceus* is one of the commonest species in most parts of Europe and is to be found at a wide range of altitudes. It hides away in the daytime and during the winter and has a life span of 2−3 years.

3 *Carabus irregularis,* 19−30 mm (4 : 3)

This forest-dwelling species occurs at moderately high and high altitudes in central Europe. The beetle has a flat and mostly copper-coloured body with a metallic sheen, pitted with a number of striking gold-green depressions.

4 *Carabus depressus,* 18−28 mm (4 : 4)

This species has broad, flat elytra irregularly pitted with metallic, gleaming depressions. It is represented in central Europe by the subspecies *C. depressus bonelli* which is to be found in the Alps, except for the extreme east. The adult beetles can be seen from July to September.

5 **Carabus violaceus* − Violet Ground Beetle, 22−35 mm (4 : 7)

This widely distributed species, which extends to eastern Siberia and Japan, includes many subspecies. These various geographical races undoubtedly result from isolation of populations during glacial periods. In regions where subspecies meet they interbreed to produce intermediate forms. The two most important groups of races in central Europe are the more easterly subspecies *violaceus,* with a stouter body and unfurrowed elytra, and the more westerly *purpurascens,* with a longer and narrower body and weakly striate elytra. The beetles are to be found at all altitudes, but mostly in wooded country. It is the commonest *Carabus* over much of the British Isles and well-known even to the city dweller as it is quite often found in gardens.

6 **Carabus intricatus* − Blue Ground Beetle, 24−36 mm (4 : 8)

This species is coloured a mostly very distinctive, uniform shade of blue. It likes warmth, occurs almost entirely in southern Europe and is seldom seen north of the river Main. It is known to have occurred in south-west England but may now be extinct there. The adult beetles can be found from May to August in moist, mostly deciduous forests at moderate altitudes.

7 *Carabus auronitens,* 18−34 mm (4 : 9)

This gleaming golden red or golden green (but occasionally blue) central European species resembles *Carabus auratus.* Variation in its colour is related partly to humidity levels and to the amount of sunlight received during pupation. The beetles can be seen from May to August in woods on hills and mountains.

8 **Carabus problematicus,* 20−30 mm (4 : 10)

This beetle, which has dark elytra with fine longitudinal ribbing, is to be found from June to September. It is generally the commonest *Carabus* on heaths and moors in Britain.

9 **Carabus granulatus,* 17−23 mm (4 : 12)

This species, whose colouring varies from copper red to almost black, can easily be mistaken for several other species, but the first segment of its antennae is always black while the antennae as a whole are particularly long, extending in the male almost halfway down the elytra. This is a widely distributed species inhabiting the whole of the palaearctic region and it has also become established in North America. The beetles can be found from the plains of central Europe to high up in the mountains, from April to September. The membranous hindwings are generally vestigial, but may occasionally be fully developed.

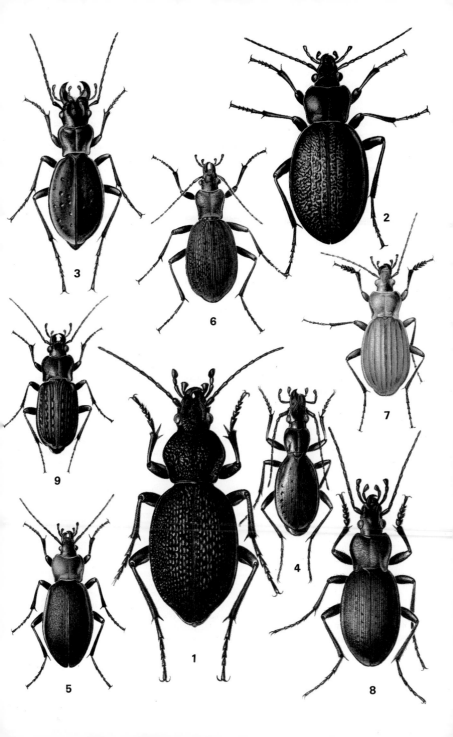

1 *Carabus menetriesi,* 18−24 mm (4 : 13)

This species closely resembles *Carabus granulatus,* but has shorter antennae. It is a north-east European species left behind in isolated regions (chiefly in forest bogs) after the Ice Ages. Its most westerly limits are the Bavarian and Bohemian Forests, the Ore Mountains and upper Silesia. The beetles can be found from April to September, but in the summer months they have a resting period or diapause.

2 *Carabus clathratus,* 20−36 mm (4 : 14)

This beetle is easy to recognize from the gleaming gold dimples in its elytra. Its flight wings are not infrequently fully developed. Its range covers the breadth of the palaearctic region, from western Europe east to Japan, although there are large gaps in which it is completely absent. In the British Isles it is local and more or less confined to Scotland and Ireland. It is to be found only in damp regions at low altitudes, e.g. in bogs and by the side of lakes. Occasionally the adult beetles spend time under water, which they reach by climbing down aquatic plants.

3 *Carabus cancellatus,* 17−32 mm (4 : 15)

While resembling *Carabus granulatus,* this beetle is usually a lighter colour and has a red basal segment to its antennae. This is not an absolutely diagnostic character, however, as the species is very variable. Together with *C. granulatus, C. cancellatus* is one of the commonest and most widespread *Carabus* species in central Europe and the beetles are found almost throughout the palaearctic region at altitudes of up to 1,000 m. It has been recorded from Britain but is not an established British species. It is one of the relatively few carabids which are active by day.

4 *Carabus auratus,* 17−30 mm (4 : 16)

Known as the 'Goldsmith' in Germany, this species resembles *Carabus auronitens,* but has a notch in the posterior margin of its elytra. It is a western species, ranging east roughly as far as the Oder, although lately it has started to extend its area of distribution. In recent years a thriving population has become established in the Harwich area, and it may now be regarded as a resident British species. The beetle likes warmth, is active during the daytime and avoids sandy ground; it is to be seen from April to August and occurs chiefly in fields and gardens at low and moderate altitudes.

5 *Carabus convexus,* 14−20 mm (4 : 17)

Apart from *Carabus nitens,* this is the smallest member of the genus in central Europe. It is generally plain black seen from above, although the edges of its elytra may have a bluish tinge. Its area of distribution stretches from western Europe to Siberia. Here and there in central Europe, from April to September, the beetle is quite common in fields and open country, from the plains to an altitude of 2,000 metres. In southern Europe it displays a tendency to form races.

6 *Carabus nitens,* 13−18 mm (4 : 18)

This − the smallest *Carabus* species in central Europe − is coloured a gleaming green-gold, with prominent black ridges down its elytra. The beetles are to be found only sporadically in central Europe, and are mostly confined to sandy regions, moors and boggy country. Further east they are somewhat more numerous, but few have been found in southern Germany. In Britain the species is very local. This generally rare species can be seen from April to October.

7 *Carabus variolosus,* 20−33 mm (4 : 19)

This species can easily be identified from its uniformly black, only weakly shining back, with rows of prominent tuberosities down its elytra. This species was formerly distributed throughout central and southern Europe, but in northern and central Germany it has now disappeared. In mountainous country it lives beside streams and in swampy areas and can sometimes be seen running under water.

8 *Carabus ullrichi,* 20−34 mm (4 : 20)

This large and robust species is very variable in colour, although mostly bronze. The elytra are not notched at the tip. There are only a few places in central Europe where this warmth-loving beetle is known, but towards the south-east it becomes more abundant. It is found in mountainous country but not at very high altitudes; it is active during the day and prefers heavy soil.

9 *Carabus arvensis,* 16−22 mm (4 : 21)

This Eurasian forest species, which extends from Europe across the whole of Siberia as far as Japan, has very variable colouring. The adult beetles can be seen from June to August, from low to very high altitudes. A great many subspecies and forms have been described.

84

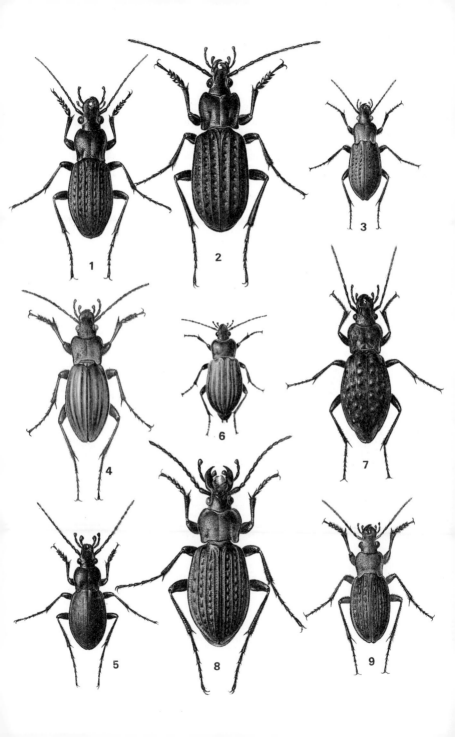

1 **Carabus monilis,* 17−32 mm (4 : 32)

In central Europe this species is mostly bronze, but may also be green or blue. Adults can be seen from June to August in lowland meadows, arable land, gardens and woods. In even years they seem to be more numerous.

2 *Carabus scheidleri,* 25−35 mm (4 : 24)

This closely resembles the preceding species, but occurs further east; the two species are separated by a wide distribution gap. This species is likewise very variably coloured, but in central Europe dark individuals predominate. The beetles prefer woods, but they also visit fields and vineyards. In central Europe the species is restricted to Bavaria, Czechoslovakia and Austria and its main area of distribution lies further to the east and south-east.

3 **Carabus nemoralis,* 18−28 mm (4 : 26)

This short-bodied, sturdy species lives mainly in and at the margin of forests, but is also to be seen in gardens. In central Europe it is to be found everywhere in flat country and at low altitudes in the mountains, usually singly. It has also found its way to North America and settled there.

4 *Carabus hortensis,* 22−30 mm (4 : 28)

This species can easily be identified by the regular rows of reddish gold or green depressions in its elytra and from the similarly coloured, projecting margins of the elytra. Its name (*hortensis*) is misleading, since it inhabits lowland and mountain woods. Although widespread in Europe as a whole, it is absent from large stretches of central Europe and is generally not very common. The beetles are to be found from July to October.

5 **Carabus glabratus,* 22−34 mm (4 : 29)

As indicated by its name (*glabratus*), this beetle has a particularly smooth back with none of the ridges or rows of depressions observed in its relatives. It is distributed over northern, central and eastern Europe, where it lives in lowland and mountain forests up to an altitude of 2,000 m. In Britain it is confined to the north where it is found mostly in hilly and mountainous districts. It can be found from July to October, chiefly in damp localities; in rainy weather it is also active by day.

6 *Carabus linnei,* 16−22 mm (4 : 30)

This daintily built species is usually copper-coloured, but often has a greenish sheen. It is a strictly montane insect occurring in central Europe at subalpine and alpine altitudes, where it can be seen from July to September in damp woods and forest bogs. The beetles are active only at night and by day they are to be found beneath bark and under logs. Like many other carabids, they spend the winter gregariously in rotting tree stumps.

7 *Carabus silvestris,* 17−25 mm (4 : 33)

While closely related to the preceding species, this beetle is more robust and more variably coloured. It likewise lives in the mountain forests of central Europe, but occurs at both lower and higher altitudes than *C. linnei.* It also spends the winter in the company of its fellows in rotting conifer stumps.

8 **Cychrus caraboides,* 12.5−20 mm (5 : 3)

The members of the genus *Cychrus* of which there are 4 in central Europe − resemble *Carabus* species, but have an unmistakably longer head. The beetles eat snails (although they by no means despise worms and other small creatures) and their long head enables them to reach inside the shells. The beetles come out at night and hide under moss and loose bark by day. *C. caraboides,* the only British species, is the most widely distributed member of the genus in north and central Europe, where it occurs mostly in damp woodland, from the lowlands up to altitudes of about 2,000 m.

9 *Cychrus attenuatus,* 11−17 mm (5 : 4)

This beetle differs from the preceding black species by its bronze lustre and its yellowish red tibiae. It has the same habits as *C. caraboides,* but is absent in the lowlands and is also much rarer in the mountains of central Europe.

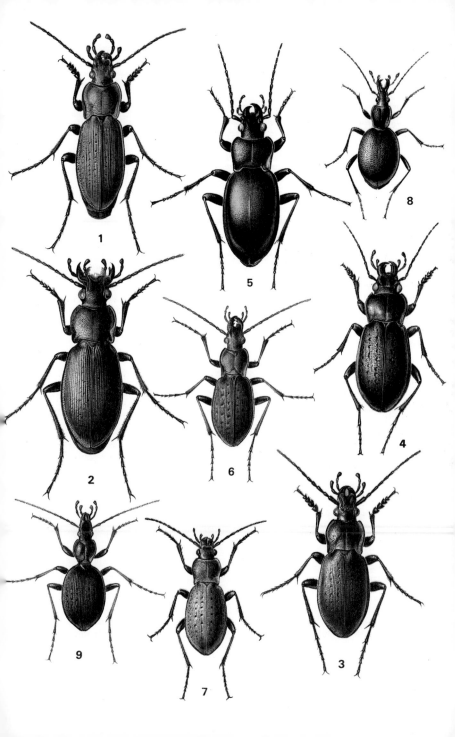

1 *Leistus rufomarginatus, 7.5−9.5 mm (6 : 2)

This genus is represented by 9 species in central Europe, 6 of which are found in the British Isles. They can be recognized by their very wide mandibles, their large head, with its prominent eyes, and their heart-shaped pronotum. Whereas the colouring of the various species differs, their size is much the same and varies only from 5 to 10 mm. Leistus rufomarginatus occurs chiefly in deciduous woods, but not throughout the whole of central Europe. It is doubtful whether it occurs in south-western Germany, but it has extended its range to the north and west in recent years, reaching Britain, where it is now quite widely distributed, by the 1950s.

2 *Leistus spinibarbis, 7.5−9 mm (6 : 1)

At low altitudes this species is bright blue or violet in colour, while montane populations are mostly brown, with less of a metallic sheen, and also differ from the nominate form in the structure of the elytra. L. spinibarbis likes warmth and its numbers diminish in a west-to-east direction.

3 *Leistus ferrugineus, 5.5−7 mm (6 : 9)

This species, which also likes warmth, is to be found throughout central Europe, where it is usually fairly common. Unlike most other species of the genus, L. ferrugineus is to be found in dry as well as wet places. Reproduction takes place in the autumn.

4 *Nebria livida, 12−15 mm (7 : 1)

The 19 central European species of the genus Nebria live mainly near running water, where they can be found under stones, 6 species are found in the British Isles. They are mostly flat-bodied insects with long antennae and long legs. A few species are able to fly. The large species C. livida is black, with a distinctive yellow border, although in insects living in northern Germany and Holland the border can be very narrow. The pronotum is always mainly yellow. The area of distribution of this widespread species stretches from northern, central and eastern Europe across Siberia as far as Japan, but in Germany the beetles are rare to very rare; they live only on damp, clayey ground beside rivers and lakes and can be found there hiding under stones. In the British Isles the species is very local and confined to the south and west coast.

5 Nebria picicornis, 10−15 mm (7 : 2)

In central Europe this species is to be found under stones beside rivers in mountainous country and in some places it is fairly common. It is also found in the northern part of southern Europe. Reproduction takes place in the autumn.

6 *Nebria brevicollis, 10−13 mm (7 : 6)

This species has different habits from most Nebria, since it is found in woods, gardens and parkland away from water, although it likes damp places with plenty of humus. It is a common species in the British Isles and most of northern and western Europe. The beetles are pitch black, but their antennae and terminal limb segments are brownish red.

7 Nebria castanea, 6−10.5 mm (7 : 16)

This dark to light brown species which inhabits mountainous regions of central and southern Europe has been divided into many subspecies which, though geographically isolated from each other, display few obvious morphological differences. The beetles are to be found under stones throughout the whole of the Alpine region; they also occur in the uplands of southern Germany and in the Black Forest.

8 *Notiophilus biguttatus, 3.5−5.5 mm (9 : 8)

In central Europe (and in the British Isles) there are 8 species of these minute dark to bronze brown beetles, whose main distinctive characteristics are a very large head and large eyes; it is usually very hard to tell the various species from each other. The adult beetles, which hibernate, may have short or long wings. The species illustrated here is generally the commonest; it occurs from the plains to high up in the mountains. Adults are active during the day and may be found under moss and stones or darting rapidly from one piece of cover to another.

9 *Omophron limbatum, 4.5−6.5 mm (10 : 1)

This species is the only central European representative of the subfamily Omophroninae and its dytiscoid form singles it out from other ground beetles. The beetles have pale yellow and green markings; they have been recorded from all over Europe, but occur only on sandy ground beside fresh water, where they live in burrows. Their incidence is very local indeed, but where they do occur can often be found living gregariously in large numbers. It is apparently a recent immigrant to Britain where it is found in one or two localities on the south coast.

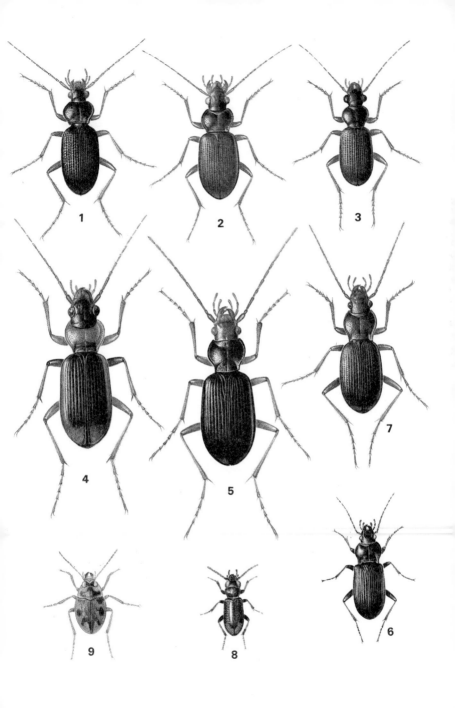

1 *Blethisa multipunctata, 10−12.5 mm (11 : 1)
This is the only species of this genus in central Europe. The beetle is black, with a bronze sheen; it has rather short antennae and on its elytra has rows of fine punctures and two rows of large dimples. The beetles are to be found on swampy ground beside stagnant water; they are more numerous in the lowlands than in mountainous country and in the west and south there are whole regions where the species is absent. The drainage of marshes has also caused this species to disappear from many of its former haunts.

2 *Elaphrus riparius, 5.5−7 mm (12 : 3)
The five species of this genus in central Europe look like small and dainty tiger beetles. On their elytra they have characteristic and conspicuous eye-spots or 'mirrors', which are usually blue or green. They are very fast runners and live on muddy ground beside water. E. riparius has circumpolar distribution and is the commonest species of the genus in central Europe.

3 *Elaphrus cupreus, 7−9 mm (12 : 2)
This closely resembles the preceding species, but is larger, generally more bronze in colour, has metallic blue (rather than green) tarsi, and ocelli which are particularly deep and sharply outlined. The two species live in the same habitats as E. riparius and are often equally common.

4 *Loricera pilicornis, 6−8 mm (13 : 1)
A close look at this beetle − the only member of the genus in central Europe − will enable its immediate recognition. Unlike any other ground beetle, it has long bristles on the first 6 segments of its antennae. On the elytra there are 11 regular striae and on either side, in the third interval, there are three round depressions − another typical feature. The beetles are to be found on wet, swampy ground, in bogs and beside water. In central Europe they are generally numerous everywhere and they hibernate in company.

5 Scarites terricola, 14−22 mm (14 : 1)
This and the next two genera belong to a particular ground beetle subfamily (Scaritinae), in which the broad tibiae of the forelegs are adapted for digging. Another special feature is the 'wasp waist' which separates the thorax and abdomen. There is only one Scarites species in central Europe; it occurs on the shores of the Neusiedler lake in Austria and even there it is rare and appears only from time to time. This large beetle is also found in the Mediterranean region, both on the coast and in salty localities inland. The beetles spend the day in burrows which they dig in the sand and at night they come out to seek their prey.

6 *Clivina fossor, 5−6 mm (15 : 1)
The 3 Clivina species found in central Europe (2 in Britain) resemble those of the following genus, but are somewhat larger, have a less spherical pronotum and 4 bristle-bearing pores on the third elytral interval (Dyschirius species do not have more than 3 such pores). The species illustrated here is the commonest in central Europe; it burrows in damp ground anywhere, often well away from water.

7 *Dyschirius thoracicus, 3.5−4.5 mm (16 : 2)
This genus is represented by 32 species in central Europe, 11 of which are found in the British Isles. They are the smallest members of the subfamily, but are clearly recognizable as scaritines from their thickened forelegs and 'wasp waist'. Their colouring varies from black to light brown and some of them have a metallic lustre. The principal prey of both the beetles and their larvae are rove beetles of the genus Bledius. D. thoracicus occurs along the coasts of Europe, north Africa and Asia Minor, but is not bound to salt water, and is also found by rivers and stagnant water. In central Europe the species is common in low-lying country, but in mountainous districts it is of sporadic occurrence and hard to find.

8 *Dyschirius angustatus, 2.5−3.5 mm (16 : 23)
This bronze-black species with yellowish red legs inhabits northern and central Europe, where it is commoner in the north and rare in the south. It is rare in Britain. The beetles like argillaceous soil and brickyards are therefore a good place to look for them.

9 *Dyschirius globosus, 2−2.8 mm (16 : 32)
This is one of the smallest members of the genus and in central Europe it is the commonest. The species favours damp clayey soil but is also found in other situations, at various altitudes, from sea level to high up in the mountains.

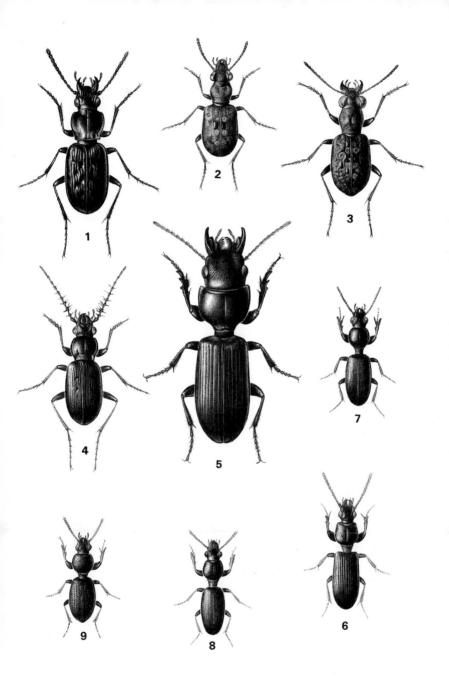

1 *Broscus cephalotes,* 17−22 mm (17 : 1)

The only member of this genus in central Europe, *B. cephalotes* may be recognized by its large head and short feelers; the pronotum is wider in front than behind. This species is found throughout central Europe, but is rarer in the south. It can be found on dry, often sandy ground with plenty of sunshine, where the beetles dig burrows and lie in wait for prey at their entrance. In Britain the species is found mostly on the coast. The beetles' legs are adapted for digging, although not as extensively as in Scaritinae.

2 *Miscodera arctica,* 6.5−8 mm (18 : 1)

This genus likewise has only one species in central Europe. It somewhat resembles the preceding species, but is much smaller; its head is not so broad and its pronotum is more rounded. This species has a circumpolar distribution, but is found only in the cooler regions of Europe. In Britain it is restricted to the northern parts of England and Wales, and Scotland. The beetle lives on sandy ground under moss and hunts the larvae of pill beetles.

3 *Perileptus areolatus,* 2.2−2.8 mm (19 : 1)

This relative of the large genus *Trechus* is the only member of the genus *Perileptus* in central Europe. The beetles are found in gravel on the banks of streams and rivers, mostly in mountain areas. In the British Isles the species is restricted to the north and west.

4 *Thalassophilus longicornis,* 3.4−4.5 mm (20 : 1)

This trechine beetle is also the only species of its genus in central Europe. It is interesting to note that the northern limit of its range coincides with the southern limit of the last inland ice sheet. The beetles are to be found by mountain streams in the middle and southern part of central Europe, but they are very rare. In Britain it inhabits the same regions as the previous species, but again is very rare.

5 *Trechus quadristriatus,* 3.5−4.5 mm (21 : 6)

In central Europe there are 46 *Trechus* species, only 9 of which are found in the British Isles. Only two of them are illustrated here as, although in many respects very variable, the various species often cannot be distinguished by their external characters; dissection and examination of the male sex organs is frequently necessary. Most species are mountain-dwellers and some are endemic to a specific mountain or range of mountains. The species illustrated here is widely distributed, however, and is generally common; it occurs in both lowland and mountainous regions, and may be found in a variety of habitats.

6 *Trechus discus,* 4.5−5.5 mm (21a : 1)

Sometimes placed in a separate genus − *Lasiotrechus* − this species has been widely recorded in central Europe. However, its incidence is sporadic and the beetles are rarely found. It is most frequently discovered following floods. This is probably related to its mode of life, since the beetles inhabit crevices and the burrows of small mammals in waterside situations; they are also to be found under stones deeply embedded in damp ground.

7 *Anophthalmus gobanzi,* 3.6−4 mm (25 : 3)

The 4 species of *Anophthalmus* belong to a rather extensive group of trechine ground beetles which are specialist cave-dwellers. Most of the species are confined to one or a few cave systems. The one illustrated here has three subspecies which inhabit mountainous areas in the south of Austria (Carinthia) and the northern part of former Yugoslavia. Their eyes have completely degenerated and their greatly lengthened antennae, legs and tactile bristles are used to feel their way about.

8 *Tachys quadrisignatus,* 2.3−2.7 mm (27 : 8)

In central Europe there are 10 species of the genus *Tachys* (6 in Britain); they mostly have a brown or dark-coloured body and are among the smallest of ground beetles, measuring only 2−3 mm in length. This is the commonest species in southern and central Europe, but is absent in the north. Like other *Tachys* it is a waterside species and is found beside running water at both low and high altitudes.

9 *Tachyta nana,* 2.6−3.1 mm (28 : 1)

This is the only species of the genus to be found in central Europe. It is a relative of *Tachys,* but has very different habits, since the beetles live beneath bark. It has a boreomontane distribution.

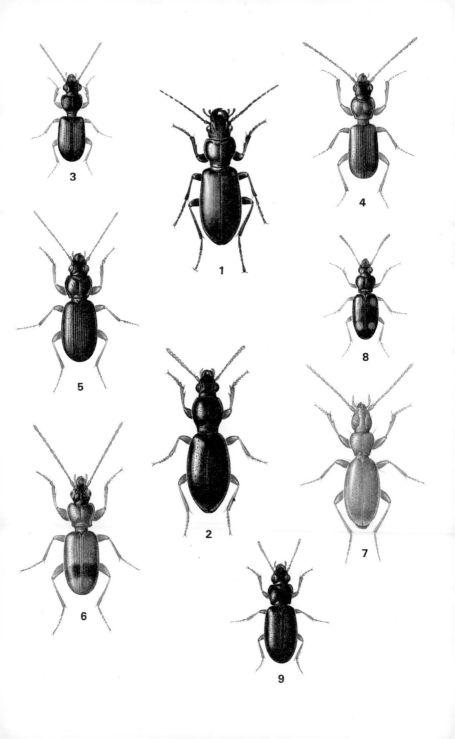

1 *Bembidion lampros,* 3−4 mm (29 : 10)
This genus is represented in central Europe by 100 species (57 in the British Isles). A characteristic feature of the genus, shared with *Asaphidion* and *Tachys,* is the small, peg-like terminal segment of their maxillary palps. They are small beetles, often with distinctive elytral markings, but many are very difficult to distinguish from one another. As far as we know, the adults of practically all species hibernate. Most of them are to be found beside stagnant and running water; some occur near salt water while a small minority are to be found in dry situations. *B. lampros* is a uniform dark, generally bronze colour with only its legs lighter. The beetles are to be found all over central Europe, on cultivated land, in woods and in the mountains. They occur in all types of habitats except sandy and stony river banks and are common everywhere.

2 *Bembidion tricolor,* 4.3−5.2 mm (29 : 31)
This species may be recognized by its bicoloured elytra, the anterior half of which is reddish yellow and the posterior half a metallic black or blue; there is no sharp dividing line between the two colours. This is often a common species beside torrential streams in the Alps and their foothills.

3 *Bembidion tetracolum,* 4.9−6.1 mm (29 : 54)
This species, formerly known as *B. ustulatum,* has two pale marks on each elytron. The species, with several subspecies distributed over Europe, Asia Minor, the Caucasus and Siberia, has also become established in North America. It is common in the British Isles and found on moist ground with vegetation, not necessarily by open water.

4 *Bembidion genei,* 4−4.9 mm (29 : 67)
The body of this species, formerly known as *B. quadriguttatus,* is black or a metallic green, with four yellow elytral spots of which the anterior pair are triangular and the posterior pair circular. The beetles live on clayey ground, usually near water, and are abundant everywhere in central Europe.

5 *Bembidion articulatum,* 3−3.9 mm (29 : 93)
The forebody of these beetles is metallic green, while the elytra are brown with a rather variable pattern of pale spots. The species is distributed from Europe across Asia Minor and Siberia, as far as Japan. It is found beside fresh water, preferring clayey soil, and is common everywhere in central Europe.

6 *Bembidion biguttatum,* 3.5−4.5 mm (29 : 98)
This beetle has a black body, with a blue-green reflection. The posterior part of the elytra is of a brownish colour and each has an oblique, yellowish red spot near the tip. This species is abundant in most of central Europe and common throughout the British Isles.

7 *Asaphidion flavipes,* 3.9−5.4 mm (30 : 4)
This genus has four representatives in central Europe (two in the British Isles). The adults resemble those of *Bembidion* but have particularly large eyes and pores on their elytra which are reminiscent of those found in *Elaphrus* species. *Asaphidion* species are mostly to be found under stones on sandy ground near water. The species illustrated here is not bound to water, however, and is common in fairly dry situations. Reproduction occurs in the spring.

8 *Pogonus luridipennis,* 6−8.7 mm (31 : 1)
All 4 species of this genus in central Europe (3 in the British Isles) are from 5 to 9 mm long and live near the sea or on salty ground inland. The species shown here is the only one with yellowish brown elytra; the others are of a uniform metallic (usually greenish) colour. In central Europe *P. luridipennis* is known from the shores of the North Sea and the Neusiedler lake in Austria. Its wider distribution covers much of Europe, north Africa, the Caucasus and western Siberia.

9 *Patrobus atrorufus,* 7−9.5 mm (32 : 3)
This genus has 5 species in central Europe, 3 of which occur in the British Isles. They are dark-bodied, are to be found in damp localities under stones and are mostly wingless. The species shown here was formerly termed *P. excavatus.* It lives mostly in damp woods and is common in the plains of northern Germany; further south, in more mountainous country, it becomes much rarer. It is known to occur in northern Europe, the Caucasus and western Siberia.

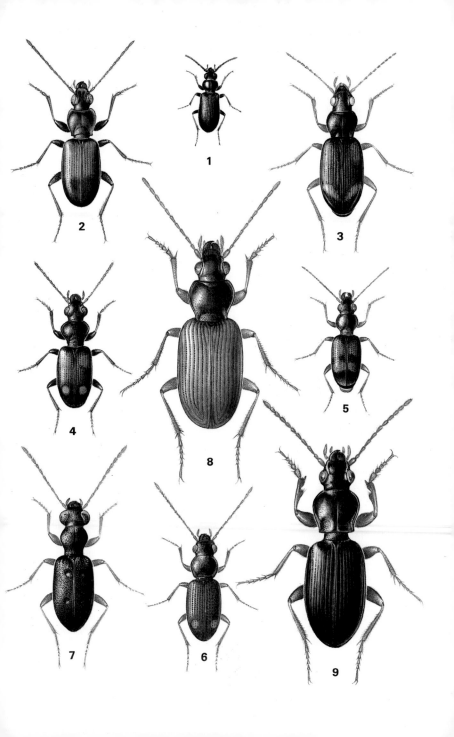

1 *Anisodactylus binotatus,* 9−13 mm (37 : 1)
The 4 species of *Anisodactylus* found in central Europe are each about 10 mm in length. Three species of the genus occur in the British Isles. They resemble the members of the much more numerous genus *Harpalus,* but have a distinctively longer first segment of their hind tarsi, which is the same length as the second and third segments together, while in *Harpalus* it is shorter. The species shown here can have black (chiefly in the north) or yellow legs (in the south). The beetles are to be found everywhere in central Europe in open country and are usually quite numerous.

2 *Harpalus rufipes,* 11−16 mm (41 : 21)
The genus *Harpalus* is represented in central Europe by 65 species whose length ranges from 4.6 to 17 mm; 33 species are found in the British Isles. All have a similar body form − long oval or straight-sided − relatively short legs and only moderately long antennae. The beetles like dry, sandy situations and are mostly found in open country, at both low and high altitudes. Unlike many other ground beetles, *Harpalus* species are not entirely carnivorous, but also eat seeds. The species *H. rufipes* − known in older works under the name *Ophonus* or *Pseudophonus pubescens* − is to be found on all types of ground, including cultivated land, but prefers clayey soils. It occurs throughout the whole of the palaearctic region and is common everywhere in Europe. The beetles like to visit umbelliferous flower-heads to eat the half-ripe seeds. Since they also eat the acini (seeds) of strawberries, they are sometimes a pest.

3 *Harpalus aeneus,* 9−12 mm (41 : 30)
The colour of this beetle's back can vary from green to copper, bronze, black or blue, almost always with a metallic lustre. Its antennae are always yellowish red and so, usually, are its legs, although these may be a darker colour. The beetles occur in fields and on sandy ground at both low and high altitudes and are common everywhere.

4 *Harpalus rubripes,* 8−11 mm (41 : 49)
This species is also somewhat variable in colour, but is generally bluish or greenish. Like *H. aeneus,* it is distributed throughout central Europe, but prefers warm and dry situations and is much more local than *H. aeneus* in Britain.

5 *Harpalus latus,* 8−11 mm (41 : 45)
The males of this species are glossy black, whereas the females have duller elytra − a difference between the sexes exhibited by several other *Harpalus* species. The beetle is to be found at both low and high altitudes, in open woods and on sandy ground, and in central Europe it is fairly common everywhere.

6 *Stenolophus teutonus,* 5.5−7 mm (42 : 1)
In central Europe there are 5 *Stenolophus* species, 3 of which occur in the British Isles. The beetles are brightly coloured and live mostly in wet, marshy localities or in waterside detritus. The species *S. teutonus* used to be abundant everywhere in central Europe, in waterside situations and swamps, but reclamation of marshlands has resulted in a fall in its numbers.

7 *Dicheirotrichus gustavi,* 5−7.5 mm (43 : 1)
Three species of this genus live in central Europe (two in Britain). They are variable in colour, from almost completely pale yellowish brown to completely black. All three species are found near salt water. Formerly known as *D. pubescens,* this species is common around the North Sea, but rare by the Baltic. In central Europe the species has also been found in a few salty inland localities. Damage caused to turnips in Holstein (Germany) shows that this species can at least occasionally turn vegetarian.

8 *Trichocellus cognatus,* 4−4.8 mm (44 : 2)
In central Europe there are three species of this genus; two are found in the British Isles. They closely resemble the foregoing species, but are smaller and not associated with salt water. *T. cognatus* is to be found under heather and on boggy ground. In the British Isles it is largely a northern species.

9 *Bradycellus ruficollis,* 2.8−3.5 mm (45 : 1)
The central European species of this genus are all small, measuring only 2.8−5.5 mm, and are a light or darker shade of reddish brown; they are often very difficult to distinguish from one another. *B. ruficollis* (known in earlier works as *B. similis*), is the smallest member of the genus. It is common under heather on sandy or peaty soil; other species of the genus are also to be found in open woods, grassland and waterside situations.

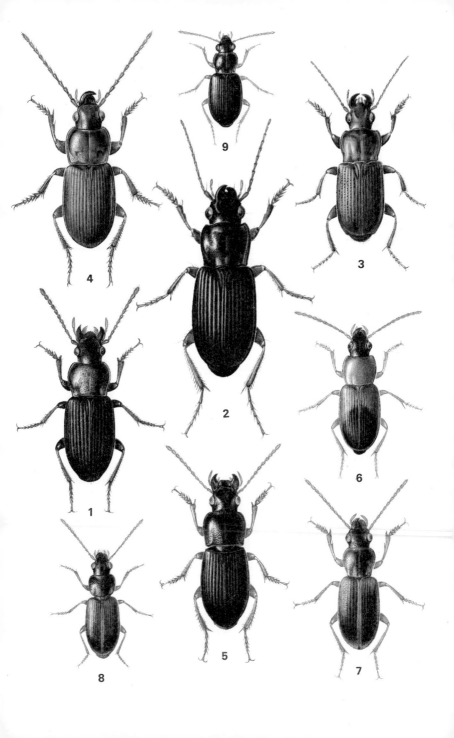

1 *Acupalpus meridianus, 3−4.4 mm (46 : 4)
The 13 species of this genus in central Europe (8 in the British Isles) are all of small size, most of them measuring less than 4 mm in length. Most of the species live in damp, swampy localities. The one shown here has a dark brown or black pronotum and a large black patch on its yellow elytra which tapers off anteriorly to a point. It is not a waterside species and the beetles are to be found in sunny, open situations, often on agricultural land.

2 *Acupalpus dorsalis, 3.4−4.2 mm (46 : 6)
This species has a lighter coloured back and the pronotum in particular has at least a broad light border. In central Europe the beetles are to be found mostly beside water; they are common at low and moderate altitudes, but are absent in the Alps.

3 *Acupalpus consputus, 3.7−5 mm (47 : 1)
Sometimes referred to as a separate genus − *Anthracus* − this species is widely distributed in central Europe, but it is commoner in the east than in the west. The beetles live in shaded places beside water, often under fallen leaves; they hibernate and then reproduce in the spring.

4 *Stomis pumicatus, 6.5−8.3 mm (49 : 1)
This genus has 2 species in central Europe, of which only the one illustrated is found in Britain. The long, slim-bodied beetles are black or dark brown, with red legs and antennae. This species lives in damp places, chiefly on clayey ground. The beetles are to be found under boards and stones, especially in the spring, before the onset of the breeding season. The species is sporadically abundant in central Europe, but does not occur everywhere.

5 *Pterostichus cupreus, 9−13 mm (50 : 7)
In central Europe there are 68 species of this genus, some of them widespread, others with a restricted montane distribution. Their lengths vary from 4.6 to 22 mm. Most species are dark in colour, often black, although some are metallic. Many of them inhabit woods, meadows and fields, mostly in damp places. Some are to be found commonly under stones or other objects on the ground in gardens. 22 species occur in the British Isles. *P. cupreus* is generally of a bronze colour, but may be a metallic green, red, coppery, blue or violet. This insect is common in meadows and fields and on footpaths throughout Europe, but likes damp localities and is not to be found at high altitudes.

6 *Pterostichus versicolor, 8−11.5 mm (50 : 8)
Formerly known under the name *P. coerulescens,* this species, like the preceding one, is variable in colour, but always has pitch black legs (in *P. cupreus* parts of the legs are usually light-coloured); the two species are often mistaken for each other. In central Europe the beetles are to be found everywhere, especially in meadows, and even at high altitudes. Unlike most *Pterostichus*, *P. cupreus* and *P. versicolor* are active in daytime.

7 *Pterostichus vernalis, 6−7.3 mm (51 : 15)
P. vernalis is mostly of a uniform black, with only the first antennal segment and the apices of the leg segments sometimes a little lighter. In central Europe the beetles are to be found in damp localities everywhere, often in large numbers; the best place to catch them is under wet moss in damp woods, swamps and marshy meadows.

8 Pterostichus metallicus, 12−14.5 mm (51 : 39)
This species has very smooth, and only very finely striate, short oval elytra with a coppery, blue, green, violet or gold lustre. It has an alpine and montane distribution and the beetles are common in all central European woods at high altitudes.

9 *Pterostichus melanarius, 13−17 mm (51 : 27)
In earlier works this completely black ground beetle was referred to as *P. vulgaris,* intimating that it is common everywhere and very numerous. The beetles occur in all types of habitat, including cultivated land. They live mainly on caterpillars, but also eat seeds and are sometimes a pest of strawberries.

98

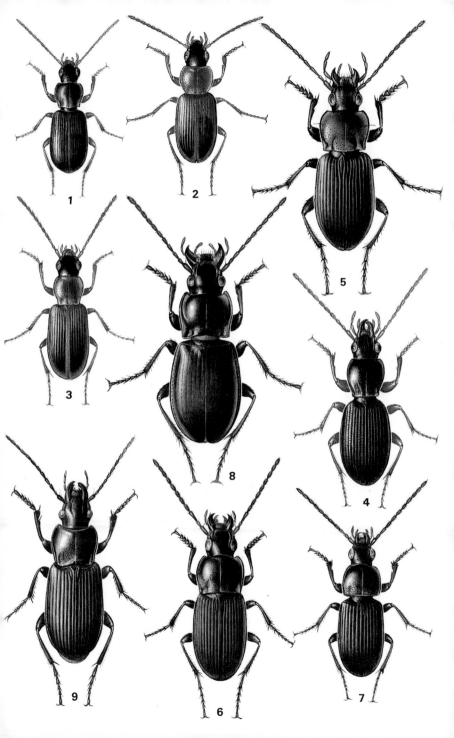

1 *Pterostichus strenuus, 5−7 mm   (51 : 11)
This tiny beetle has a clearly heart-shaped pronotum. In central Europe it is particularly common in damp woods everywhere, in ground litter or in moss.

2 *Pterostichus niger, 15−21 mm   (51 : 26)
This uniformly black beetle, in which only the outer segments of the antennae are lighter, is one of several very similar species which are often mistaken for one another; it is one of the commonest members of the genus. The beetles are to be found in woods, fields, gardens and riverside meadows throughout the whole of central Europe, where they are usually common.

3 *Pterostichus oblongopunctatus, 9−12 mm   (51 : 24)
This beetle can be distinguished from the preceding species by its smaller size and the 4−7 deep pores in its third elytral stria. It is black, but usually has a greenish sheen. It is common in all central European forests and can also be caught in the winter, hiding in rotting tree stumps or under moss.

4 Molops piceus, 9−14 mm   (52 : 2)
The 4 species of this genus in central Europe have shorter feelers and a more compact body than the preceding species and the sides of their pronotum are even more distinctly heart-shaped. The beetles have a glossy black or brownish black back and light or dark brown antennae and legs; they live under stones and moss in the woods. Unlike the other species of the genus, which are strictly mountain-dwellers, M. piceus also occurs in low-lying country in central Europe; it is rare in the north, however, and is probably absent altogether in the north-east. No Molops species are found in the British Isles.

5 *Abax parallelepipedus, 16−21 mm   (53 : 2)
The 7 central European species of this genus are all uniformly black, robustly built insects. Unlike many Pterostichus species they lack elytral pores. The beetles are fairly large and measure from 11 to 25 mm in length. In earlier works P. parallelepipedus is referred to under the name P. ater. In central Europe it occurs chiefly in mountain forests, where the beetles are numerous, although further north their numbers diminish. It is the only species of Abax found in the British Isles, where it is not confined to woodlands, and is also found in gardens and other situations, although always in the shade.

6 Abax ovalis, 11−15 mm   (53 : 5)
This is the smallest species of Abax and has a compactly oval shape. Since the pronotum is narrower in front than it is behind, it forms a continuous curve with the margins of the elytra. In central Europe the species is found in forests, under stones and wood. While commonest in the mountains, this species also occurs in the lowlands, but is absent in north-eastern Germany.

7 *Synuchus nivalis, 6−9 mm   (55 : 1)
The only member of the genus occurring in central Europe, this species is to be found chiefly in open woods, often under moss, but also in open country where shade is available. Reproduction takes place in autumn and the larvae hibernate.

8 *Calathus fuscipes, 9−14 mm   (56 : 1)
In central Europe there are 8 species of this genus, all but one of which are to be found in Britain. All have a similar elongate oval form, and vary in length from 6 to 14 mm. The beetles are to be found mostly in dry places. They hide under leaves, moss and stones or between grass roots by day and are active at night. C. fuscipes is black, but its legs and feelers are mostly a light reddish brown. The beetles are numerous throughout central Europe; they live in open country and also occur at high altitudes. The hind wings are rudimentary and the beetles are unable to fly.

9 *Calathus melanocephalus, 6−9 mm   (56 : 6)
This beetle has very characteristic colouring, with a yellowish red pronotum, black head and elytra and yellow antennae. In central Europe this species abounds in sunny, open country everywhere, including cultivated land. Two races with a darker pronotum, which is much the same colour as the elytra, live in the Alps; it is possible that they form a separate species.

100

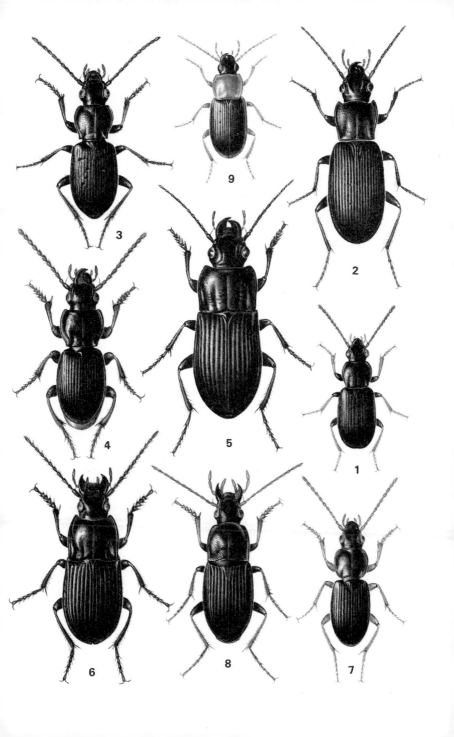

1 *Pristonychus terricola, 12—16 mm (59 : 2)
Formerly referred to as *Laemostenus* or *Laemosthenes,* this genus includes 3 central European species, all of which have elytra with a bluish lustre. Two species are found in the British Isles. Adults and larvae like the dark and are to be found chiefly under stones. *P. terricola* is the most widely distributed species in Europe, and has also successfully colonized North America. The species is chiefly to be found in cellars, stables, and other buildings, but may also be found in other dark places, such as small caves, mines and mammal burrows.

2 *Olisthopus rotundatus, 6—7.2 mm (61 : 1)
Two species of this genus occur in central Europe. *O. rotundatus,* the only species found in Britain, is the more widely distributed of the two; it likes warmth and occurs in open, often sandy country, on dry ground warmed by the sun.

3 *Agonum sexpunctatum, 7—9.5 mm (62 : 4)
Including the species sometimes placed in a separate genus — *Platynus* — there are 37 species of *Agonum* to be found in central Europe; 22 occur in the British Isles. Most often black or metallic in colour, the various species measure from 4.5 to 10.5 mm in length. They are rather flat-bodied, with slender antennae and legs. Most of the species are to be found in wet and marshy localities, beside water or in damp woods. They hibernate as adults and then reproduce in the spring. *A. sexpunctatum* usually has a bright green head and pronotum and red-gold elytra, but occasionally it may be a uniform green, blue or black. The beetles are to be found — often in numbers — in sunny, but not too dry, localities throughout central Europe, at both low and high altitudes.

4 *Agonum muelleri, 6.9—9 mm (62 : 9)
Somewhat variable in colouring, the forebody in this species is usually a bright metallic green, with the elytra bronze. The antennae and legs are blackish brown with only the first antennal segment and the tibiae constantly lighter in colour. These beetles abound in damp localities everywhere in central Europe.

5 *Agonum viduum, 7—9 mm (62 : 12)
This is one of several *Agonum* species of very similar appearance which can be reliably identified only after a detailed morphological examination. *A. viduum* is common throughout central Europe and is found in a variety of waterside situations.

6 *Agonum fuliginosum, 6—7 mm (62 : 28)
This is the commonest of 8 central European *Agonum* species belonging to the subgenus *Europhilus.* The beetles abound in marshy places and waterside situations, usually in the shade, everywhere in central Europe, and are rare only in the Alps.

7 *Agonum dorsale, 5.8—7.5 mm (63 : 8)
This member of the subgenus *Platynus* has very characteristic colouring and can hardly be mistaken for any other ground beetle. The beetle abounds practically everywhere in central Europe. Unlike most *Agonum,* it is not restricted to very wet situations and may be found commonly in gardens and on cultivated land; in the mountains it is to be found only in the valleys.

8 *Agonum assimile, 10—12 mm (63 : 2)
This black beetle, with its more or less brown legs and feelers, is one of the commonest ground beetles in central Europe, where it occurs everywhere in large numbers under moss and beneath loose bark. In Britain it is most often found in deciduous woodland.

9 *Zabrus tenebrioides, 12—15 mm (64 : 1)
The body of this species is unusually convex, deep and clumsy for a ground beetle. It is one of 3 species representing this genus in central Europe, and the only one to occur in Britain. Both the larvae and adults are vegetarian. The larvae in particular can do serious damage to the young shoots of cereal plants, while the adults, which eat the grains of corn, are less destructive. Only the species shown here is widely distributed. In central Europe it occurs in the lowlands where today, as in Britain, it is generally very rare.

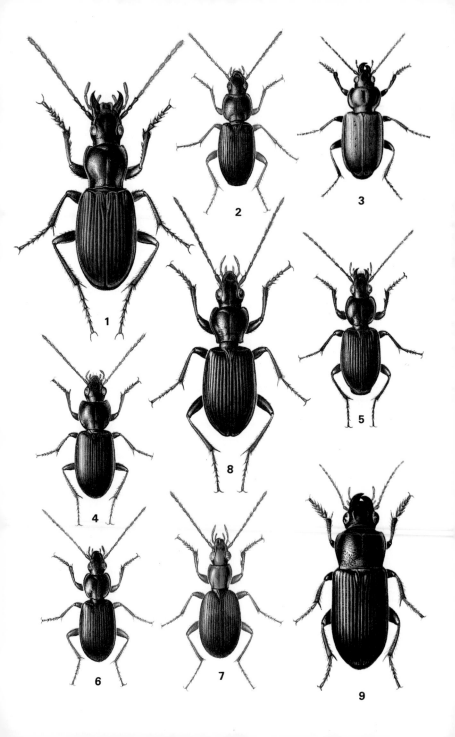

1 *Amara apricaria,* 7−8.5 mm   (65 : 55)
The genus *Amara* is represented in central Europe by 57 species, and by 35 in the British Isles. The shape of the species is not uniform, but the majority have an elongate or compactly oval body. Their size is also somewhat variable, ranging from 4 to 15 mm, and they may be black or brown, often with a metallic sheen. Some species are very hard to distinguish and often need to be identified by study of the male genitalia. In general, the beetles prefer dry localities. When the sun shines they can be seen in fields, on footpaths and on waste ground; they like to hide under stones, moss and leaves and between grass roots. They live on a mixed diet including both insect larvae and vegetable material; not infrequently they can be seen on grasses and other plants, eating the seeds. *A. apricaria* occurs in most of the holarctic region and is common everywhere in central Europe.

2 *Amara plebeja,* 6−8 mm   (65 : 1)
This species has finely grooved elytra, which are mostly a glossy green and less often black or coppery. The species is common throughout central Europe and tends to be found in damper places than most members of the genus.

3 *Amara similata,* 7.5−10 mm   (65 : 8)
This beetle is usually of a light bluish green colour, but may be copper, bluish or jet black. It is common in central Europe, especially in dry places.

4 *Amara familiaris,* 5.5−7.5 mm   (65 : 26)
From front to back, the grooves on this beetle's elytra grow gradually deeper. In colour it is usually bright bluish green and less often bluish or black. These insects are common everywhere in central Europe, especially in flat country.

5 *Amara aenea,* 6.5−8.5 mm   (65 : 21)
The colouring of this species is also very variable; the beetles are mostly a light copper colour, but may be a darker shade, greenish, bluish or almost black. Conspicuous in this and some other species of *Amara* are the first 3 segments of the antennae, whose yellowish red colour contrasts sharply with the dark remaining joints. The beetles, which love sunshine, are very numerous on dry ground everywhere in central Europe.

6 *Amara bifrons,* 5.5−7.5 mm   (65 : 36)
This species, found mainly in sandy localities in flat country, is common to very common throughout the whole of central Europe.

7 *Chlaenius vestitus,* 8.5−11 mm   (66 : 8)
The length of the 13 species of *Chlaenius* found in central Europe ranges from 8 to 18 mm; only 3 occur with any certainty in Britain. Most of them are green or black and are more or less distinctly hairy. They are to be found in damp or wet localities. *C. vestitus* can be distinguished by the yellow margin of its elytra, which is wider at the tip. It is common in central Europe, where it lives beside rivers and in damp spots up to altitudes of about 600 m; sometimes the beetles occur in large numbers, but in the north they are rare.

8 *Chlaenius nigricornis,* 9.5−12.5 mm   (66 : 5)
This green species has a more coppery pronotum and at most the first segment of its antennae is a light yellowish brown. The beetles are to be found in wet spots with luxuriant vegetation; they occur everywhere in central Europe and are sometimes very numerous.

9 *Chlaenius nitidulus,* 10−12.5 mm   (66 : 6)
While the green species of this genus with a narrow yellow lateral border are distributed very locally and the black species are hard to find, *C. nitidulus,* which has greenish to greenish blue and occasionally coppery elytra, occurs almost everywhere in central Europe. In Britain, however, the species is very rare and confined to a few localities on the south coast. The beetles like damp but sunny clayey spots like brick pits, for example; in the Alps they are often to be found only in the valleys and are seldom seen at high altitudes.

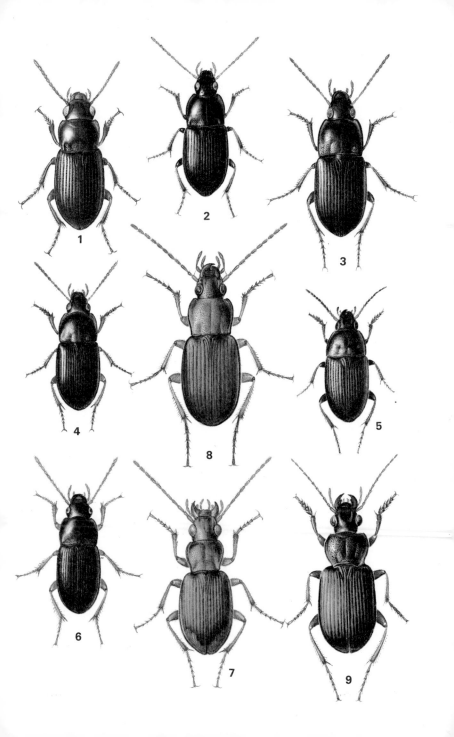

1 *Callistus lunatus*, 4.2−7 mm   (67 : 1)
This ground beetle is related to the genus *Chlaenius,* but is easily distinguished by its conspicuous markings.
It is the only central European member of the genus and is thus unmistakable. The dark spots on its elytra
may vary slightly, but otherwise their pattern is fairly constant. The beetles are thermophilic and are to be
found chiefly on dry and warm chalky hillsides, where they are sometimes very numerous. They are common
only in the southern part of central Europe and are rare or absent further north. In Britain the species is very
rare and restricted to a few localities in the London district.

2 *Oodes helopioides*, 7.5−9.5 mm   (68 : 1)
There are two species of this genus in central Europe, the adults of both having a similar general form to
Amara species. They are virtually amphibious in their habits and inhabit swampy localities where they live
among reeds and sedges. This is the commoner of the two central European species, which closely resemble
each other; it is the only species found in Britain, where it is very local.

3 *Licinus hoffmannseggi*, 9−15 mm   (69 : 1)
The 5 central European species of this genus are large, black ground beetles with a flat head and pincer-like
jaws; the male's first two tarsal segments are very wide. The beetles hide under stones during the daytime;
they mostly inhabit dry and often sandy or chalky localities and also occur in forests up to quite high
altitudes. Like those of *Badister,* the species of this genus appear to feed mainly on snails. The central and
southern European distribution of the species depicted here is montane to alpine. The two British species of
the genus are local and restricted to the south of the country.

4 *Badister bipustulatus*, 4.8−6 mm   (70 : 2)
The 9 species of this genus in central Europe (7 in Britain) are closely related to the preceding genus, but the
beetles are smaller, none measuring more than about 9 mm in length. They are to be found in damp spots
under stones and wood and among grass roots; some species are confined to marshy or waterside situations.
In central Europe this species occurs in marshy country everywhere. Further north, for example in Britain, it
is to be found in open and less damp deciduous woods and gardens.

5 *Panagaeus crux-major*, 7.5−9 mm   (71 : 1)
Their conspicuous colouring makes the two central European species of this genus easy to identify. *P.
crux-major* is the larger and its posterior red spots usually stretch to the outer margin of its elytra. The
beetles are to be found beside water or in damp meadows, and in winter at the foot of willows or poplars or
behind loose bark. The species has been recorded from all parts of central Europe, but is not generally
common. In Britain it is very local.

6 *Panagaeus bipustulatus*, 6.5−7.5 mm   (71 : 2)
The posterior spots on the elytra of this smaller species do not reach right to their edge. The beetles are to be
found in dry and often chalky or sandy districts, but in the mountains of central Europe they also occur in
damper spots.

7 *Odacantha melanura*, 6−7.8 mm   (72 : 1)
The only member of this genus in central Europe, the beetle can be easily recognized by its long, cylindrical
pronotum, its slender body and its distinctive colouring. The species is found on clayey ground on and among
water-side plants, especially reeds, where the adults hibernate and reproduce in the spring. In Britain the
species is restricted to the south-east, where it is very local, although sometimes found in numbers.

8 *Lebia chlorocephala*, 4.8−8.5 mm   (74 : 1)
This genus has 6 species in central Europe, most of them brightly coloured beetles. As many as 5 species may
occur in Britain but all of them are local and rare. They live chiefly in shrubs and trees, where the adults catch
insect larvae and aphids and the larvae are parasites of leaf-beetle pupae. This species is generally
distributed in central Europe, although rarer in the north. It occurs on the outskirts of woods and in
meadows, hiding by day and hunting in the evening.

9 *Demetrias atricapillus*, 4.5−6 mm   (76 : 1)
In central Europe there are 6 *Demetrias* species, small plant-climbing ground beetles with a long, narrow
pronotum, a yellowish red body and a black head. They are to be found mostly near stagnant water.
However, *D. atricapillus,* the commonest of the 3 species found in the British Isles, is found in grassy places
in both dry and wet situations, where it is often abundant.

106

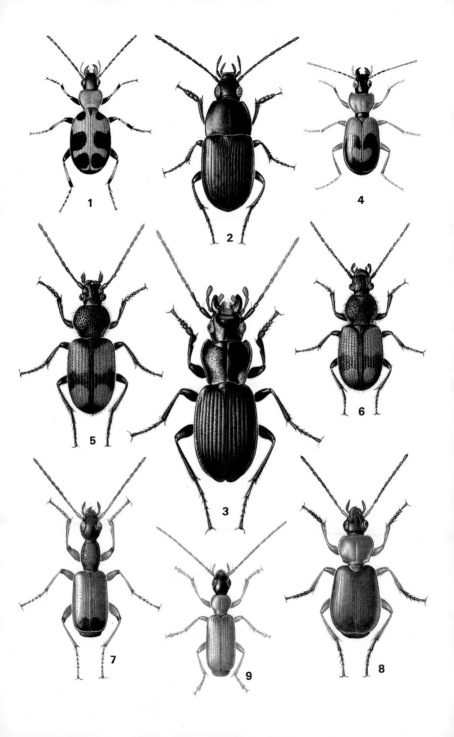

1 *Cymindis humeralis*, 8—11.5 mm   (78 : 1)
The genus *Cymindis* is represented by 9 species in central Europe (3 in Britain). The insects are to be found under stones and in moss on heathland and at the margins of woods; many of the species are confined to mountain regions. The species shown here used to be commoner in central Europe than it is today and its numbers continue to dwindle, especially in the north. The beetles can be found on the sunny outskirts of woods, in stretches of dry grassland and on moors. They reproduce in the autumn and both beetles and larvae can hibernate.

2 *Dromius agilis*, 5.2—7 mm   (79 : 4)
In central Europe there are 17 species of the genus *Dromius* of which 12 occur in Britain. Many of the species live in trees and are often to be found beneath loose bark during the day, although a few species are to be found in ground litter and grass. The beetles are active at night. *D. agilis* is one of the commonest tree-inhabiting species in central Europe and is to be found everywhere beneath the bark of old trees.

3 *Dromius quadrimaculatus*, 4.7—6.1 mm   (79 : 12)
This beetle is likewise found beneath bark and under moss everywhere in central Europe and is fairly common. It displays a preference for places with pines and firs.

4 *Dromius notatus*, 3—3.9 mm   (79 : 17)
This small *Dromius* species was formerly known as *D. nigriventris*. In central Europe it is fairly common in dry and sunny spots everywhere, but in Britain the species is more local and found mostly in grassy places on the coast.

5 *Metabletus truncatellus*, 2.6—3.3 mm   (80 : 4)
The 4 central European species of this genus (sometimes referred to as *Syntomus*) are small, flat-bodied and usually dark-coloured beetles with large eyes and short temples; their elytra are obliquely truncate at the tip. The beetles can be found on tree roots, beneath bark and in dry places under stones. This species is almost completely black and only its antennae and legs are usually somewhat lighter. It is the commonest species in central Europe, while the commonest of the species (of 3) in Britain is the similar *M. foveatus*.

6 *Lionychus quadrillum*, 3—4 mm   (81 : 1)
This, the only species of *Lionychus* found in central Europe, is easy to recognize by the yellow spots on its black elytra. The shoulder spots are always present, but the two posterior spots may be separate, joined to the anterior spots or absent altogether. The beetles are to be found on sandy ground beside water. This species is absent in the low-lying plains of northern Germany, but is fairly common in the south. In Britain it is rare and found in only a few localities in the south-east, mostly on the coast.

7 *Microlestes minutulus*, 3—3.2 mm   (82 : 1)
The 6 species of this genus in central Europe closely resemble those of *Metabletus* in general appearance. Most of them are a uniform glossy black, but one species occurring in the extreme south of the region has a whitish yellow stripe along its elytral suture. The species depicted here is mostly quite common, but is rare in the north and in the Alps; it prefers sunny localities. The only British species of the genus — *M. maurus* — is of a similar appearance.

8 *Brachinus explodens* — Bombardier Beetle, 4.9—7.9 mm   (86 : 3)
The last group of ground beetles are the bombardier beetles, which include the genus *Brachinus* (also spelt *Brachynus*), 4 species of which live in central Europe, but only one in Britain. The beetles have 'shorn-off' elytra and defend themselves by squirting from their anus a liquid which explodes audibly on coming into contact with the air. The species shown here can be found in many parts of central Europe under wayside stones and hedges and in open woods, but is absent in the north and the Alps. The only British species of bombardier beetle — *B. crepitans* — is found mostly in chalky districts in the south of the country.

9 *Aptinus bombardus*, 9.5—15 mm   (87 : 1)
This genus, which has only one species in central Europe, is closely related to *Brachinus,* but the beetles are black with only the antennae and legs yellowish red. Being larger than the preceding species, they also make a louder 'bang'. This species occurs in south-eastern Europe, but in central Europe only in the south-east and westwards as far as eastern Bavaria, where these beetles are already rare.

108

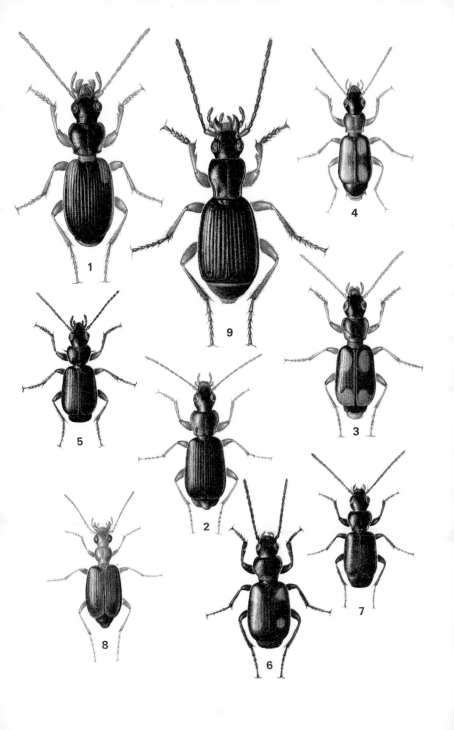

Family Haliplidae — crawling water beetles

In central Europe there are only 20 species of these tiny boat-shaped water beetles, all but one of which are also found in the British Isles. They are all less than 5 mm long and are yellowish or reddish brown with black markings. The beetles can be found among aquatic plants in slow-flowing or stagnant water. They feed on plant material and are not very good swimmers, moving their legs alternately as if they were walking.

1 *Peltodytes caesus, 3.5−4 mm   (2 : 1)

In central Europe there are 2 species of this genus, which in older works goes under the name of *Cnemidotus*. The beetles can be distinguished from those of the next genus by the form of the elytra which do not fit exactly at the apex, a gap being left between them. The species shown here is the commoner of the two everywhere in central Europe. It can be found among aquatic plants in stagnant water.

2 *Haliplus ruficollis, 2.5−2.9 mm   (3 : 5)

The 18 species of this genus are often very difficult to distinguish from one another. The yellowish elytra are variously patterned with rows of black dots. Adults and larvae live in clean stagnant or slowly running water, among aquatic plants. This species is widely distributed and common everywhere in central Europe.

Family Dytiscidae — predacious diving beetles

This family has 31 genera and 154 species in central Europe. 111 species are found in the British Isles. The adult beetles are clearly adapted for life in water, since their long-haired hind legs have been modified for use as paddles and they have a stream-lined body. They also fly very well, however, and can move to new waters when necessary. When in the water they surface from time to time to collect an air supply which is carried beneath their elytra. Both adults and larvae are strictly predacious.

3 *Hyphydrus ovatus, 4.5−5 mm   (1 : 1)

Beetles of this genus have a very deep body and are the most convex of European Dytiscidae. Two species live in central Europe. The beetles live in stagnant (seldom in running) water. *H. ovatus* is the only species found in the British Isles where it is common, as it is everywhere in central Europe.

4 *Guignotus pusillus, 1.75−2.25 mm   (2 : 1)

This genus, with 2 central European species, was formerly included within the genus *Bidessus*. The species illustrated here, formerly known as *Bidessus geminus,* is one of the smallest Dytiscidae. The beetles are abundant everywhere in central Europe.

5 *Bidessus unistriatus, 1.75−2 mm   (3 : 3)

There are 5 species of this genus in central Europe (2 in Britain), and together with those of the preceding genus they are the smallest members of the family. This beetle is to be found practically everywhere in central Europe, but in the west and south it is rarer.

6 *Coelambus impressopunctatus, 4−5 mm   (6 : 1)

This genus, 4 species of which occur in central Europe, and the British Isles, used to form part of the genus *Hygrotus*. Practically all *Coelambus* species have black longitudinal stripes on a yellow to yellow-red background, but the markings are highly variable, even within one species. The species shown here is common throughout the whole of central Europe.

7 *Hygrotus inaequalis, 3−3.7 mm   (7 : 2)

The 4 central European and British species of this genus have a more broadly oval body than the members of the preceding genus. They are to be found in stagnant water with abundant vegetation. This species is common everywhere in central Europe.

8 *Hydroporus palustris, 3−3.2 mm   (8 : 9)

This genus has 34 species, all measuring 1.75−5.5 mm, in central Europe; 29 of them are found in the British Isles. Their determination is often difficult and hardly possible without recourse to specialist literature. The species depicted here has very variable colouring; it occurs everywhere in central Europe and is one of the commonest members of the genus.

9 *Graptodytes granularis, 2.2 mm   (11 : 2)

Five species of this genus, which used to form part of *Hydroporus,* live in central Europe, all but one of them also occurring in Britain. The reddish yellow spots and stripes on their elytra are very variable, even within the same species. The species shown here is fairly common in central Europe. The beetles occur chiefly in the slime and sludge of stagnant ponds and slow-flowing streams.

110

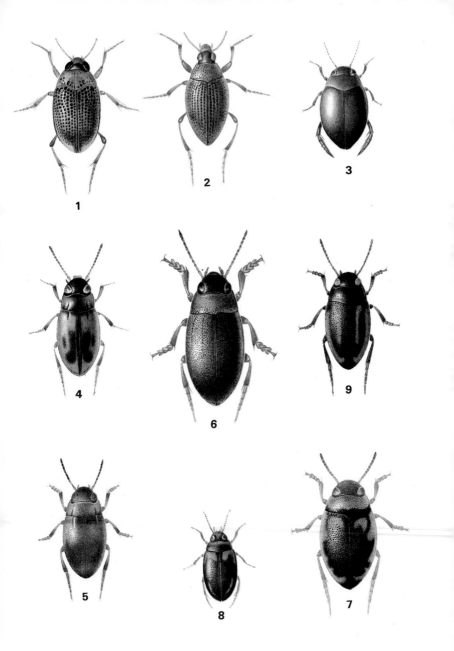

1 *Porhydrus lineatus, 3−3.5 mm   (13 : 1)
In central Europe there are 2 species of this genus, which used to be included in *Graptodytes*. In both species the elytra are very finely granular between the punctures. This species, the more widely distributed of the two and the only one found in Britain, is generally common in central Europe.

2 *Potamonectes assimilis, 4−4.5 mm   (16 : 4)
This genus has four central European and British species, which were formerly included in either *Hydroporus* or *Deronectes*. The beetles are very densely punctured dorsally and have black stripes down their yellow to yellowish red elytra. *P. assimilis* has a boreomontane distribution in northern and central Europe and in Siberia. In north-eastern and southern Germany the beetles are to be found in mountain streams and lakes.

3 *Scarodytes halensis, 4−4.5 mm   (18 : 1)
This single species of *Scarodytes* found in central Europe was likewise formerly included in the genus *Hydroporus* or *Deronectes*. The six black bands down its ochre-coloured elytra often merge with each other. In central Europe the beetles are to be found mostly in stagnant water, but occasionally in slow-running water, preferably with a gravel and clay bottom, where they are often very numerous.

4 *Noterus clavicornis, 4.2−4.5 mm   (19 : 1)
The genus *Noterus*, along with other non-European genera, is often given separate family status. The two species native to central Europe and the British Isles have a reddish brown back, often with a somewhat lighter pronotum. Although convex dorsally the adult beetles are rather flat underneath. They occur in stagnant and flowing water at low to moderate altitudes and also in brackish water. The species depicted here (the illustration is of a male, with somewhat clubbed antennae) is abundant everywhere.

5 *Laccophilus minutus, 4.2−4.8 mm   (20 : 2)
There are 3 species of this genus in central Europe and the British Isles. The mostly olive-brown beetles are easy to recognize when caught as they have a characteristic way of jumping about once out of water. This species − known as *L. obscurus* in earlier works − is distributed from Europe and north Africa to western Asia and Turkestan. In central Europe it is common to very common in stagnant water.

6 *Copelatus haemorrhoidalis, 6.5−8 mm   (21 : 1)
The only species of *Copelatus* found in central Europe and Britain formerly went under the name of *C. ruficollis*. The rather elongate oval adult beetle has a reddish brown back, red antennae and legs. It is distributed from the southern part of northern Europe to north Africa and stretches eastwards as far as the Caucasus. In central Europe it occurs in stagnant water, including ditches and small pools, as long as there is sufficient vegetation, when it is by no means rare.

7 *Platambus maculatus, 7−8.5 mm   (22 : 1)
This genus has only one central European species, which is closely related to *Agabus*. The vivid yellow and black markings on the beetle's back are very variable. This species, whose distribution extends from Europe to Armenia, occurs in central Europe in gently flowing water or near the influx of streams and rivers into lakes. The beetles like to sit on aquatic plants or on submerged wood.

8 *Agabus bipustulatus, 8−11 mm   (23 : 9)
There are 27 species of this genus in central Europe, 20 of which are found in the British Isles, all measuring from 8 to 11 mm. The beetles are mostly dark brown and only rarely have yellow and red or yellow and black markings. The males have tiny suction pads or patches of adhesive hairs on the under side of the widened first segments of their fore and middle tarsi. The beetles live chiefly in clear, cold water. The species shown here extends from Europe and north Africa as far as western Siberia and in central Europe, as in the British Isles, it is common.

9 *Ilybius fuliginosus, 10−11.3 mm   (24 : 3)
This genus has 10 species in central Europe (7 in Britain). Except for the species illustrated here the adult beetles, which measure 9−14 mm, are more or less uniformly dark brown to black, and are difficult to distinguish. The beetles are to be found in stagnant and running water. This species occurs in Europe, north Africa, Siberia and North America. In central Europe it is common everywhere.

112

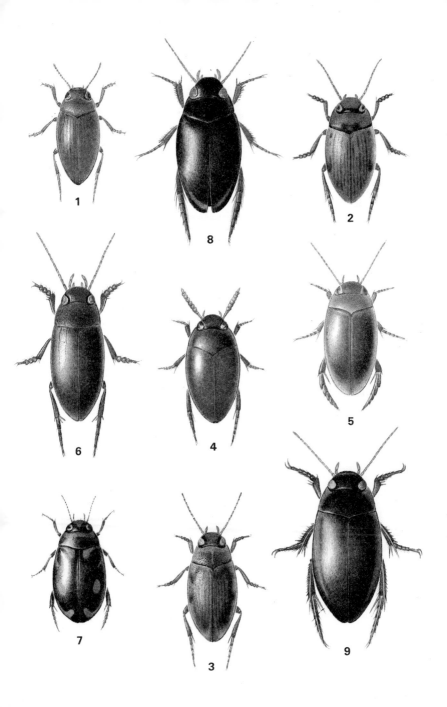

1 *Rhantus exsoletus, 9–10 mm   (26 : 8)
The 10 species of this genus in central Europe (6 in the British Isles) are all rather flat-bodied insects with distinctive colouring and measuring 9–12 mm. Except for one species their pronotum is yellowish, often with dark edges, while their elytra appear to be dark, but have a yellow stripe down the sides and sometimes along the elytral suture. The beetles mainly frequent the vegetation in stagnant water. The species shown here is common in central Europe and widely distributed in the British Isles.

2 *Colymbetes fuscus, 17–19 mm   (27 : 1)
There are 3 species of this genus in central Europe, all with characteristic fine transverse striations on their elytra. The beetles are to be found mainly in stagnant water. C. fuscus, the only British species, is fairly abundant in central Europe and occasionally it can even be very abundant.

3 *Hydaticus transversalis, 12–13 mm   (28 : 1)
The 5 species of this genus in central Europe, only 2 of which occur in Britain, measure 9–15 mm and have an apparently smooth back. The pronotum and elytra are dark, but have varied yellow markings. On the forelegs, the tarsi are expanded and equipped with suction pads. Some females have a wrinkled pronotum. The beetles live primarily in stagnant water with plenty of mud. The species shown here is commoner in the northern part of central Europe than in the south.

4 *Acilius sulcatus, 15–18 mm   (30 : 1)
Two very similar species of this genus occur in stagnant water in central Europe and the British Isles. The males differ markedly from the females in respect of their smooth back (the female's elytra are deeply grooved): in addition, the males have suction pads on the underside of their widened tarsi. The species shown here is the commoner of the two; the related A. canaliculatus shows a preference for bog-water and, in Britain, is found mostly in the north.

5 Dytiscus latissimus, 36–44 mm   (31 : 1)
In central Europe there are 7 large species of this genus of true predacious diving beetles, all but one of which also occur in the British Isles. They are dark brown – often with an olive-green reflection – and have a yellow marginal stripe. On their first pair of tarsi the males have one large, one medium sized and a number of small suction discs: their elytra are smooth, while those of the females generally have deep longitudinal grooves. The beetles and the larvae are both predacious, but accounts of the damage they do in fishponds are greatly exaggerated. D. latissimus is the largest species of Dytiscidae found in central Europe. At one time it was to be found everywhere, but in recent years its numbers have dwindled and in many places it is now absent altogether. It is not found in the British Isles.

6 *Dytiscus marginalis, male – Great Water Beetle, 27–35 mm   (31 : 4)
This is the commonest and most widely distributed species of the genus. The males have 1 large, 1 medium sized and 160 small suction discs on their first pair of tarsi. Like a number of water beetles, those of this species often fly, especially at night. Sometimes they land on glass roofs and on roads, which they mistake in the dark for stretches of water.

7 *Dytiscus marginalis, female
The females generally – though not always – have deep grooves in their elytra. They can also be identified by the absence of suction discs on their tarsi.

Family Gyrinidae — whirligig beetles
In central Europe there are 3 genera of this family, with a total of 13 species; 12 species of the family are found in Britain. They spend much of their time on the surface of water, where they swim sometimes slowly, but often very fast, in circles. Their last two pairs of legs are modified as oars and their eyes are horizontally halved to enable them to see simultaneously both above and below the water.

8 *Gyrinus substriatus, 5–7 mm   (2 : 6)
All the 11 species of this genus have a smooth, dark back. G. substriatus is common in stagnant water everywhere in central Europe.

9 *Orectochilus villosus, 5–7 mm   (3 : 1)
This genus, only 1 species of which is found in central Europe, has a hairy back. It also has different habits from the preceding genus, since it occurs near weirs and mill-wheels, i.e. in running water. The beetles are no doubt more abundant than they seem to be, but they hide in the vegetation during the daytime and do not come out until it is dark.

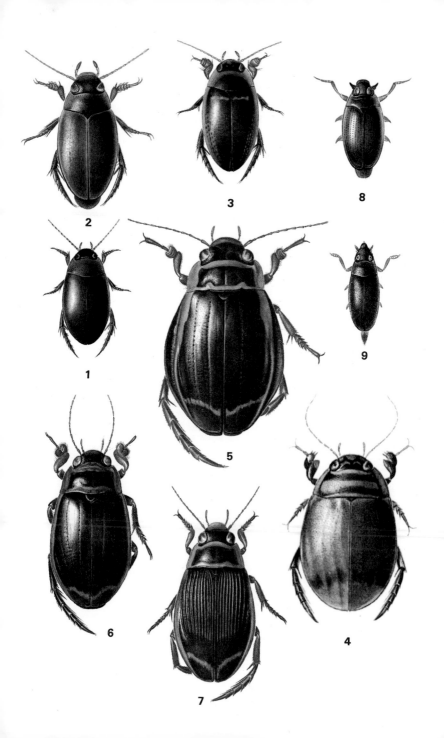

Family Hydraenidae

The beetles of this family, which has 5 genera (if *Hydrochus* and *Helephorus* are included) and 93 species in central Europe, measure 1−7.5 mm and live in or near water. Some authors regard the Hydraenidae as being related to the Hydrophilidae, while others consider their similarities to hydrophilids as due to parallel adaptations to a life in water, and consider the family more closely related to the rove beetles.

1 *Hydraena gracilis, 2−2.3 mm   (1 : 19)
The 27 *Hydraena* species found in central Europe (10 in Britain) are small, narrow beetles whose extremely long maxillary palps are considerably longer than their short antennae which have a small, three-jointed club. The beetles are to be found in flowing water, under stones, in moss, under wood and on aquatic plants, and less often in stagnant water. The species shown here is the commonest: it is rare in low-lying country, however, and occurs chiefly in the water of mountain springs.

2 *Ochthebius minimus, 1.6−2.2 mm   (2 : 8)
This genus is represented by 21 species in central Europe (15 in the British Isles). The beetles are of a less narrow form than those of the preceding genus, but may be distinguished from *Hydraena* species easily by their short maxillary palps. Some species are found chiefly in running water, but others occur on muddy ground at the water's edge or by salty pools. *O. minimus* (formerly known as *O. impressus*) is common in central and northern Europe (including Britain) and is found by both running and stagnant water.

3 *Limnebius papposus, 1.8−2.1 mm   (3 : 2)
In central Europe the genus *Limnebius* has 9 species (4 of which occur in the British Isles) which closely resemble small members of the family Hydrophilidae. These tiny beetles, measuring only 1−2.5 mm, are easy to distinguish from hydrophilids, however, as their elytra do not completely cover their abdomen and leave the pygidium free. The beetles live mostly in stagnant pools and small brooks. *L. papposus* is generally common in small pools in central Europe, but is rare in the west and south-west.

4 *Helophorus flavipes, 2.5−3.8 mm   (5 : 22)
This genus is represented by 31 species in central Europe, 20 of which are found in the British Isles. In the majority of recent works the genus is attributed to the Hydrophilidae rather than the Hydraenidae. The adult beetles have a distinctive pronotum on which 5 long grooves are separated by swollen ridges. Most of these beetles live beside stagnant water. *H. flavipes* (formerly known as *H. viridicollis*) is common to very common everywhere in central Europe, even at high altitudes.

Family Hydrophilidae − water scavenger beetles

This family is represented in central Europe by 18 genera (excluding *Hydrochus*, *Helophorus* and *Georissus*) with a total of 72 species. The mostly round- or oval-bodied beetles differ from Dytiscidae most obviously in respect of their antennae, which have a 3- to 5-jointed club. Many species live in water and have swimming hairs on their legs, while some also inhabit damp spots, rotting vegetation, or fresh dung.

5 *Coelostoma orbiculare, 3.5−4.5 mm   (1 : 1)
The only species of the genus in central Europe, this beetle lives in shallow stagnant water and moss and detritus at the water's edge.

6 *Sphaeridium scarabaeoides, 5.5−7.5 mm   (2 : 3)
The 4 central European species of this genus (3 in Britain) are hard to distinguish from one another, and have rather variable colouring, but all live in fresh cow-dung. *S. scarabaeoides* is very common.

7 *Cercyon analis, 1.7−2.4 mm   (3 : 23)
This species, referred to in earlier works as *C. flavipes*, is one of 23 *Cercyon* species inhabiting central Europe (21 in Britain). The beetles have a round or oval, convex body and are only 1.3−4 mm long. They live in dung, compost and waterside debris. *C. analis* is to be found in decaying organic matter of various kinds and is common everywhere in central Europe.

8 *Megasternum obscurum, 1.7−2.2 mm   (4 : 1)
The only species of this genus in central Europe, this beetle is common in all kinds of decaying organic matter everywhere.

9 *Cryptopleurum minutum, 1.6−2 mm   (5 : 1)
Like the preceding species, this beetle resembles *Cercyon*, but the members of the genus *Cryptopleurum* have a hairy back. The one shown here is the most widely distributed species in central Europe and is to be found in dung in large numbers everywhere.

116

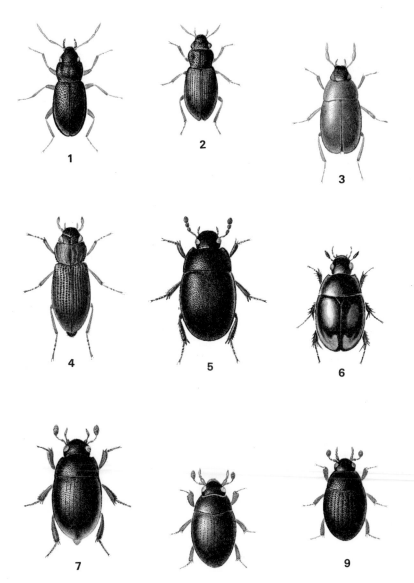

1 *Hydrobius fuscipes, 6−9 mm (8 : 1)
The only species of this genus found in central Europe is black, with a somewhat metallic sheen. It can be distinguished by the striae on its elytra, which posteriorly become deep furrows. It occurs throughout the whole of the palaearctic region and also in North America. In central Europe it has 3 forms, regarded by some as separate species, but whose differences are ecological rather than morphological. H. fuscipes is common everywhere in central Europe.

2 *Anacaena limbata, 2.3−3.2 mm (10 : 2)
The 3 central European and British species of this genus are small and round to oval beetles no longer than 3.5 mm, with extremely spiny tibiae. A. limbata occurs throughout the whole of the palaearctic region and in central Europe is common in and at the edge of all types of stagnant water.

3 *Laccobius minutus, 2.5−3.4 mm (11 : 9)
This genus has 12 species in central Europe, 9 of which are found in Britain. All are very similar, with a short oval and almost hemispherical body measuring some 2−4.2 mm. Their pronotum has a yellow margin and their elytra are brownish or yellowish grey, often with blackish spots: their legs are yellow. The species are often difficult to tell apart without examining the male sex organs. L. minutus is distributed from Europe, across Siberia, as far as Japan: in central Europe it is abundant everywhere, especially in acid water.

4 *Helochares obscurus, 4.5−6.5 mm (12 : 2)
This is one of three similar reddish brown species occurring in stagnant water. The species shown here (formerly known as H. griseus) is distributed over the whole of Europe and abounds in pools everywhere in central Europe. However, it is the least common of the three species in Britain.

5 *Enochrus affinis, 3.5−3.9 mm (13 : 8)
This genus has 9 species in central Europe, all but one of which also occurs in Britain. The yellowish brown beetles have an elongate oval body and their maxillary palps are longer than their antennae. This species is distributed over the whole of the palaearctic region and is common everywhere in central Europe.

6 *Chaetarthria seminulum, 1.1−1.7 mm (15 : 1)
The single central European species of Chaetarthria has a round, hemispherical body, which can be rolled up into an almost complete ball. Its tarsi are extremely short. This tiny species occurs throughout the whole of the palaearctic region and in central Europe it is abundant under débris on wet ground beside stagnant water.

7 *Hydrous caraboides, 14−19 mm (16 : 1)
In central Europe there are 2 species of this genus and, with the exception of Hydrophilus, they are the largest of Hydrophilidae. The species shown here, which is distributed over most of the palaearctic region, occurs throughout central Europe, while the range of the other species extends just into central Europe from the south. H. caraboides could formerly be found in ponds and pools everywhere, but lately it has begun to decline and in some places it is already completely absent. It is the only species found in Britain, where today it is rare.

8 *Hydrophilus piceus − Great Silver Water-beetle, 34−50 mm (17 : 1)
In central Europe there are 2 species belonging to this genus. They are among the largest members of our beetle fauna. Unlike Dytiscidae, they do not collect air at the surface of the water upside down, but use their head and guide the fresh air to the under side of their abdomen by means of their antennae. The eggs are accommodated in a little 'raft' drifting on the surface of the water. Although the larvae are predacious, the beetles are herbivorous and are thus to be found chiefly in pools with plenty of vegetation. The species depicted here, the only one occurring in Britain, used to be abundant everywhere, but in many places it has recently become rare. Conversely, the other species (H. aterrimus) has displayed a local increase in parts of its range. H. piceus is distributed throughout the whole of the palaearctic region.

9 *Berosus luridus, 3.5−4.6 mm (18 : 2)
Their shape makes the 4 central European species of this genus easy to identify, since the hind part of the abdomen is noticeably wider and more convex than the front. The beetles live in stagnant water, are good swimmers and can produce sounds with their abdomen. The species illustrated here occurs throughout the palaearctic region and is fairly common in central Europe.

118

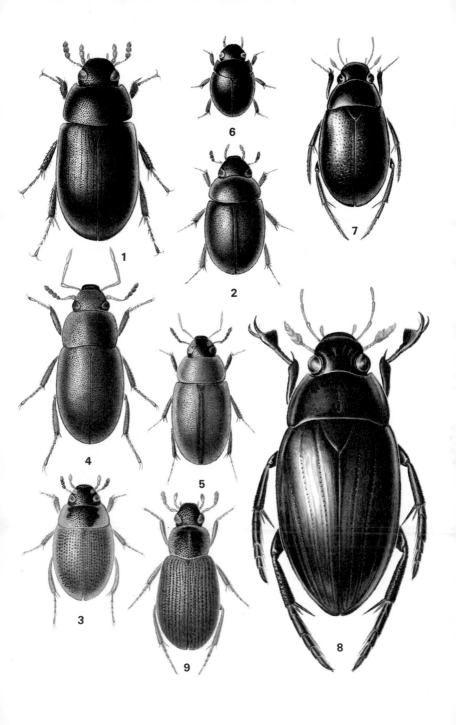

Family Histeridae

In central Europe there are 32 genera of this family, with a total of 94 species. 50 species are known to occur in the British Isles. The beetles have a number of characteristic features. Their body is particularly hard and chitinous, they have geniculate antennae with a thick, button-like club and their elytra leave the last two abdominal tergites exposed. They are able to retract their head beneath their pronotum. Both the larvae and the adult beetles are predacious and hunt the larvae of other insects in decaying plant and animal matter. They are found chiefly in carrion, dung, rotting fungi, and under bark: a few frequent ants' nests.

1 *Plegaderus caesus*, 1.2−1.7 mm (2 : 3)
The 5 central European species of this genus can be distinguished from other members of the family by the thick border on their pronotum. The beetles live beneath bark and in rotten wood, and catch the larvae of bark beetles. Their small size makes it easy to overlook them. *P. caesus,* the commonest species in central Europe, is to be found chiefly under the bark of deciduous trees. Two other species of the genus are found in Britain.

2 *Onthophilus striatus*, 2−2.5 mm (3 : 1)
The 3 species of this genus found in central Europe live under rotting vegetation, in dung and in mammals' nests. The beetles are round-bodied and have prominent ridges on their elytra. *O. striatus* is the commonest species and it is to be found everywhere, under rotting plants, in dung, on carrion and on fungi.

3 *Abraeus globosus*, 1−1.5 mm (5 : 3)
None of the 3 species of this genus in central Europe (2 in Britain) is very common, but their domed body makes them easy to identify. The species shown here occurs beneath bark and in the nests of ants belonging to the genus *Lasius*.

4 *Acritus nigricornis,* 1 mm (7 : 4)
This genus is represented in central Europe by 5 species, all of which measure at most 1 mm or so in length and are thus easily overlooked. They live under decaying vegetable matter, in rotting wood, under bark and in ants' nests. The species depicted here is the commonest species of the genus in central and northern Europe, including Britain, and is to be found in decaying plant matter.

5 *Gnathoncus nanus,* 1.8−3 mm (9 : 1)
5 species of this genus occur in central Europe (4 in Britain). All of them live in birds' nests and poultry-sheds and only the occasional individual is found elsewhere, on carrion or in rotten fungi. The species shown here was formerly known under the names *G. rotundatus* or *G. punctulatus.* It occurs throughout the whole of Europe and Asia and is the commonest species in central Europe.

6 *Saprinus semistriatus,* 3.5−5.5 mm (10 : 5)
There are 15 species of this genus in central Europe, only 6 of which also occur in the British Isles. The beetles' most distinctive feature is the prominent groove in front of the posterior margin of their elytra, which curves round to a groove beside the suture. The beetles can be found under decaying plant and animal matter. The species shown here is the commonest member of the genus and is everywhere especially abundant on carrion.

7 Chalcionellus decemstriatus, 2.8−4 mm (11 : 2)
The two central European members of this genus were formerly included in the genus *Saprinus,* but they lack the deep grooves at the end of the elytra. This species ranges east from central Europe to southern Siberia. Neither species is common in central Europe, but occasionally they can be found on sandy ground under animal excrement.

8 *Hypocaccus rugiceps,* 3−4 mm (13 : 4)
The 4 central European species of the genus were likewise formerly considered to belong to *Saprinus.* 3 species are found in Britain, but none of them commonly. They are to be found chiefly on sandy ground close to water. This species is generally quite common in central Europe, where it occurs on dung and carrion in the vicinity of water.

9 *Dendrophilus pygmaeus,* 3 mm (16 : 2)
Two members of this genus occur in central Europe and the British Isles. The beetles' most distinctive feature is that the tibiae of all legs are extremely broad: they are not toothed, however, but only finely notched. In central Europe, the species depicted here occurs only in ants' nests (chiefly of *Formica rufa*), but is quite common in such situations.

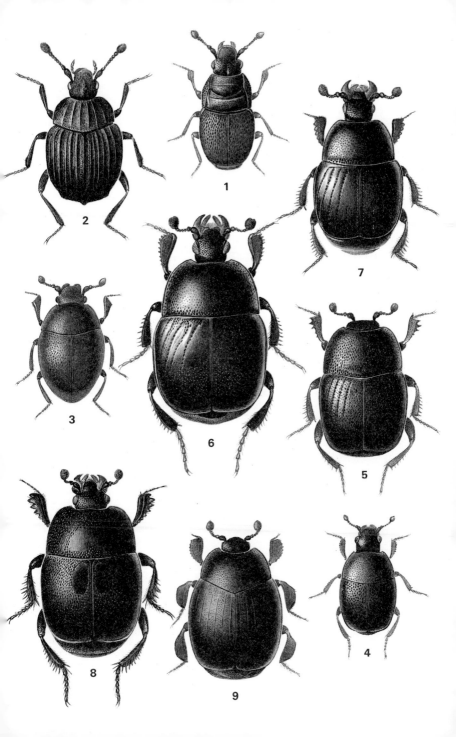

1 *Paromalus flavicornis, 1.5−2.2 mm (20 : 1)
In central Europe and the British Isles there are 2 species of this genus, which earlier authors included under *Micromalus* or *Microlomalus*. The glossy black beetles live under bark. The species shown here is the commonest in central and northern Europe: it is mostly to be found under the bark of deciduous trees, while the other species favours conifers.

2 *Hololepta plana,* 8−9 mm (21 : 1)
This gleaming black beetle − the only species of this genus in central Europe − is conspicuous for its long, sickle-shaped mandibles and its flattened body. It is to be found beneath the bark of deciduous trees (mainly poplars), is not very abundant and is absent in the north of Germany.

3 *Platysoma frontale,* 3−4 mm (24 : 1)
The genus *Platysoma* has 3 species in central Europe, none of which occur in Britain. The beetles can be recognized by their wide tibiae, which have a toothed outer edge, and from the deep S-shaped grooves on the first pair of tibiae. Both the beetles and the larvae prey on bark beetles and fly larvae under bark. This species is fairly common in natural forests and is to be found chiefly beneath the bark of dead deciduous trees.

4 *Cylister oblongum,* 3.5−4 mm (25 : 1)
In earlier works this genus, which has 3 species in central Europe, was included in *Platysoma*. None of them occur in Britain. The beetles are very similar, but *Cylister* species have a longer body. They also have similar habits to *Platysoma*. *C. oblongum* occurs mainly in eastern Europe and extends into Siberia: in central Europe it is to be found chiefly under the bark of conifers, where it hunts for bark beetles. It is not generally common, however; it is most abundant in the south-east and possibly does not occur at all in the north-west.

5 *Paralister stercorarius,* 3−5.5 mm (29 : 1)
In central Europe there are 7 species of this genus, which was formerly included in the genus *Hister*. 4 species of the genus are found in Britain. This species extends from southern and central Europe to western Asia: it is one of the commonest histerids and is to be found chiefly in dung.

6 *Hister cadaverinus,* 6−8.5 mm (32 : 9)
There are 12 species of this genus in central Europe, only 6 of which are to be found in Britain. Of the 3 grooves in the anterior corners of the pronotum, the middle one is usually shorter than the others. These beetles are to be found mainly on and in animal excrement, hunting other insects, but they also occur under decaying plant matter, in decaying fungi and on escaping sap. The distribution of this species extends from Europe, across Siberia, to Japan. In central and northern Europe it is one of the commonest histerids, especially on carrion.

7 *Hister quadrimaculatus,* 7−11 mm (32 : 1)
Several *Hister* species have red spots on their elytra, but this is a very variable character, since in this species, for example, the red may occasionally be missing. *H. quadrimaculatus* occurs in central and southern Europe, north Africa, western Asia and the Caucasus. In central Europe the beetles are to be found chiefly in cow and horse dung, but also under decomposing vegetation. This is a thermophilic species: it is usually fairly common in central Europe, but does not occur at high altitudes, and is very rare in Britain where it is found only in the south.

8 *Atholus corvinus,* 3.5−4.5 mm (33 : 4)
This genus, which has 4 species in central Europe, but only one in Britain, used to be included in the genus *Hister,* but the beetles have only 2, and not 3, striae in the anterior corner of their pronotum. The species illustrated here is very common in the south of central Europe, but northwards it grows steadily rarer.

9 *Hetaerius ferrugineus,* 1.5−2 mm (35 : 1)
This sole species of *Hetaerius* in central Europe is a distinctive round-bodied beetle with 3−4 fine grooves and with rows of erect yellow hairs down the elytra. It is distributed from central Europe as far as the Caucasus, but is nowhere common. The rust-red beetles live in the nests of various ants, mostly *Formica fusca* and *F. sanguinea,* and eat dead and sickly individuals.

Family Silphidae — carrion beetles

In central Europe this family has 12 genera, with 30 species. 20 species occur in the British Isles. Most of the beetles are fairly large, measuring over 10 mm, while the total range is 4 to 30 mm. The beetles usually have a flattened body and their antennae either have a thickened, button-like tip, or grow gradually thicker from base to tip. Not all species deserve the name of 'carrion' beetle: many do live on carrion, but some are predators, while others live on decaying plants and a few on living plant tissues.

1 *Nicrophorus humator* – Sexton or Burying Beetle, 18−26 mm (1 : 2)
This genus has 10 species in central Europe, 6 of which also occur in Britain. The beetles measure 10−30 mm and are either plain black or have red bands on their elytra. They are able to produce chirping sounds with their abdomen. They are to be found on carrion and bury small animals as future food for their brood. A few can also be found on decaying plants or fungi. This species − one of 2 with black elytra (but the only uniformly black *Nicrophorus* in Britain) − is fairly common in central and northern Europe, where it occurs on cadavers and decayed fungi.

2 *Nicrophorus vespillo* – Common Sexton or Burying Beetle, 12−22 mm (1 : 18)
This sexton beetle is distributed over the whole palaearctic region and North America. In many parts of Europe it is the commonest member of the genus. The beetles, which are active by night, can be caught by using meat as bait.

3 *Necrodes littoralis*, 15−22 mm (2 : 1)
The only member of the genus found in central Europe, this beetle has sharply ribbed elytra and unusually large eyes for a carrion beetle. In central Europe it is to be found on large cadavers, but today it is not so abundant as it used to be. In the British Isles it is commonest on or near the coast.

4 *Thanatophilus sinuatus*, 9−12 mm (3 : 2)
There are 3 species of this genus in central Europe and the British Isles. The beetles also have sharply ribbed elytra, but their distinctive pronotum has the appearance of beaten metal. They live on carrion. This species occurs over the entire palaeartic region, and in central Europe it is very plentiful.

5 *Oiceoptoma thoracica*, 11−16 mm (4 : 1)
Only a few European beetles are as unmistakable as the only representative of this genus in central Europe, since its orange-red pronotum distinguishes it from all other carrion beetles. Its range extends from Europe to Japan. In central Europe it abounds everywhere; it is often found on carrion, but especially favours the fruit bodies of the stinkhorn.

6 *Aclypea opaca*, 9−12 mm (5 : 1)
The ground colour of both the species of this genus (referred to as *Blitophaga* in many works) is black, but the one shown here is covered with golden hairs, while the other appears to be hairless. Both are vegetarians and may damage beet and turnip crops. *A. opaca* is distributed over the whole of the holarctic region: in central Europe it occurs chiefly in the north and east and is rarer in the west and south.

7 *Dendroxena quadripunctata*, 12−14 mm (6 : 1)
This is the only central European species of *Dendroxena* (termed *Xylodrepa* in many works); its yellow elytra, each with 2 black spots, make it unmistakable. It has unusual habits for a carrion beetle, since the adult beetles run about on bushes and trees hunting caterpillars, including serious pests like procession caterpillars. In central Europe it is locally and occasionally abundant, but is absent at high altitudes.

8 *Silpha obscura*, 13−17 mm (7 : 4)
The true carrion beetles have 8 species in central Europe (6 in Britain). The beetles are slightly convex, black or brown in colour and measure from 11 to 20 mm: many live on carrion, but some are predacious. *S. obscura* is common everywhere in central Europe, except in the high Alps. In Britain it is of very local occurrence.

9 *Silpha atrata* – Black Carrion Beetle, 10−15 mm (9 : 1)
This black or brown beetle (referred to the genus *Phosphuga* in many works) can be recognized by its long, shout-like head, which, as a snail-eater, it uses to break into snail-shells. In central and northern Europe the beetles are common everywhere and are to be found under loose bark and in moss.

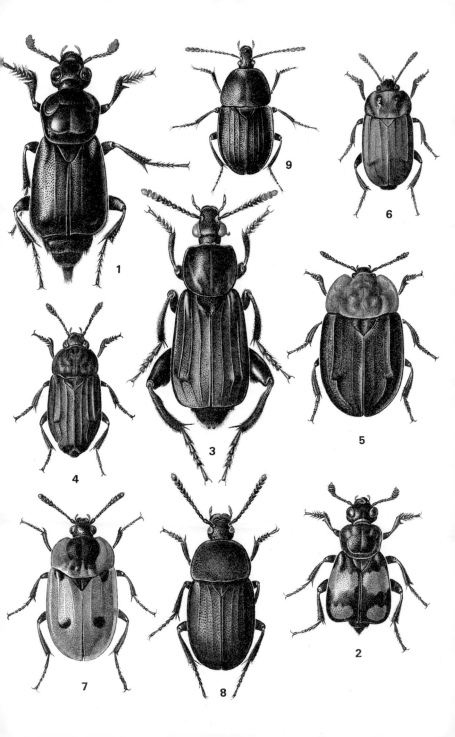

1 *Pteroloma forsstroemi*, 5—7 mm   (10 : 1)
The only member of the genus in central Europe, this beetle closely resembles certain ground beetles (e.g. *Nebria* or *Platynus*) in form. It has a boreomontane distribution in north and central Europe, where the beetles scuttle about beside mountain streams when the sun is shining and hide among the stones when the weather is cold and cloudy. In central Europe they occur in and to the south-east of the Harz Mountains and in the eastern Austrian Alps and have lately been reported in the Black Forest.

2 *Necrophilus subterraneus*, 6—8 mm   (11 : 1)
The only member of this genus found in central Europe has a round, discoid, red-brown body and is a montane species. Since the beetles are active at night, they have to be caught with bait or found under stones. They live primarily on snails.

Family Leptinidae
The central European fauna includes only 3 species of this family, belonging to 2 genera. All 3 species are highly modified for life as commensals with mammals.

3 *Leptinus testaceus*, 2—22 mm   (1 : 1)
Of the 2 species of this genus in central Europe, only the one shown here is widely distributed. The tiny, pale beetles lack both eyes and wings. *L. testaceus* is not rare, but is hard to catch, since it lives in the nests of small mammals (chiefly mice and moles) and in caves, in bat excrement.

4 *Platypsyllus castoris* — Beaver Beetle, 2.2—3 mm   (2 : 1)
The only species of this genus is one of the strangest of all beetles. It lives in the fur of beavers — both in zoos and on wild beavers in Europe and North America. Until quite recently it was wrongly thought to be a parasite, but it actually catches mites specifically parasitic on beavers.

Family Catopidae
There are 15 genera and 63 species of this family in central Europe; 32 species are found in the British Isles. They were formerly classed together with the silphids but, in most modern works, they are placed as a subfamily of the Leiodidae. The tiny beetles, which measure only 1—6.5 mm, lead a secretive existence and are to be found mainly on animal cadavers, decaying fungi or in leaf litter. Some species inhabit mammals' burrows, nests and caves; some of the species with a more southerly European distribution are exclusively cave-dwellers.

5 *Ptomaphagus sericatus*, 1.8—3 mm   (1 : 4)
There are 5 species of this genus in central Europe (3 in Britain). The beetles live chiefly in the burrows and nests of small rodents and on cadavers. The species shown here is in some places common. It is doubtful whether it occurs in north-western Germany, since in central Europe it is a montane species.

6 *Nargus velox*, 2.7—3.2 mm   (5 : 1)
This genus, which is represented by 5 species in central Europe (3 in Britain), is closely related to *Choleva*. The beetles of the 2 genera are similar, but *Nargus* have shorter antennae and legs and a shorter and broader body. They live mainly in mammals' burrows and can be found by sieving fallen leaves. The species shown here is fairly common in central and northern Europe, but is rarer in the north-east and in Austria.

7 *Choleva oblonga*, 4.5—5.5 mm   (6 : 5)
With its 18 species, this is one of the largest genera of the family in central Europe. 8 species are found in the British Isles. The fairly large, slender beetles, with long legs and antennae, are usually hard to distinguish from one another. They live chiefly in the burrows of mice or moles or in caves: a few also live in decomposing plant matter. This species is fairly common everywhere.

8 *Sciodrepoides watsoni*, 2.6—3.4 mm   (10 : 1)
This genus, which in central Europe and Britain has 3 species, used to be included in the genus *Catops*. The beetles live on carrion, in mammals' burrows and in birds' nests. The species depicted here is to be found on cadavers everywhere and is the commonest member of the genus in central Europe.

9 *Catops nigrita*, 3.5—4.5 mm   (11 : 12)
With its 20 European species, this is the largest genus of the family. 12 species occur in the British Isles. The beetles, whose lengths range from 2.5 to 6.5 mm, live on carrion, on decayed fungi, in mammals' burrows and the entrances to caves. They can be caught by using meat or cheese as bait. The species shown here is one of the commonest: it occurs mainly on cadavers and is found less often in burrows.

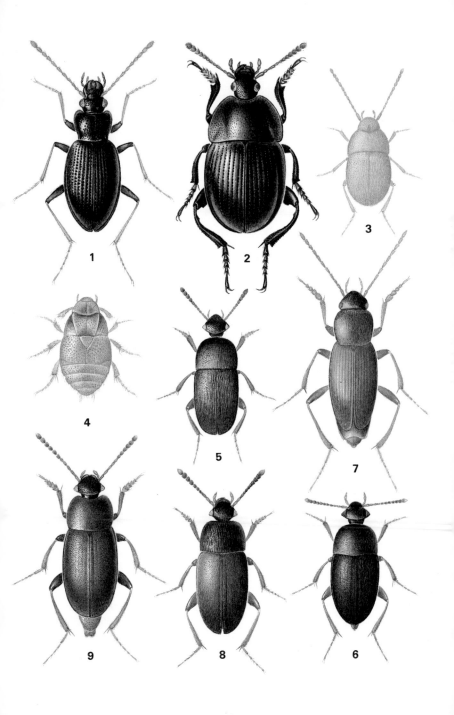

Family Colonidae

Like the Catopidae, of which it is sometimes regarded as a subfamily, this family was placed under the Silphidae in many early works, but many modern authors treat it as a subfamily of the Leiodidae. It contains only one genus which is represented by 20 species in central Europe (9 in Britain).

1 *Colon brunneum, 1.4−2.7 mm   (1 : 15)
All central European species of *Colon* have an elongate oval body, measure only 1.3−3.5 mm and have short antennae with claviform tips. They probably live on fungal mycelia. They are to be found in moss on old tree stumps and also under the bark, but most species are found rarely. The species shown here is fairly common everywhere in central Europe, and is the commonest species of the genus in Britain.

Family Leiodidae

This family, in which the Colonidae and Catopidae are included by many authors, has 11 genera in central Europe, with a total of 82 species measuring from 1.3 to 7 mm; 52 species occur in Britain. The majority have a round, domed body, but some are more elongate. Their colour ranges from light brown to black and they have claviform antennae. All Leiodidae eat fungi; some live on underground fungi and have legs adapted for digging, while others live on fungi above the ground and have normal legs.

2 *Hydnobius spinipes, 2−2.6 mm   (2 : 4)
In central Europe this genus has 7 species (4 in Britain), most of which are rare. *H. spinipes* is one of the commoner species, but it seems to be completely absent in parts of northern and western Europe.

3 *Leiodes calcarata, 2−3.4 mm   (3 : 20)
This genus (sometimes spelled *Liodes*) has 37 species in central Europe, 25 of which are found in Britain. The beetles have a light to dark brown and usually high-domed body and their legs, which are adapted for digging, are equipped with strong spines. They live on underground fungi (truffles and moulds) and swarm from half an hour before to half an hour after sunset in forest clearings and beside water. The species illustrated here is common in central Europe, and is the commonest *Leiodes* in most parts of Britain.

4 *Colenis immunda, 1.3−2 mm   (4 : 1)
This is the only species of the genus in central Europe and the British Isles. It is found in mouldy leaves and moss and often in large numbers on soil fungi. They can be locally numerous and rare in other places.

5 *Cyrtusa minuta, 1.6−1.8 mm   (6 : 1)
There are 6 species of this genus in central Europe, 2 in Britain. The beetles are almost spherical; they have antennae with a wide, four-jointed claviform tip and their legs are adapted for digging. They are to be found on both soil fungi and on mushrooms. This species is the commonest of the genus, but is not abundant.

6 *Anisotoma humeralis, 2.7−4 mm   (7 : 1)
Members of this and the following genus have 'normal' legs, i.e. without spines for digging. The five central European species are of a convex shape with an interrupted 5-segmented antennal club. They live chiefly under the bark of old tree stumps. *A. humeralis* is fairly common everywhere in central Europe.

7 *Agathidium seminulum, 2−2.5 mm   (11 : 15)
This genus has 19 species in central Europe (12 in Britain). The beetles have a pronotum with completely rounded posterior corners and are more or less able to roll themselves up into a ball. They live on wood, in mouldy fallen leaves and less often in mushrooms. The species shown here is abundant everywhere.

Family Clambidae

In central Europe this family has 13 species belonging to 2 genera. 9 species occur in the British Isles. The tiny beetles are able to roll themselves up into a ball. They have a broad head of characteristic shape, which is almost the same width as the pronotum. Little is known of their life and habits.

8 *Clambus armadillo, 1−1.3 mm   (2 : 7)
This genus alone has 11 species in central Europe. The beetles live under rotting plants and can be caught by sieving them out of flood debris or wet, rotting leaves. The species shown here is everywhere abundant.

9 *Calyptomerus dubius, 1.1−1.6 mm   (1 : 2)
The two central European members of this genus are a uniform reddish brown and are covered with long, thick, yellowish hairs. *C. dubius,* the only species found in Britain, occurs throughout the region.

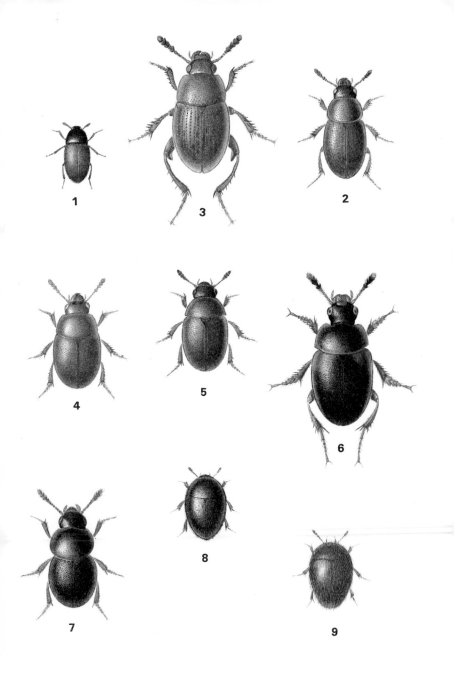

Family Scydmaenidae

Ten genera of this family, with 84 species, are found in central Europe. The family is much less well represented in the British Isles, where only 30 species occur. The beetles are minute, measuring only 0.7−2.3 mm, and have an elongate body with fine, loose bristles on the back. The antennae have clavate tips. The beetles live chiefly in moss and in damp fallen leaves, in dung, in rotting wood, under bark or under stones. A few species live in ants' or mammals' nests. Both larvae and adults feed on mites.

1 *Cephennium thoracicum*, 1.1−1.3 mm (4 : 3)
This genus is represented by 13 species in central Europe. The beetles' membranous wings have degenerated and the elytra are often fused. This species occurs mainly in western and southern Germany north of the Alps. One species of the genus − *C. gallicum* − is found in Britain.

2 **Neuraphes elongatulus*, 1.4−1.5 mm (5 : 1)
In central Europe there are 27 species belonging to this genus, 6 of which are found in Britain. The beetles are to be found in moss, in woodland leaf litter and in soil rich in humus; a few species live in ants' nests. The species depicted here is the commonest member of the genus in central and northern Europe.

3 **Scydmoraphes minutus*, 1.1−1.15 mm (6 : 4)
The 5 species of this genus in central Europe (2 in Britain) live similarly to *Neuraphes*. This species is to be found in the nests of ants belonging to the genera *Formica* and *Lasius*.

4 **Stenichnus collaris*, 1.55−1.7 mm (7 : 8)
Most of the 9 species of this genus in central Europe (6 in Britain) are black and have an elongate body. They live in ground litter, in moss, in rotting and powdered wood and a few with ants. *S. collaris* is the commonest species of the genus in central and northern Europe. The determination of *Stenichnus* species is difficult and is often impossible without examination of the male sex organs.

5 **Microscydmus nanus*, 0.9 mm (8 : 1)
There are 2 species of this genus in central Europe and the British Isles. The beetles, which measure only 0.7−0.9 mm, live in the top layer of forest humus and in well rotted wood. *M. nanus* is widely distributed in central Europe. In Britain it is largely restricted to areas of ancient deciduous woodland.

6 *Euconnus wetterhali*, 1.6 mm (9 : 17)
The genus *Euconnus* has a worldwide distribution, and is particularly well represented in the tropics. In central Europe there are 17 species belonging to 6 subgenera; 6 species occur in Britain. The gleaming black species shown here is abundant under rotting plant matter everywhere in central Europe.

7 **Scydmaenus tarsatus*, 2−2.1 mm (10 : 1)
This genus has 2 subgenera and 4 species in Europe (2 in Britain). The antennae are set very close together on the front of the beetles' head. The other species lives in ants' nests, but *S. tarsatus* abounds everywhere in mouldy straw, decaying plants and compost. It is particularly widespread in Europe, north Africa and the Near East.

Family Corylophidae

This family (referred to as Orthoperidae in some works) has 7 genera and 20 species in central Europe (10 in Britain). The beetles are tiny (barely over 2 mm) and oval or round and their head is invisible from behind as it is hidden under the pronotum. The beetles are to be found on mouldy wood, under bark, on rotting vegetation, in fungi and in wet, marshy situations.

8 **Sericoderus lateralis*, 0.8−1 mm (4 : 1)
This single species of *Sericoderus* found in central Europe is virtually cosmopolitan in its general distribution. The beetles, which become rarer towards the north, can be found under rotting plant matter.

9 **Orthoperus atomus*, 0.8−0.9 mm (8 : 3)
In central Europe there are 9 species of this genus, 6 of which occur in Britain. The minute, round-bodied, black beetles are particularly difficult to identify. They live under bark, on mouldy wood, under rotting leaves, in fungi, straw and plant matter, in pine and fir cones and even in damp cellars and the nests of birds of prey. The species shown here is much lighter than the others. Its incidence is often sporadic and it is not very common.

Family Sphaeriidae
The single genus contained in this family has 18 species, known from various parts of the world. Only one of them lives in central and northern Europe.

1 *Sphaerius acaroides, 0.7 mm   (1 : 1)
The beetles have a hemispherical and shining black or dark brown body. The antennae have a 3-jointed club and the wings are fringed with hairs. Although placed next to the Ptiliidae here, the two families are not closely related. This species lives in central and southern Europe, the south of northern Europe and the Caucasus. It is fairly common in sand and debris at the edge of fresh water, but is often overlooked because of its size. In Britain the species is extremely rare.

Family Ptiliidae — featherwing beetles
This family is very incompletely known, even in Europe. The central European fauna is likely to include at least 100 species, while at least 70 occur in the British Isles. They have a very variable form and the family includes the smallest of beetles measuring from about 0.5 to 1.2 mm. Their wings are made up of a narrow central strap fringed with long hairs to augment their surface area. Both adults and larvae feed on fungal spores.

2 *Nossidium pilosellum, 1.15−1.3 mm   (1 : 1)
The only member of the genus in central and northern Europe is to be found in rotting wood and in fungi growing on wood. It is fairly common.

3 *Ptenidium pusillum, 0.9−1.1 mm   (2 : 10)
This genus has 13 species in central Europe (11 in Britain). The head and pronotum are usually dark brown or black, while the elytra are often lighter brown. Most species live in decaying plant material and in dung, while a few live in ants' nests or other situations. The species shown here is widely distributed in Europe and north Africa and also occurs in North America. It abounds in rotting plant matter and in dung.

4 *Actidium aterrimum, 0.6−0.65 mm   (3 : 5)
There are 5 members of this genus in central Europe (2 in Britain). The beetles are a dull black, inhabit damp places, marshes, river banks and the sea shore. This species is distributed over practically the whole of Europe except Scandinavia, and is found in shingle on river banks.

5 *Oligella foveolata, 0.55−0.58 mm   (4 : 1)
The 3 species of this genus found in central Europe and the British Isles have a characteristic median longitudinal groove and an impression at the base of their pronotum. O. foveolata, inhabits central Europe and the southern part of northern Europe. It is quite common under rotting straw and dung.

6 *Ptilium exaratum, 0.63−0.7 mm   (6 : 12)
There are 14 species of this genus in central Europe (5 in the British Isles). The beetles can generally be recognized by the 3 longitudinal grooves on their pronotum. The various species, which are hard to distinguish from one another, live mainly in decaying plant matter. This species occurs all over Europe and is quite common in manure and in partly dry cow and horse dung.

7 *Nanoptilium kunzei, 0.55−0.65 mm   (8 : 1)
The 2 central European and British species of this genus formerly belonged to the genus Ptiliolum. The species shown here is dark brown or black. In central Europe it is to be found chiefly in manure and in partly dry cow and horse dung, where it is generally abundant.

8 *Ptiliolum fuscum, 0.65−0.75 mm   (9 : 6)
This genus has 7 species in central Europe, all but one of which also occur in Britain. The beetles live in decaying plant material and in excrement. P. fuscum is widespread in Europe and north Africa and in central Europe it is fairly common.

9 *Ptinella aptera, 0.6−0.8 mm   (12 : 4)
Like certain other Ptiliidae which inhabit rotting wood the members of this genus found in Europe are characterized by a remarkable dimorphism in the adult stage. One form of adult is full-winged and has well-developed eyes while the other, usually much the commoner, is wingless and eyeless. 7 species of the genus are known to occur in Britain and about the same number in central Europe. All of them live in rotting wood and under bark. The various species are extremely difficult to distinguish and are often confused. P. aptera is widespread in central and northern Europe.

132

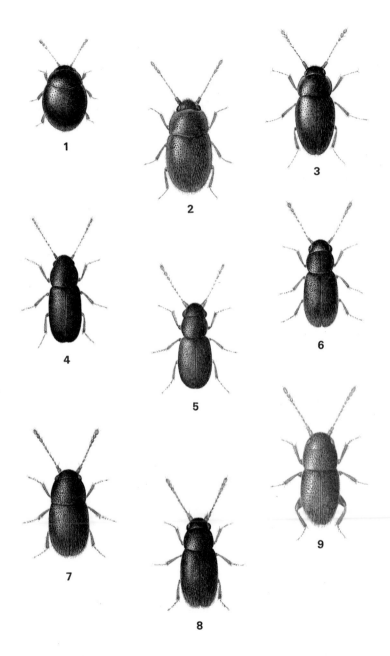

1 **Pteryx suturalis*, 0.75—0.85 mm (13 : 1)

This central European species has another relative in the south of Norway and Finland. In both sexes the beetles can occur in 2 forms. One is darker in colour, has well developed wings and large eyes, while the other is lighter, wingless and has distinctly smaller eyes. The beetles live chiefly in rotting wood and under bark. The species shown here occurs all over Europe and is common in central Europe.

2 **Nephanes titan*, 0.55—0.65 mm (15 : 1)

This only member of the genus found in central Europe resembles the preceding species, but its pronotum has a different form. It is known to occur throughout the whole of Europe and in central Europe it is fairly common. The beetles are found chiefly in manure, such as dry cow and horse dung, and in compost.

3 **Smicrus filicornis*, 0.8—0.9 mm (16 : 1)

The only member of the genus found in central Europe, this beetle has very long antennae with particularly long middle segments. In earlier works the genus was named *Micrus*. The beetles are fairly common everywhere in Europe and are to be found mainly in decaying plant matter.

4 **Baeocrara variolosa*, 0.9—1 mm (17 : 1)

This is the only central European representative of the genus. It resembles the preceding species, but has a more shining back, which can be brown or black. In some works this species is also referred to as *B. litoralis*. It occurs in central and northern Europe and can be found chiefly in hollow fir stumps.

5 **Actinopteryx fucicola*, 0.75—0.85 mm (18 : 1)

This species — also the only member of the genus in central Europe — has 2 not always clearly discernible impressions on its pronotum. It is a seashore species known from the coasts of Holland, Denmark and Sweden as well as the British Isles, where it is found under drifted seaweed.

6 **Acrotrichis intermedia*, 1—1.1 mm (19 : 15)

Acrotrichis is a large genus with at least 24 species in the British Isles and probably a greater number in central Europe. The beetles are relatively broad but not very convex, are dark in colour and measure from 0.5 to 1.1 mm in length. The posterior margin of the pronotum partly overlaps the anterior part of the elytra. The beetles live in various situations but mostly in decaying plant matter. In central Europe *A. intermedia* is a common woodland species, found in leaf litter, or in compost, dung or carrion.

Family Scaphidiidae — shining fungus beetles

These beetles have a scaphoid, i.e. boat-shaped body. In central Europe there are 4 genera comprising 11 species; 5 species occur in Britain. The beetles' elytra are somewhat abbreviated, so that the tip of the abdomen is generally exposed. The beetles are fast runners and live on fungi, especially tree fungi.

7 **Scaphium immaculatum*, 5—6.5 mm (1 : 1)

This genus is represented in central Europe and the British Isles by a single black species. It is distributed over much of southern and western Europe and its range extends to the south-western part of central Europe, but is not common there. In Britain it is extremely rare and found only in the south-east. The beetles can be found in warm places in moss, ground litter, mouldy wood or decayed mushrooms.

8 **Scaphidium quadrimaculatum*, 4.5—6 mm (2 : 1)

This single species of this genus found in central Europe is quite unmistakable. The beetles are glossy black and have 2 red spots on each elytron; in rare cases the anterior spot may be missing. The beetles are quite often to be found on wood overgrown by moss or fungi and on various fungi, particularly in deciduous woods.

9 **Scaphisoma agaricinum*, 1.5—1.9 mm (3 : 1)

The genus *Scaphisoma* (termed *Scaphosoma* by earlier authors) has 8 species in central Europe, 3 of which are found in Britain. The beetles are a squatter boat shape than other related genera. The species depicted here is the commonest of the genus and is fairly abundant on fungi.

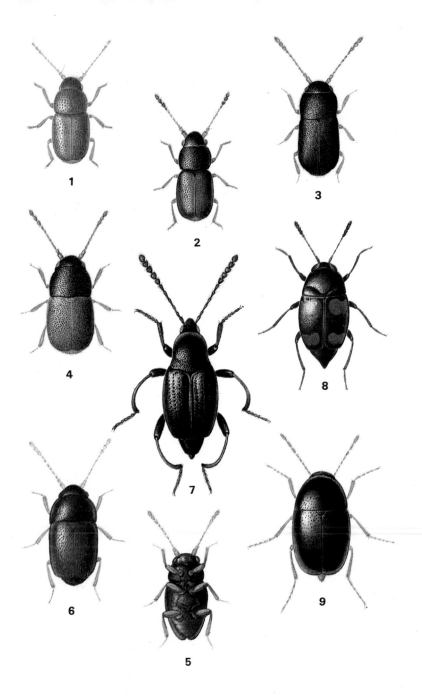

Family Staphylinidae — rove beetles

With almost 2,000 species, the rove beetles are the largest beetle family in central Europe (994 species in Britain). They can generally be recognized by their short elytra, although in some species these are fairly long and conversely, some beetles belonging to other families have short elytra and might well be taken for staphylinids. Most of the members of this family have well developed membranous wings and are able to fly. The size of the different species is usually very constant and less variable than that of herbivorous beetles. Most rove beetles are predators, although others feed on fungi, algae, decaying plant matter or parasitise other insects. Their habitats will be mentioned in connection with the separate genera.

1 *Micropeplus porcatus*, 2.3 mm   (1 : 6)
The 8 central European species of this genus differ from other staphylinids in respect of their 9-segmented and clubbed antennae (in other staphylinids the antennae are 11-segmented or, less usually, 10-segmented); they are also characterized by the thick ribs down their elytra and pronotum and the deep depressions in their abdominal tergites. They mostly live on rotting and mouldy plant matter. *M. porcatus* is widely distributed in Europe, but is rarely common.

2 *Phloeocharis subtilissima*, 1.5−2 mm   (5 : 1)
The only species of *Phloeocharis* found in central Europe and the British Isles is brown in colour, covered with clearly discernible yellow hairs, and of a rather depressed form. It is distributed throughout the whole of Europe, and occurs everywhere in central Europe, but is not common in Britain. Found under bark.

3 *Metopsia clypeata*, 2.5−3 mm   (7 : 1)
In earlier works, this genus, which has one species in central Europe, was termed *Phloeobium*. In western Europe, including the British Isles, there is a second species which may occur in the western part of central Europe. In central Europe *M. clypeata* is to be found under decaying matter, moss and leaves, especially on sandy ground; it has also been found in mouse burrows. Towards the north-east it becomes rarer.

4 *Megarthrus depressus*, 2.5−3 mm   (8 : 1)
There are 8 *Megarthrus* species in central Europe (5 in Britain). The beetles' pronotum is characterized by a groove down the midline and 'cut-away' posterior corners. The beetles measure from 1.9 to 3 mm and are to be found in decomposing animal and vegetable matter; they swarm on warm evenings. The species shown here is common everywhere in central Europe and throughout the British Isles.

5 *Proteinus brachypterus*, 1.6−1.9 mm   (9 : 4)
The genus *Proteinus* has 6 species in central Europe (5 in Britain). The beetles can often be found early in the spring, usually on fungi, but also on carrion. This species is abundant everywhere in central Europe and throughout the British Isles.

6 *Eusphalerum minutum*, 2−2.5 mm   (10 : 10)
There are 33 species of this genus in central Europe, many of them found only or mostly in mountain areas. Only 6 species occur in Britain. The adult beetles can often be found in large numbers on flowers, where they feed on pollen and the sexual parts of the flowers. *E. minutum* is found only in wet places, particularly on the flowers of sedges and rushes. It is very common in central Europe, and is widely distributed in the British Isles. In earlier works the genus goes under the name of *Anthobium*.

7 *Acrolocha minuta*, 2 mm   (13 : 2)
Four species of this genus live in central Europe (2 in Britain). The beetles' most striking features are the narrow third segment of their antennae and the punctured striae on their elytra. They live in dung, decomposing fungi and plant material. *A. minuta*, a winter-active species, is widely distributed in central Europe and is usually fairly common. In Britain it is scarce and found only in the south-east.

8 *Phyllodrepa floralis*, 3.5−4.5 mm   (14 : 6)
This genus has 7 species in central Europe (4 in Britain). The majority are to be found, especially in spring, on flowering shrubs, but nests and burrows are their true habitat. *P. floralis* is the commonest species of the genus in central and northern Europe.

9 *Omalium rivulare*, 3.5−4 mm   (15 : 5)
There are 21 species of *Omalium* in central Europe (13 in the British Isles). The beetles are black or brownish red and generally have 2 deep lengthwise impressions in their pronotum. They are to be found on decaying material of animal and plant origin. Some species are strictly confined to the seashore. *O. rivulare* is the commonest and is more or less ubiquitous in central and northern Europe, including the British Isles.

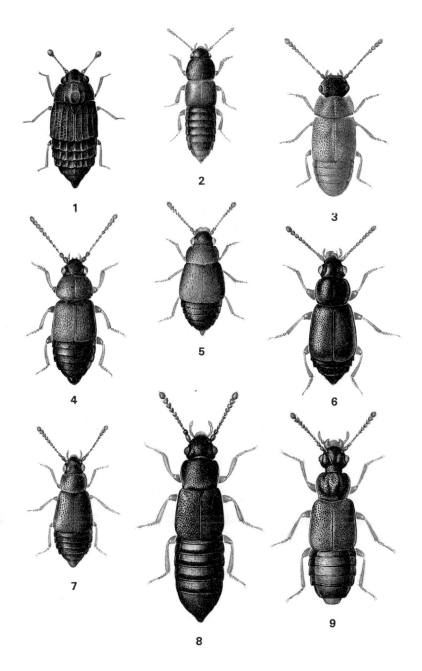

1 *Phloeonomus pusillus,* 1.7−2 mm (16 : 5)
The 3 species of this genus in central Europe (2 in Britain) closely resemble *Omalium* species. Their sizes vary from 1.3 to about 2 mm and they are to be found mainly under the bark of trees. This species occurs over the entire holarctic region and in central Europe can be found in abundance under the bark of conifers.

2 *Xylodromus depressus,* 3−3.5 mm (17 : 1)
The 4 central European members of this genus also resemble the preceding genera. *X. depressus* is distributed over almost the whole of Europe and in central Europe it is very common. The beetles can be found in the summer, in meadows, in mouldy hay and in hay and straw in barns.

3 *Anthobium atrocephalum,* 3−3.5 mm (25 : 2)
In central Europe there are 5 species of *Anthobium* (referred to as *Lathrimaeum* in some works), 2 species occur in Britain. They have particularly long elytra, which sometimes cover almost the entire abdomen. The beetles are to be found in woods, under leaves and moss and in tree fungi. This species, whose head is darker than its reddish brown body, occurs over most of the palaearctic region from Europe to Japan. In central Europe the beetles live in damp ground litter, mostly in woodland, where they can be very abundant.

4 *Olophrum piceum,* 5−6 mm (26 : 1)
The 12 *Olophrum* species in central Europe (4 in Britain) have a very wide pronotum, a relatively small head, a smooth and shining surface and a convex general form. *O. piceum* is flightless but widely distributed in central Europe and the southern part of northern Europe. In central Europe the beetles can be found on heaths and in bogs, where they are fairly common. The species is to be found in marshes, bogs, and on the banks of ponds throughout the British Isles.

5 *Arpedium brachypterum,* 3−4.5 mm (28 : 1)
This, the only British *Arpedium,* is sometimes placed in the genus *Eucnecosum, A. brachypterum* lives in damp moss in bogs and is commoner in the mountains than in the lowlands. In the British Isles it is restricted to areas of moorland and mountains in the north.

6 *Amphichroum canaliculatum,* 4.5−5 mm (31 : 1)
Two species of this genus occur in central Europe, but neither of them is to be found in Britain. They both have a hairy back and closely resemble each other. They live on shrubs and bushes at montane and subalpine altitudes and swarm in the middle of the day, often in large numbers. *A. canaliculatum* is to be found in mountainous regions in the middle and south of central Europe and in some places the beetles may even be abundant.

7 *Lesteva longoelytrata,* 3.5−4.5 mm (32 : 3)
All 13 central European species of this genus, 6 of which occur in the British Isles, are discernibly hairy. They can be identified with certainty by the last segment of their maxillary palps, which is four times the length of the preceding one. Most of the species are found in waterside situations, some in wet moss by waterfalls and weirs, others in bogs and marshes. The species shown here is common everywhere in central Europe, and occurs throughout the British Isles.

8 *Geodromicus nigrita,* 5−6 mm (33 : 3)
The 4 species of this genus found in central Europe (2 in Britain) are black or brown with long, relatively slender antennae. They can be found in wet moss by fast-flowing water and a few at the edge of snowfields at high altitudes. This species is the commonest in the west of central Europe, but is absent in the plains of northern Germany. In the British Isles it is found only in the north and west.

9 *Anthophagus caraboides,* 4.5−5.5 mm (35 : 4)
Most of the 17 species of this genus in central Europe are confined to montane and Alpine regions, where the beetles can be found − often in large numbers − on shrubs and flowers in the vicinity of running water. Only 2 species of the genus are found in Britain. Their elytra and legs are almost always brownish yellow. The species shown here occurs everywhere in central Europe, but while it is generally fairly common in the mountains, it is rare in the plains. In Britain it is confined to the north and west, where it is found mostly in the hills and mountains.

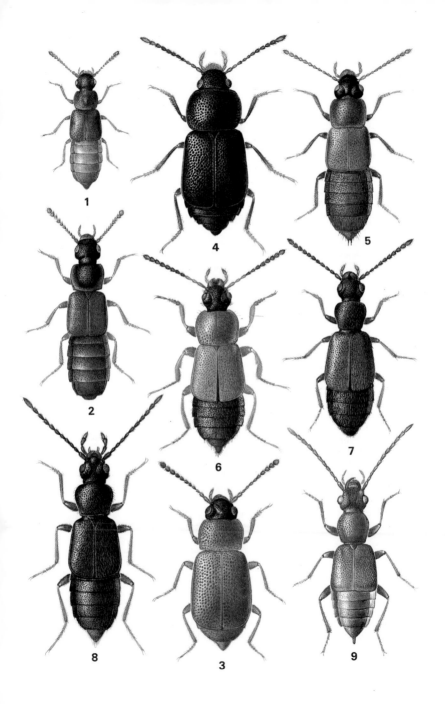

1 *Syntomium aeneum,* 2−3 mm (40 : 1)

Beetles of the genus *Syntomium* have a characteristically short, bulky body, whose head and thorax have a pronounced metallic sheen. The only species found in central and northern Europe is widely distributed and by no means rare, but easily missed because of the beetles' very sluggish movements. They are to be found in moss on trees and in bogs. They swarm on summer evenings and can be caught in the winter by sieving.

2 *Coprophilus striatulus,* 5−7 mm (42 : 1)

This genus, referred to in earlier works as *Elonium,* has 2 species in central Europe. Both species have irregular rows of large punctures on their elytra. *C. striatulus,* the only one occurring in Britain, is common in decomposing plant matter and compost. The beetles can be found chiefly in the spring.

3 *Manda mandibularis,* 6−8 mm (43 : 1)

The only species of this genus (referred to in many works as *Acrognathus*) in central Europe differs from the preceding species chiefly in respect of its hairy back and lighter colour. It is distributed from northern, via central, to southern Europe, and in central Europe lives beside water. In Britain the species is confined to the southern counties, where it is rare. The beetles swarm in the evening, often in large numbers, near wet meadows; they are also attracted by lights.

4 *Ochthephilus omalinus,* 2.5−3 mm (45 : 3)

There are 8 species of this genus (*Ancyrophorus* in some works) in central Europe, four of them being found in the British Isles. The beetles have very long, flat elytra. They are to be found chiefly in the mountains, by waterfalls and weirs, where they crawl about on damp moss with members of the genus *Lesteva.* This is an uncommon species, found in northern and central Europe and in Italy.

5 *Carpelimus elongatulus,* 2.2−2.5 mm (46 : 32)

In central Europe this genus, often also referred to as *Trogophloeus,* has 33 species, mostly uniform black or dark brown and elongate. They are often very difficult to distinguish from one another. A few species have definitely been shown to live on algae and it is likely that most species share this habit. The beetles live mostly beside water, on parts of the banks devoid of vegetation. If one stamps or knocks on the ground at such spots, they come out of hiding. A few species live in compost or mud walls. *C. elongatulus* is not confined to waterside situations, occurs everywhere and is generally abundant.

6 *Anotylus tetracarinatus,* 1.7−2.2 mm (48 : 26)

The 23 species of this genus in central Europe (13 in Britain) have characteristic surface sculpture and closely resemble each other. The beetles can be found, often in large numbers, in dung and soil, under decomposing plants or in excrement, and occasionally in mammals' nests. The beetles swarm on warm evenings. The species depicted here is the commonest species of the genus and is sometimes regarded as the most abundant of European beetles.

7 *Anotylus sculpturatus,* 3.5−4.5 mm (48 : 11)

This much larger member of the genus occurs throughout much of the palaearctic region and is very common everywhere in central Europe.

8 *Platystethus arenarius,* 2.8−5 mm (49 : 1)

The size of the body of some of the 10 central European members of this genus, 7 of which occur in Britain, is more variable than is usual in rove beetles. The males of most species have 2 distinct spines on their head. The beetles can be found mostly in dung or on muddy river banks. *P. arenarius* occurs over the whole palaearctic region and is abundant everywhere in central and northern Europe.

9 *Bledius gallicus,* 4−4.5 mm (50 : 20)

47 species of this genus occur in central Europe, of which 25 are found in Britain. The beetles have typical spines on their first pair of tibiae for digging, their body is cylindrical and their pronotum and abdomen are clearly separated. The various species, which are often difficult to tell apart, burrow in flat sandy or clayey soil or in vertical banks, mostly in waterside situations; the loose material thrown out of the entrances to their burrows gives them away. They live in colonies and evidently feed entirely on algae. They swarm on warm evenings and are attracted by lights. The best way to catch them is to flood them out. The species illustrated here, referred to as *B. fracticornis* in many works, is abundant everywhere in central Europe.

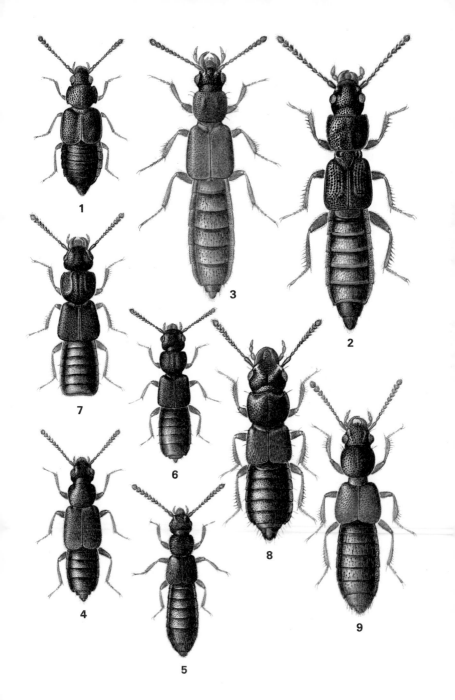

1 **Oxyporus rufus*, 7−12 mm (54 : 1)

The 2 species of this genus found in central Europe are brightly coloured and conspicuous for their large, prominent, crossed mandibles. They also have a strikingly large head, wider than their pronotum. In the summer the beetles are to be found on mushrooms. The species shown here is widely distributed in the palaearctic region; in central Europe it is fairly common everywhere on gill fungi.

2 **Stenus clavicornis*, 5−5.5 mm (56 : 22)

This genus is represented in central Europe by 114 species (72 in Britain). The various species are all of a similar general appearance, with large eyes and generally dark coloration; a few have red spots on their elytra and others have lighter-coloured legs. Their lengths range from 1.7 to 7.5 mm. In view of the large number of species in this genus, it is not surprising that their determination is often very difficult and that microscopic examination of their legs, the under side of their abdomen or their sex organs is frequently necessary. The beetles lead very diverse lives. The majority are found in waterside situations and wet places such as marshes, but some live in forest litter, at the edge of snowfields, on heaths and even in ants' nests. The beetle depicted here is widely distributed in the Palaearctic region and is abundant everywhere in central Europe and throughout the British Isles.

3 **Dianous coerulescens*, 5−6 mm (56 : 1)

The only central European species of *Dianous* resembles *Stenus*, but is at once distinguishable by its metallic blue colouring and the large red spots (smaller in *Stenus*) on its elytra. It lives in northern and central Europe, where the beetles are to be found almost everywhere by waterfalls and, in low-lying country, by weirs.

4 **Euaesthetus ruficapillus*, 1.4−1.7 mm (58 : 2)

The species depicted here is by far the commonest of the 3 members of the genus found in central Europe and the British Isles. The beetles can be found in marshes and on river banks, especially in the spring.

5 **Paederus riparius*, 7.5−8 mm (59 : 8)

The 10 species of this genus in central Europe, 4 of which occur in Britain, are conspicuous for their bright colouring; all have a red pronotum and metallic blue elytra. With abdomen erect they run about nimbly in the sunshine, mostly on sandy ground beside water. *P. riparius* is very common on river banks and in marshes everywhere in central Europe.

6 **Rugilus rufipes*, 5.5−6 mm (61 : 3)

The 8 species of *Rugilus* (referred to as *Stilicus* in many works) found in central Europe have a large head attached to their thorax by a narrow neck. The beetles are to be found in a variety of situations, including leaf litter and vegetable debris. *R. rufipes* is widespread in Europe and east to the Caucasus; in central and northern Europe it is generally common.

7 *Hypomedon debilicornis*, 2.5 mm (63 : 1)

Formerly included in the genus *Medon*, this almost cosmopolitan species is found in compost and other man-made accumulations of vegetable matter. Its continuing spread across Europe is no doubt aided by the fact that the species reproduces parthenogenetically.

8 **Lithocharis nigriceps*, 3.5−4 mm (65 : 2)

The 2 central European and British members of this genus resemble the preceding species, but have larger eyes. *L. nigriceps*, originally a native of Asia, but now almost cosmopolitan, has spread right across central Europe since 1940 and is now abundant in compost heaps and under rotting plant matter everywhere.

9 **Scopaeus sulcicollis*, 2.8−3 mm (66 : 4)

There are 14 species of this genus in central Europe, five of which occur in the British Isles. The tiny beetles (only 2.5−3.5 mm long) have an almost square head attached to the thorax by a very narrow neck. The beetles are to be found in the vicinity of water, under stones and in sand and gravel. *S. sulcicollis*, referred to as *S. cognatus* in some works, occurs everywhere in central Europe, but it is not particularly common and the other species are rarer still.

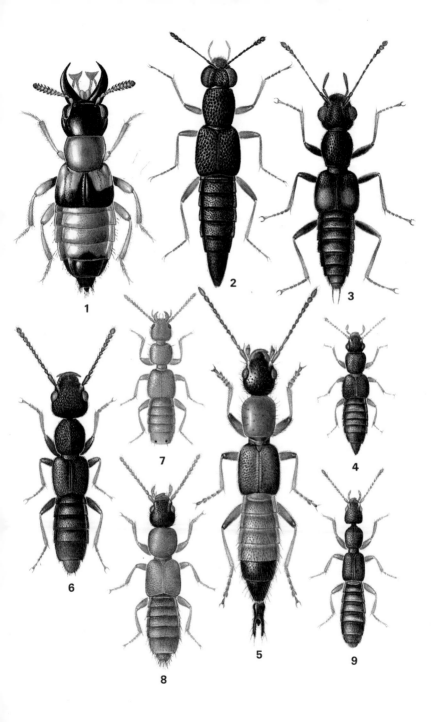

1 *Lathrobium fulvipenne, 7−8 mm   (68 : 21)
37 species of this genus live in central Europe (18 in Britain). They are long-bodied, parallel-sided beetles with irregularly punctured elytra. In some species the membranous wings may be absent, in others fully developed. The beetles can be found in damp spots − many beside water under stones, others in woods, under moss and leaves. *L. fulvipenne* is one of the commonest species in central and northern Europe.

2 *Leptacinus intermedius, 3.5−4.5 mm   (75 : 2)
Five species of this genus live in central Europe (4 of them in Britain). The beetles are mostly dark brown or black, but have brownish yellow legs. The species cannot always be determined from their external appearance, as they closely resemble each other and their distinguishing characters are rather variable; the only sure way is to examine the sex organs. Most *Leptacinus* species are to be found in compost containing straw. The species shown here is common in central and northern Europe.

3 *Gyrohypnus punctulatus, 7.5−9 mm   (79 : 1)
Earlier authors placed the 4 *Gyrohypnus* species living in central Europe and the British Isles in the genus *Xantholinus*, as a separate subgenus. Like related genera, the beetles have a frontal process on the head − in this case strongly developed. The various species live mostly in decaying plant matter or in ground litter and one lives in ants' nests. *G. punctulatus* is widespread in the Palaearctic region. In Europe and the British Isles the species has been much confused with the very similar *G. fracticornis,* which is also found in other continents.

4 *Xantholinus linearis, 6−9 mm   (80 : 10)
The large, long, posteriorly wider head of the 17 central European species of this genus, 8 of which occur in Britain, is the same width as the pronotum, while the frontal process on the head is short, blunt and much smaller than in related genera. A further distinctive character is the long first segment of the antennae. The various species often cannot be told apart without examining the sex organs. The species illustrated here is found throughout the palaearctic region and is the commonest in central Europe.

5 *Xantholinus tricolor, 7.5−11 mm   (80 : 5)
This species, which is widely distributed in the palaearctic region, is to be found in central Europe mainly in conifer forests. It occurs in the Alps at high altitudes and is fairly common over much of Europe but is very local in the British Isles.

6 *Atrecus affinis, 6−7.5 mm   (81 : 1)
The 3 central European species of this genus have a squarish head the same width as or wider than the pronotum. The beetles live beneath bark or in the powdered wood of old, rotten trees. This species, the only one found in the British Isles, is the commonest member of the genus.

7 *Othius punctulatus, 10−14 mm   (82 : 1)
In central Europe there are 7 species of this genus, 5 of which occur in the British Isles. All of them are to be found in leaf litter. The species shown here is much larger than most; it occurs in Europe, Siberia and north Africa and in central Europe it is fairly abundant under leaves, moss and stones.

8 *Cafius xantholoma, 6−9 mm   (85 : 1)
There are 4 species of this genus in the British Isles but only 2 occur in central Europe. They may be distinguished from related species of other genera by the close dimpled puncturation on the pronotum and the patches of fine bristles on the abdomen. All of the species are halophilic (salt-loving). *C. xantholoma* is widespread on the Atlantic coasts of Europe and Africa. It is also found in the Mediterranean, by the North Sea and the Baltic, where the beetles abound under seaweed on sandy shores.

9 *Philonthus politus, 10.5−13 mm   (88 : 25)
This genus has 75 species in central Europe, and 55 in the British Isles. On the pronotum, on either side of the midline, the beetles have a row of pores. They are to be found chiefly in decaying plant matter, in compost and on carrion, dung and fungi. Some species are found in marshes and in waterside situations. *P. politus* occurs throughout the palaearctic region, North America and in the cooler parts of the southern hemisphere; it is very common everywhere in central and northern Europe.

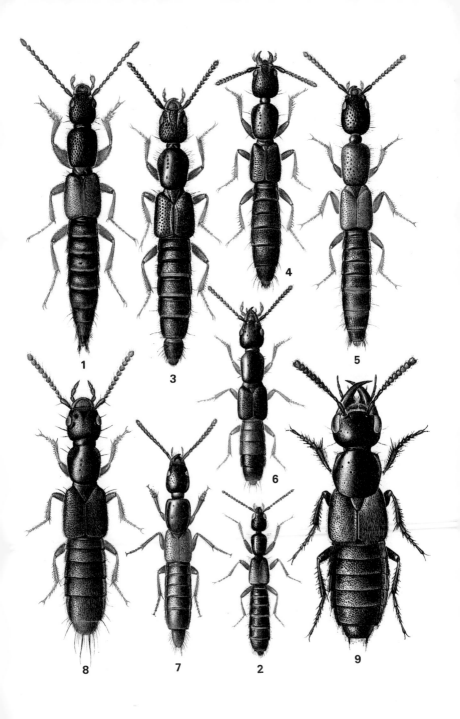

1 *Gabrius nigritulus*, 4—5.5 mm   (90 : 18)
Gabrius was formerly classified as a subgenus of *Philonthus*. Its 25 central European species, 13 of which occur in Britain, look like small members of *Philonotus*, but have a longer head and pronotum than most of them. The pronotum carries two rows of 5 or 6 pores. The beetles live in decaying organic matter and in wet places. The species depicted here occurs throughout the holarctic region and also occurs in the southern hemisphere; it is the commonest species in central Europe and is to be found there everywhere.

2 *Creophilus maxillosus*, 15—25 mm   (91 : 1)
With the black and whitish grey patches on its pronotum and abdomen, due partly to its colouring and partly to patches of fine bristles, the only species of *Creophilus* found in Europe is unmistakable. In central Europe the beetles are abundant everywhere; they are to be found mainly on carrion and less often on other decomposing matter.

3 *Ontholestes murinus*, 10—15 mm   (92 : 2)
The 3 central European members of this genus (2 of which occur in Britain), somewhat resemble the preceding species, but have a slimmer body. The golden yellow and black marbling effect is produced entirely by hairs. The species shown here occurs throughout the palaearctic region; in central Europe the beetles can be found everywhere in large numbers on carrion and fresh dung.

4 *Emus hirtus*, 18—28 mm   (93 : 1)
The only species of *Emus* found in central Europe is thickly covered with golden yellow, grey and black hairs. It has been found everywhere in central Europe, but only singly and rarely. In Britain *E. hirtus* is very rare and found, only occasionally, in Kent. The handsome beetles are to be found chiefly on fresh manure and less often on carrion.

5 *Staphylinus fossor*, 15—20 mm   (97 : 1)
Although not found in Britain, *S. fossor* is one of the commoner species in the western and southern part of central Europe. The striking-looking beetles live mainly in woods and forests.

6 *Staphylinus caesareus*, 17—22 mm   (98 : 2)
In earlier works the species now placed in *Ocypus* and *Platydracus* were included in *Staphylinus*. However, as presently constituted, the latter genus contains only central European species. They are among the most impressive and handsome of staphylinids. Several of the species, including *S. caesareus,* have a black body, red elytra and golden patches of hair on their abdomen. *S. caesareus* is usually fairly common in central Europe, but in the plains of northern Germany it is rare or absent and it is rare in Britain.

7 *Ocypus olens*, 22—32 mm   (99 : 1)
The 25 central European species of *Ocypus* were formerly included in *Staphylinus*. 13 species are found in the British Isles. Most of the beetles are pitch black, but a few have a dark metallic or blue sheen. The species illustrated here, which is one of the largest staphylinids, is found in woods, gardens and open situations. The beetles often hide under wood and other objects by day; they have powerful mandibles and their bite can be quite painful.

8 *Heterothops dissimilis*, 3.8—4.5 mm   (100 : 5)
Seven species of this genus live in central Europe (5 in Britain). The tiny beetles have a large head. They live in damp places under leaves and plant debris. One species is a regular guest in moles' nests and others may also be closely associated with mammals' burrows. This species occurs throughout the palaearctic region; in central Europe it is one of the commonest members of the genus and is to be found everywhere.

9 *Velleius dilatatus*, 15—24 mm   (103 : 1)
The single species of *Velleius* found in central Europe is not only conspicuous for its length and girth; as distinct from other rove beetles, its antennal segments, from the 4th onwards, are distinctly serrate (like the teeth of a saw). The beetles also have remarkable habits. They are regularly to be found in hornets' nests, but since it is a ticklish job to get them out, they are often thought to be rarer than they really are. At night they come out and make for escaping sap on trees and this is one way of catching them. This species has been recorded from all parts of central Europe, but it also occurs as far afield as China and Japan.

146

1 *Quedius nitipennis, 5.5−7 mm   (104 : 64)
There are 70 species of this genus in central Europe, varying in length from about 5 mm to 15 mm. 43 species occur in Britain. On the beetles' head and pronotum we can find bristle-bearing pores whose position and pattern are important for determination of the many species. The majority of *Quedius* species live in ground litter and moss, mostly in wet places. Some inhabit dead wood and decaying fungi, while a few live in nests and holes in trees. *Q. nitipennis* (in earlier works also named *attenuatus* or *picipennis*) is abundant everywhere in central Europe, and in the British Isles is particularly common on heathland and moorland.

2 *Habrocerus capillaricornis, 3−3.5 mm   (107 : 1)
The single European species of *Habrocerus* is readily distinguished by its thread-like antennae. The beetles are abundant everywhere in central Europe; they are to be found in woods, under damp and mouldy leaves, and also in mouldy straw and hay.

3 *Mycetoporus lepidus, 4−5 mm   (109 : 8)
In central Europe there are 33 species of this genus, 15 of which are found in Britain. The boat-shaped beetles are slim and glossy; they live in moss and ground litter and under mouldy twigs and bark and are mostly found singly. This species, which is widely distributed in Europe, Siberia and North America, is the commonest in central Europe and one of the commonest in Britain.

4 *Bolitobius analis, 6−7 mm   (112 : 2)
The 4 central European species of *Bolitobius* (*Bryocharis* in many works) are brightly coloured. *B. analis* and the very similar *B. cingulatus* have a black body, red elytra and a dark, red-tipped abdomen. The beetles of both species can be found in damp spots with ground litter and (less often) in open country. *B. analis* is found in practically the whole of Europe except the north; in central Europe it occurs everywhere, but, like the other species, is rather rare.

5 *Lordithon thoracicus, 2.5−4.5 mm   (111 : 3)
The 9 species of *Lordithon* (referred to as *Bolitobius* in many works) in central Europe, 5 of which are found in Britain, are built on somewhat broader lines than the preceding species. The beetles are mostly brightly coloured and can often be found in large numbers on mushrooms and a few on tree fungi; they are all predacious. *L. thoracicus* (in earlier works termed *pygmaeus*) is the smallest species of the genus in central Europe, where it is abundant everywhere; it is distributed over the whole of the holarctic region.

6 *Sepedophilus testaceus, 3.5−5 mm   (113 : 2)
In central Europe there are 7 species of this genus, referred to as *Conosoma* or *Conosomus* in many works. The beetles' abdomen tapers off to a fine point and the whole of their back is covered with fine hairs. Most species are to be found under mildewy bark, in fungusy wood, and under mouldy leaves. *S. testaceus,* known to earlier authors as *S. pubescens* and easily confused with related species, occurs throughout the holarctic region, and in central Europe it is abundant everywhere.

7 *Tachyporus chrysomelinus, 3.5−4 mm   (114 : 8)
The 18 members of this genus in central Europe (13 in the British Isles) measure only 2−4 mm in length and have a sharp-pointed abdomen. They vary from yellowish red to black and may have contrasting patches or bands of colour, but their colouring is often an unreliable aid to identification because of its variability. Like all the other species, the one depicted here is a predator, found in ground litter and, in winter, on moss growing on tree trunks. It is distributed over the whole of the holarctic region and, together with certain other *Tachyporus* species, it is one of the commonest of rove beetles.

8 *Tachinus signatus, 5−6.5 mm   (117 : 13)
There are 20 species of this genus in central Europe (14 in Britain). On their terminal abdominal segments the beetles bear protuberances and spines, by means of which the various species can be identified. The beetles live in decomposing plant matter, dung and carrion, and may be found at escaping sap; occasionally they can be found in animals' nests. *T. signatus* (known as *T. rufipes* in many works) is known over the entire holarctic region and is very common everywhere in central Europe and the British Isles.

9 *Cilea silphoides, 3−4 mm   (119 : 1)
This almost cosmopolitan rove beetle is very distinctively coloured, especially as regards the black markings on its elytra. It is the only species of the genus found in central Europe, where it lives under decaying plants and dung and in warm compost, where it tends to be present in large numbers. The beetles swarm in the evening.

148

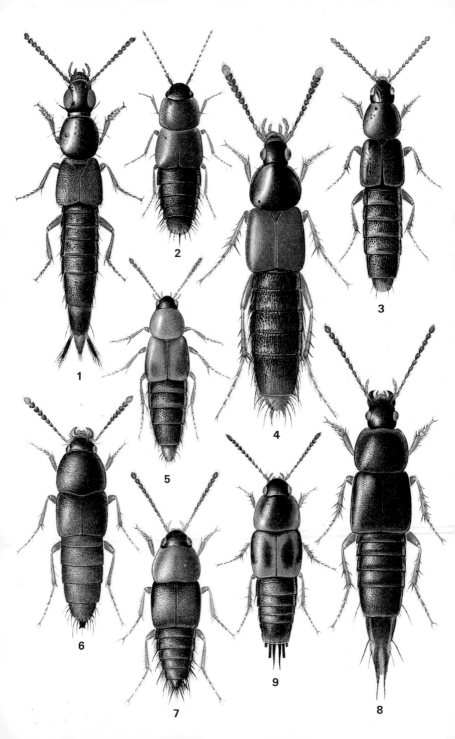

1 **Cypha longicornis*, 1–1.4 mm (120 : 1)

The 15 species of this genus (formerly known as *Hypocyptus* or *Hypocyphtus*) in central Europe are very small beetles (0.5–1.5 mm) whose pointed abdomen can be largely retracted telescope-wise below the elytra, so that the beetles can roll themselves up almost into a ball. Ten species occur in Britain. They may be found in damp spots under leaves, in moss and on vegetation. The species shown here occurs everywhere in central Europe except the Alps and is the commonest member of the genus.

2 **Myllaena intermedia*, 2.2–2.6 mm (123 : 2)

The 8 members of this genus in central Europe have a dense covering of hairs and an abdomen which tapers off to a sharp point. They are confined to waterside and marshy situations where they are found chiefly under leaves and moss. *M. intermedia* is the commonest species of the genus in central Europe. Eleven species of the genus are found in the British Isles.

3 **Oligota inflata*, 1.1–1.4 mm (126 : 6)

The 10 central European members of this genus are tiny beetles measuring only 0.7–1.5 mm. They are generally thickset, and some species are almost as broad as *Cypha*. Many of the species are very similar and difficult to identify. Most species live under decaying vegetation, leaves and moss, while a few live in the foliage of bushes and trees where they feed on mites. *O. inflata* is found in cellars and stables, in dry dung and in compost.

4 **Hygronoma dimidiata*, 2.5–3 mm (127 : 1)

The single known species of *Hygronoma* can easily be recognized from the colouring of its elytra and its slender form. The under side of the beetles' tarsi bear special hairs which enable them to run over water. In central Europe they abound on swampy ground and in the immediate vicinity of water, where they climb rushes and reeds, but to the west and in the mountains they are rare; in the winter they can be found in the sheaths of bulrushes.

5 **Gyrophaena affinis*, 1.8–2.3 mm (130 : 4)

This genus has 26 species in central Europe, 19 of which occur in Britain. The beetles, which measure only 0.9–3 mm in length, have a short, broad, glossy body. They live mostly in mushrooms and tree fungi, and may often be found in large numbers. *G. affinis* is common everywhere in central and northern Europe.

6 **Placusa tachyporoides*, 2–2.2 mm (132 : 3)

The 7 central European species of this genus, 3 of which are found in Britain, are built on somewhat similar lines to *Atheta* species. All live under bark. The one shown here is probably the commonest in central Europe.

7 **Anomognathus cuspidatus*, 1.5–1.8 mm (134 : 1)

This is the only central European species of this genus, which was formerly termed *Thectura*. The beetles have a characteristic sharp, spine-like process on their last abdominal tergite. *A. cuspidatus* lives gregariously under bark and is fairly common in central Europe, except in the southwest.

8 **Silusa rubiginosa*, 3–3.6 mm (135 : 1)

Three species of this genus live in central Europe. The beetles have a characteristic deep impression on the posterior margin of their elytra. They may be found at sap flows on tree trunks and bark. The species depicted here, the only one found in Britain, is to be found on flowing sap everywhere, especially on elms and lime-trees, but it is relatively rare.

9 **Leptusa fumida*, 2.4–3 mm (141 : 4)

The genus *Leptusa*, which used to be called *Sipalia*, has 56 currently recognized species in central Europe. They form 2 different groups. One comprises large-eyed beetles living above ground, mostly under bark. The beetles in the other group, which is not represented in Britain, live underground in damp humus, among grass roots and under stones, etc., and have very large heads and small eyes. The various species are mostly confined to small areas, especially in the mountains, and many new species are probably still waiting to be described. The species depicted here (known as *haemorrhoidalis* in earlier works) is one of those which live above ground and is common under bark and in rotten wood everywhere in central Europe.

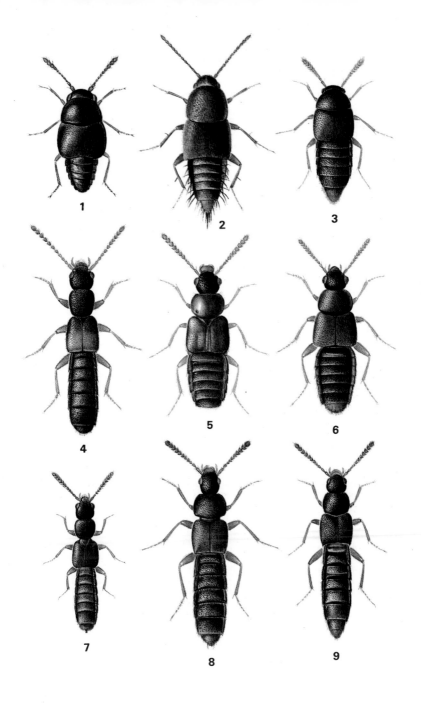

1 *Bolitochara pulchra, 3.5−4.5 mm   (147 : 4)
The 6 species of this genus found in central Europe are all brightly coloured beetles living on fungi. The one shown here (known as *B. lunulata* in many works) is distributed over the whole of Europe and Siberia; in central Europe it is the commonest species and the beetles are fairly abundant everywhere.

2 *Autalia rivularis, 1.7−2.1 mm   (148 : 3)
The 4 members of this genus found in central Europe and the British Isles are easily distinguished from allied genera by the 2 deep longitudinal grooves at the base of each of their elytra. They live in decomposing plant material, fungi, compost, dung and carrion. The species shown here abounds on carrion and compost everywhere in central and northern Europe, including the British Isles.

3 *Cordalia obscura, 2−2.8 mm   (149 : 1)
In earlier works this genus was termed *Cardiola*. Its single representative in central and northern Europe is conspicuous for the beetles' almost spherical pronotum, which is much narrower than the elytra. The species, which has an almost cosmopolitan distribution, is common in central Europe where it is found in decaying matter everywhere.

4 *Falagria sulcatula, 2−2.5 mm   (150 : 1)
Seven species of this genus live in central Europe (3 in Britain). The beetles of most species live under rotting vegetation, and have a characteristic, rather ant-like form. *F. sulcatula* is to be found everywhere and is fairly abundant.

5 *Tachyusa atra, 3−3.5 mm   (154 : 6)
This genus has 10 central European species, 6 of which occur in Britain. The beetles scuttle about beside water and on wet ground with uptilted abdomen. They are slim, have long legs and the part of their abdomen showing beyond the elytra widens towards the tip. The species is widely distributed in north and central Europe east to the Caucasus. In central Europe the beetles are abundant everywhere beside water.

6 *Gnypeta carbonaria, 2.5−3 mm   (156 : 3)
The 4 species of *Gnypeta* found in central Europe and the British Isles resemble those of the preceding genus, but have shorter legs. They also have similar habits, since *Gnypeta* species, like *Tachyusa*, run about in the sunshine on sandy and muddy ground beside water. *G. carbonaria* is a common waterside species throughout the whole of central Europe.

7 *Schistoglossa viduata, 2.5−3.5 mm   (160 : 1)
The members of this and the following genus can be reliably recognized only by microscopic examination of the structure of their mouthparts. The 5 *Schistoglossa* species in central Europe (4 in Britain) comprise black or dark brown beetles living chiefly in swamps and on wet ground beside water overgrown by vegetation. *S. viduata*, which is found in central and northern Europe, is the commonest species in central Europe; it occurs only in the northern part, however, and though not actually rare, it is generally rarely caught.

8 *Hydrosmecta thinobioides, 1.8−2.1 mm   (164 : 11)
Like a number of other genera now regarded as distinct, *Hydrosmecta* was included under the 'supergenus' *Atheta* in many earlier works. It includes slender, flat-bodied beetles with parallel sides. In central Europe there are 26 species belonging to this and 2 very similar genera. The species illustrated here is the most widely distributed, but is rather rare, especially in low-lying country; it occurs on sandy ground beside water.

9 *Aloconota gregaria, 2.7−3.8 mm   (166 : 14)
This genus used to be included in *Atheta*. The 18 species living in central Europe (12 in Britain) are all narrow, rather parallel-sided, and mostly brown beetles. They have long legs and live chiefly beside running water. The various species are frequently difficult to tell apart and the genitalia often need to be examined. *A. gregaria* is widely distributed in Europe and north Africa; in central Europe it is very common everywhere and, unlike other *Aloconota*, is often to be found in quite dry surroundings.

152

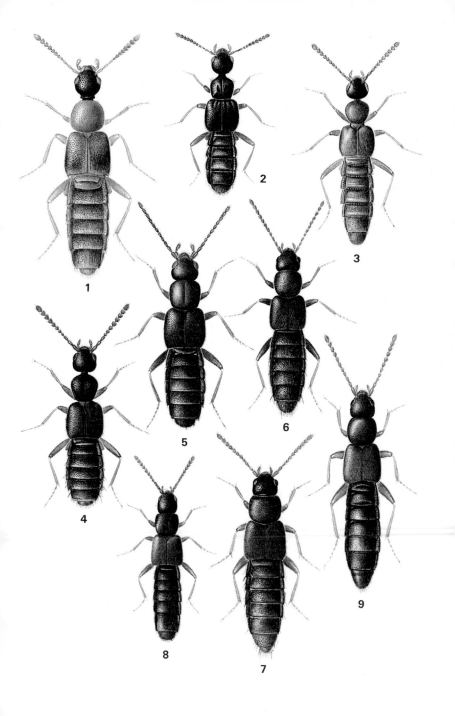

1 *Pycnota paradoxa, 2–2.5 mm (167 : 1)
This species, the only member of the genus, is also known in earlier works under the name *P. nidorum*. It closely resembles *Atheta* and a second species placed in this genus should actually be included in *Atheta*. *Pycnota paradoxa* occurs in northern and central Europe where the beetles live underground, in the nests of small mammals (mainly moles), but also occasionally in birds' nests.

2 *Amischa analis, 1.8–2 mm (168 : 1)
The 8 central European species of this genus, 5 of which are found in Britain, used to be regarded as a subgenus of *Atheta*. In most of them males are a rarity and in some regions parthenogenesis seems to be the rule. The beetles live in ground litter. The species shown here occurs over the whole of the holarctic region and has also been reported from other continents. In central Europe females are abundant everywhere, while males are rare and in some places are absent altogether.

3 *Amidobia talpa, 1.6–1.9 mm (169 : 1)
The only central European species of the given genus, which was also formerly classified as a subgenus of *Atheta*, has very small eyes, showing that it lives in the dark. The beetles are to be found in ants' nests (chiefly of *Formica rufa*), where they may be found in large numbers.

4 *Nehemitropia sordida, 3–3.5 mm (171 : 1)
This genus, which has only one species in central Europe, was also formerly included under *Atheta*. Its antennal segments fit very closely together. The species has an almost cosmopolitan distribution and, in central Europe, it is generally abundant on dung and decaying matter of various kinds.

5 *Nothotecta flavipes, 3–3.5 mm (172 : 1)
The antennal segments of the 2 central European and British species of this genus also fit closely together, but the terminal segments are strikingly long and spindle-shaped. The beetles live in ants' nests, from which they can easily be sieved out in the winter. The species depicted here associates with *Formica* species (especially *Formica rufa*) and is abundant everywhere.

6 *Ousipalia caesula, 1.4–1.9 mm (178 : 1)
The 2 central European species of this genus were included under *Atheta* in many earlier works. Most of the beetles – but not all – have very short elytra and small eyes. They live on dry sandy ground under lichens and in tufts of grass and sometimes associate with ants. They seem to be common only in flat country.

7 *Geostiba circellaris, 2.2–2.9 mm (180 : 3)
This genus, known to earlier authors as *Sipalia*, has 7 species in central Europe, only one of which is found in Britain. The beetles have very short elytra and are generally flightless. The dark or pale brown beetles inhabit moss, humus and leaf litter, mostly in woods. With the exception of the species shown here their areas of distribution are very small. *G. circellaris* ranges across northern and central Europe to the Caucasus and western Siberia; it is abundant everywhere in central Europe.

8 Taxicera deplanata, 1.9–2.2 mm (181 : 5)
The five central European species of this genus used to be included in *Atheta*. None of them occur in Britain. On their pronotum and elytra the beetles have long hairs, which are directed sideways in a characteristic manner. The various species are often difficult to distinguish from one another. The beetles live in dry sand beside water, chiefly under decaying matter, and carrion and are found mostly in the mountains. *T. deplanata* is a montane species occurring in central and southern Europe and the Caucasus; it is also present in the middle and southern part of central Europe, where it is the commonest member of the genus.

9 *Dinaraea angustula, 3–3.7 mm (182 : 1)
Formerly classified as a subgenus of *Atheta*, *Dinaraea* is now regarded as a separate genus with 4 species in central Europe, 3 of which also occur in Britain. Some species live chiefly under bark and others in marshes or damp places. The species illustrated here prefers damp surroundings, such as waterside debris or powdered wood under bark which is already turning into soil. It is common everywhere in central Europe.

154

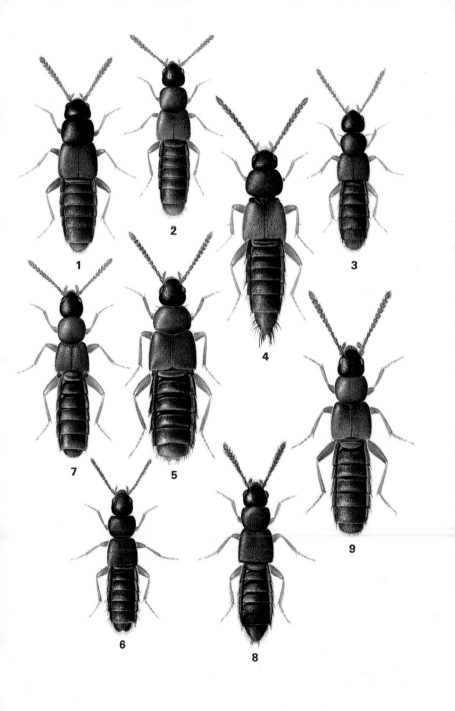

1 *Liogluta longiuscula, 3.4—4 mm (187 : 4)

Formerly classified as a subgenus of *Atheta,* the genus *Liogluta* has 10 species in central Europe (6 in Britain), ranging in length from 3.1 to 5 mm. The various species are generally hard to tell apart and the consequent frequent changes in their names have caused considerable confusion. The species shown here occurs in the southern part of northern Europe, central Europe and from southern Europe and north Africa to the Caucasus. Like the other species it lives in moist ground litter and in central Europe it is common everywhere.

2 *Atheta crassicornis, 2.8—3.4 mm (188 : 21)

Atheta is the largest beetle genus in Europe, with 226 species known from central Europe and 137 from the British Isles. The beetles, which measure from 1 to 5 mm in length, are mostly black or brown and only rarely lighter; some of them are glossy, others matt. Differentiation of the various species requires careful microscopic investigation and the genitalia must also usually be examined. The genus is divided into 22 subgenera and groups of species. *A. crassicornis* is one of the commonest central European species and abounds on fungi and other decomposing plant matter everywhere.

3 *Atheta fungi, 2.4—2.8 mm (188 : 5)

This species is very widely distributed and has been recorded from many parts of the holarctic region and elsewhere. However, like several closely related species, *A. fungi* sometimes reproduces by partheno-genesis, making for great difficulty in establishing the range of morphological variation which the species exhibits. It is no doubt often confused with related species. In central Europe the beetles are very abundant in ground litter everywhere.

4 *Halobrecta algae, 2.4—3.2 mm (191 : 1)

The 2 species of this genus in central Europe (there are 3 in Britain) used to be regarded as a subgenus of *Atheta,* but although their body structure is similar to that of *Atheta* species they have very distinctive mouthparts. The beetles are confined to the seashore where they live under rotting seaweed. *H. algae,* known as *H. puncticeps* in many works, is common on the coast of much of Europe.

5 *Drusilla canaliculata, 4—4.8 mm (195 : 1)

This genus, which has only one species in central Europe, used to be termed *Astilbus.* The beetles have short elytra and are unable to fly. They are very abundant in central Europe, where they can be found under stones and leaves, often in the company of ants.

6 *Zyras humeralis, 5.5—6.5 mm (196 : 7)

The 16 central European species of this genus used to belong to more than one genus (*Myrmedonia, Myrmoecia*). Nine of the species occur in Britain. They are very diverse in form, but they all live in the company of ants. Some have been shown to possess special tufts of bristles, indicating that they secrete a substance which attracts the ants. The species depicted here is the commonest member of the genus everywhere in central Europe.

7 *Lomechusa emarginata, 3.5—4.5 mm (198 : 1)

The 3 central European species of this genus, known as *Atemeles* in many works, have a characteristic, but very variable body structure. The beetles live together with ants. This species is distributed over the whole of Europe and is generally the commonest member of the genus. It is interesting to note that the larvae of all 3 species live with *Formica* species, while the adult beetles live with species of *Myrmica.*

8 *Dinarda dentata, 3—5.5 mm (199 : 1)

The single central European member of *Dinarda* has a characteristic body structure and lives with ants of the genus *Formica.* Four races, sometimes regarded as distinct species, can be distinguished, each of which lives with a different *Formica* species. The present species occurs in Europe and the Caucasus; when present in an ants' nest, the beetles are often to be found in large numbers.

9 *Phloeopora testacea, 2.5—3 mm (201 : 1)

In central Europe there are 6 species of this genus, all of very similar appearance, and all living under bark. Three species are found in Britain. *P. testacea* is the commonest species everywhere in central and northern Europe.

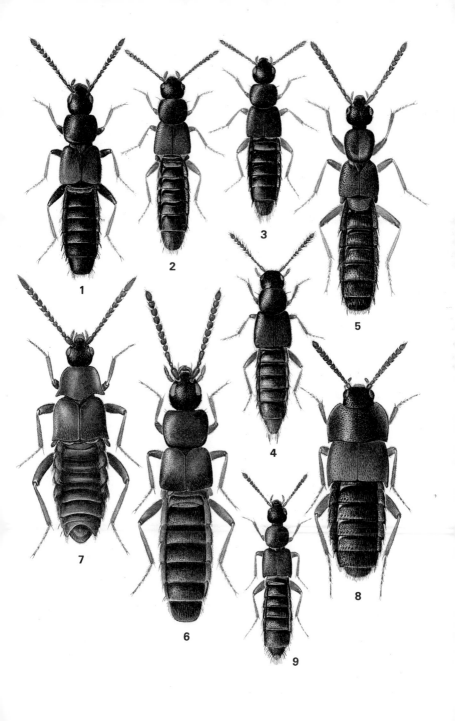

1 *Ilyobates subopacus, 3—5.5 mm (203 : 2)

This genus is represented by 6 species in central Europe, 2 of which are found in Britain. The beetles are light or dark brown, with a densely punctured back. *Ilyobates* are unusual among rove beetles in that individuals of one species are of very variable size. The beetles are to be found on damp soil, under wet leaves and in débris in the vicinity of ant-hills. The species shown here was formerly known under the name *nigricollis*; in central Europe it is the most widely distributed species and is fairly common.

2 *Chiloporata longitarsis, 3.7—4.7 mm (206 : 3)

The 8 central European species of this genus, 2 of which occur in Britain, comprise narrow-bodied beetles with long legs, which live hidden under leaves and débris on the banks of fresh water. *C. longitarsis* can be found beside running and still water; it is less common in low-lying country than in the mountains, however.

3 *Ocalea picata, 4—5 mm (210 : 2)

There are 4 species of this genus in central Europe and the British Isles. They can be distinguished from related genera by the long bristly hairs on the edge of the pronotum and the outer margin of the tibiae. Some species are found only on the banks of running water while others also favour damp moss and leaf litter in wooded areas. *O. picata* seems to be fairly abundant everywhere in central Europe and is certainly the commonest species of the genus.

4 *Meotica exilis, 1.4—1.7 mm (213 : 19)

This genus has 26 species in central Europe (5 in Britain). It is exceptional for the beetles to measure more than 1.3—2 mm. *Meotica* was once regarded as a subgenus of *Atheta*, but it has not been very closely investigated and a few species are represented by single specimens only. The beetles can be sieved out of the roots of tufts of grass or out of pieces of turf; they evidently live in topsoil in marshes and other wet places. Some species are found commonly in sphagnum and other wet moss. The species depicted here is widely distributed in central Europe and is to be found in large numbers in flood débris.

5 *Oxypoda umbrata, 2.5—3.2 mm (223 : 18)

With 60 species in central Europe (27 in Britain), this is a large genus whose members do not have an absolutely uniform shape. The beetles can be found in ground litter and decaying matter. A number of species are associated with the underground nests of mammals and Hymenoptera. Many species are consequently found only sporadically and the number of undescribed species is still undoubtedly large. This species is very common everywhere in central Europe.

6 *Thiasophila angulata, 2.3—3.3 mm (231 : 1)

The 5 central European species of this genus, 2 of which are found in Britain, comprise stocky, brownish red or brown beetles living in ants' nests. *T. angulata* is a frequent guest of *Formica rufa*.

7 *Crataraea suturalis, 2.3—3 mm (233 : 2)

The single central European species of *Crataraea* is found throughout the holarctic region and also occurs in temperate regions of the southern hemisphere. In central Europe the beetles are often to be found in the vicinity of dwellings (in mouldy straw in barns, sheep-pens and cellars), but are also found in nests. The beetles swarm frequently in the evening.

8 *Tinotus morion, 1.9—2.6 mm (235 : 1)

This genus, which has one species in central and northern Europe, used to be included in the genus *Aleochara*, which it closely resembles. The rather squat, pitch-black, brown-legged beetles are to be found in most parts of the holarctic region. In central Europe they abound everywhere in dung.

9 *Aleochara curtula, 4—8 mm (237 : 1)

The 50 species of this genus in central Europe, 29 of which occur in Britain, mostly have a broad oval, fusiform body, a small head, fusiform antennae and a coat of soft hair. They live chiefly in decomposing matter of plant and animal origin. Many species can be caught in mammals' burrows. Many species are very variable in size due to the fact that the larvae live semi-parasitically in fly pupae. *A. curtula* is found throughout the holarctic region and in South America. In central Europe the beetles abound on carrion.

Family Pselaphidae

This beetle family is particularly well represented in the wet tropics. The relatively modest number of 29 genera and 131 species is found in central Europe (50 in Britain). The beetles are very small, measuring from 0.9 to 3.5 mm. In a truly natural classification pselaphids should probably be included within the Staphylinidae. Their elytra are usually very short, like in other Staphylinidae, but the abdomen is less flexible than in most rove beetles. The beetles' body form is rather variable; their eyes are composed of relatively few, but large ommatidia. Pselaphidae subsist mainly on mites; they live in decaying vegetation, in humus and in moss and require a damp substrate. Many of them are also to be found in ants' nests.

1 *Bibloporus bicolor, 1.2–1.4 mm (2 : 2)
In central Europe this genus has 4 species, 2 of which occur in Britain, which can be distinguished by the tooth on the middle tibiae. The black-brown beetles, which have yellowish red legs and antennae, live in rotting wood and under bark. The species illustrated here is common everywhere in central Europe.

2 *Bibloplectus ambiguus, 1.1–1.25 mm (5 : 3)
The 9 species of this genus in central Europe, 6 of them found in Britain, are all tiny, narrow brownish black beetles, and are very difficult to distinguish from one another. They live in swamps and near flowing water. B. ambiguus occurs over almost the whole of Europe and is common in many places.

3 *Euplectus sanguineus, 1.4–1.6 mm (6 : 9)
The 17 central European species of this genus are of various sizes, but all have a long, narrow, flat body. Thirteen species occur in Britain. Most of them live under bark and in rotting wood. E. sanguineus occurs in Europe and the Caucasus. In central Europe it is to be found in abundance in rotting straw- and hay-stacks, in manure heaps and in compost everywhere.

4 *Plectophloeus fischeri, 1.4–1.7 mm (8 : 9)
In older works, Plectophloeus was listed as a subgenus of Euplectus. Now, as an independent genus, it includes 9 central European species, two of which are found in Britain. The beetles are all a light reddish brown and live mostly under bark and in rotting wood. P. fischeri is common in central Europe.

5 *Trimium brevicorne, 1.15–1.35 mm (11 : 1)
This genus has 4 species in central Europe. The beetles have short antennae with an outsize, ovoid terminal segment and live in moss and rotting leaves. The species shown here, the only one found in Britain, is abundant everywhere in central Europe.

6 Batrisus formicarius, 3.1–3.5 mm (14 : 1)
This only species of this genus in central Europe is the largest member of the family. It may be readily known by its stout antennae with their swollen, hooked terminal segment. The species is distributed in central and southern Europe. In central Europe the beetles live mainly in the nests of the ant Lasius brunneus, but are sometimes to be found under bark and in rotting wood; they are fairly common.

7 *Batrisodes venustus, 2–2.2 mm (15 : 2)
Seven species of this genus are known in central Europe (3 in Britain). The beetles resemble the preceding genus, but their antennae are less robust and only the two terminal segments are thicker than the others. The beetles live in the nests of ants of the genus Lasius and in rotting wood. The species shown here is fairly common in woodland over the whole of Europe.

8 *Bythinus macropalpus, 1.2–1.3 mm (17 : 1)
This genus has 6 species in central Europe (2 in Britain). The tiny beetles have a compact body and the second segment of their antennae is unusually large. The beetles live among fallen leaves and moss and under stones, preferably near water. B. macropalpus is common in central Europe.

9 *Bryaxis bulbifer, 1.3–1.5 mm (18 : 32)
In the 34 species of this genus found in central Europe, 4 of which also occur in Britain, the first and /or second antennal joints are generally of characteristic form. In some species there are 2 male forms, one with slender and the other with stouter legs. The beetles live chiefly in moss and rotting leaves, but a few live in caves or deep underground. B. bulbifer abounds in damp localities and marshes everywhere in central Europe, and is by far the commonest species in Britain.

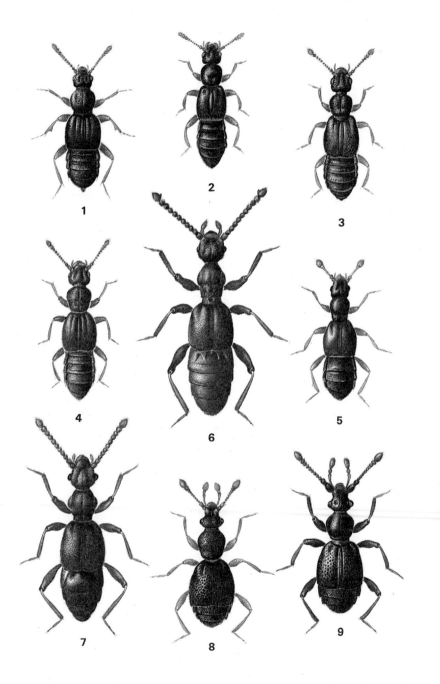

1 *Tychus niger, 1.5−1.6 mm (19 : 1)

Three species of this genus occur in central Europe (2 in Britain). The males are easy to recognize by the thickened fifth segment of their antennae. The beetles have mostly blackish brown elytra which may be a lighter reddish brown in the centre. *T. niger* occurs over much of Europe and in central Europe it is commonly found in fallen leaves.

2 *Rybaxis longicornis, 1.8−2.2 mm (20 : 1)

In earlier works this species was known as *Bryaxis sanguinea;* it is one of 2 members of the genus in central Europe. The fairly robust beetles are generally blackish brown, but may have reddish elytra or are entirely of a reddish brown colour; their legs and antennae are lighter. The species shown here, which occurs in most parts of Europe, north Africa and Asia Minor as far as inner Asia, is often very abundant in swampy regions in central Europe.

3 *Brachygluta fossulata, 1.6−2 mm (21 : 1)

Earlier authors classified *Brachygluta* − which has 13 species in central Europe (5 in Britain) − as a subgenus of *Reichenbachia.* The tiny but robustly built beetles may be plain dark black-brown to light reddish brown or variegated. The species depicted here is distributed over practically the whole of Europe.

4 *Reichenbachia juncorum, 1.6−1.8 mm (22 : 1)

In central Europe this genus has 2 species with a somewhat globose form, but only the one shown here occurs in the British Isles. It has been recorded from most parts of Europe and north Africa and is to be found in swamps and damp meadows, often in large numbers.

5 Trissemus antennatus, 1.7−1.9 mm (23 : 1)

The 2 central European species of this genus used to be included in *Reichenbachia,* to which they are closely related. The species depicted here has 2 morphologically distinguishable subspecies. The western subspecies, *T. antennatus antennatus,* occurs in southern Germany, Switzerland, France and Italy and on Elba and Corsica, while the eastern race, *T. antennatus serricornis,* stretches from Upper Austria across Slovakia, Hungary, countries of former Yugoslavia, Albania and Turkey and the Caucasus. The beetles abound in swapms and in the vicinity of water everywhere. The second species − *T. impressus* − is found in Britain.

6 *Pselaphus heisei, 1.7−1.95 mm (25 : 1)

Only 1 species of this genus occurs in central Europe and the British Isles. The beetles can be identified by their long maxillary palps, whose terminal segment has a claviform tip and is covered with spines and hairs. This species, which occurs all over Europe, forms several subspecies, especially in the Mediterranean region; they can be differentiated primarily by the structure of the male genitalia. In central Europe *P. heisei* occurs in damp and swampy regions, where it abounds under decaying vegetation and in moss and leaves.

7 Ctenistes palpalis, 1.8−2 mm (28 : 1)

The single species of this genus found in central Europe is of characteristic general form and has especially distinctive palps and antennae. It occurs in central and southern Europe, in Asia Minor and in inner Asia. In central Europe the species is confined to very warm places where the beetles are found under stones.

8 Tyrus mucronatus, 2.2−2.4 mm (29 : 1)

This is the only species of the genus occurring in central Europe. The dark black-brown beetle with reddish brown elytra, legs and antennae is to be found under bark and in rotting wood practically everywhere in Europe.

9 *Claviger testaceus, 2.1−2.3 mm (30 : 1)

This genus, represented in central Europe and Britain by 2 species, was once placed in a separate family, Clavigeridae. The beetles are easy to identify. Their antennae have only 6 segments, the first of which is hidden from sight, and they have no eyes and only very short tarsi. The beetles live with ants of the genus *Lasius.* The species shown here occurs in central and northern Europe and the beetles are to be found − often in large numbers − in the nests of the small yellow ant *Lasius flavus.*

Family Lycidae — net-winged beetles

The adults of the 8 central European species of this family, belonging to 6 genera, are very conspicuous, since in most species the elytra, at least, are bright red. Their antennae are generally robust and their head is sometimes protruded to a proboscis. The adult beetles, which have only a short life span, are found on flowers, while the longer-lived larvae live in rotting wood, feeding on other insects and their larvae.

1 *Dictyoptera aurora, 8—13 mm (1 : 1)

Two species of this genus are known in central Europe. The beetles have small heads which are usually kept tucked away under their pronotum. This species, the only one found in Britain, occurs everywhere in central Europe, but is rarer in the southern part.

2 *Platycis minutus, 5—10 mm (4 : 1)

The 2 central European and British species of this genus resemble the preceding species, but can be differentiated from them by the form of their pronotum. The lattice-work on their elytra is also less regular. P. minutus occurs everywhere in central Europe.

3 Lygistopterus sanguineus, 7—12 mm (5 : 1)

The single species of Lygistopterus found in central Europe can be distinguished from other native lycids by its long, beak-like head. The elytra have weak ribbing, but are not latticed. Fairly common.

Family Lampyridae — glowworms

This is one of the smallest families in central Europe, with only 3 genera and 3 species. Despite this, their ability to emit light has made glowworms familiar insects everywhere.

4 *Lampyris noctiluca — Common Glowworm, male 10—12 mm, female 15—20 mm (1 : 1)

This largest of central European glowworms can be seen everywhere on warm evenings from June to September, but it is not so common as it used to be. The females are completely wingless; they attract the males by means of light signals. In Britain it is rather local, mostly in chalky districts.

5 Lamprohiza splendidula, 8—10 mm (2 : 1)

This genus was formerly known as Phausis. Apart from their smaller size, the beetles differ from the preceding species in respect of the 2 large, transparent window spots on their pronotum. The females of this species have wing rudiments. The beetles swarm in central Europe in June and July; in some places they are still quite common, but become rarer towards the north.

6 *Phosphaenus hemipterus, male 6—8 mm, female 10 mm (3 : 1)

In central Europe, as in Britain, this is a rare species. The beetles emit only a very faint light. Although flightless, the males have short, rudimentary wings, whereas the females are completely wingless.

Family Melyridae

This family has 9 genera in central Europe, with a total of 29 species (8 in Britain), excluding the Malachiidae which are included in the Melyridae in many works. They are generally covered with long hairs or scales. Because of their soft cuticle they were once included in Cantharidae, but are not even closely related. The larvae of most species are predators living in old wood, while the adult beetles are found on flowers.

7 *Aplocnemus nigricornis, 4—4.8 mm (2 : 2)

The 6 species of this genus (sometimes spelled Haplocnemus) in central Europe live chiefly on flowering conifers. This species is fairly common everywhere.

8 *Dasytes plumbeus, 3.5—4.6 mm (5 : 8)

In central Europe there are 11 species of this genus, 4 of which occur in Britain. The beetles have a plain black or metallic blue back and their elytra are covered with long, outstanding hairs with a coat of short close-set hairs underneath. The larvae are predators living in rotting wood, the adult beetles are found on flowers and shrubs during spring and summer. D. plumbeus is common everywhere in central Europe.

9 Danacaea pallipes, 3.2—4.2 mm (8 : 2)

There are 5 species of this genus in central Europe, but none of them are found in the British Isles. The adult beetles have a uniform covering of hairs, giving their otherwise metallic green body a grey or yellowish tinge. D. pallipes is in general fairly common in central Europe, but is mostly absent in low-lying country.

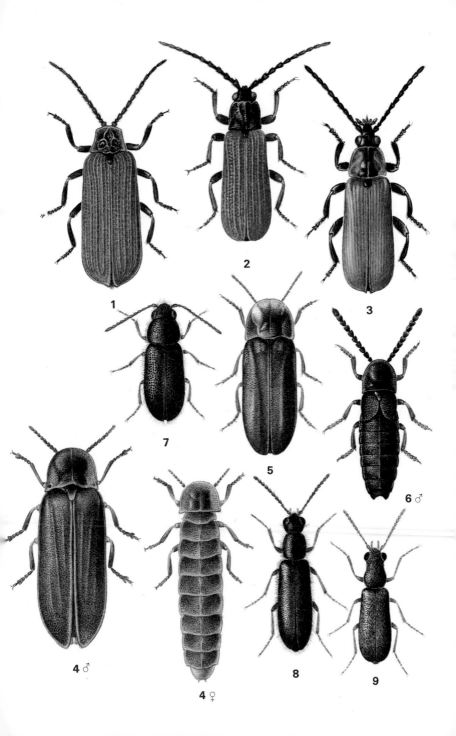

1

2

3

7

5

6 ♂

4 ♂

4 ♀

8

9

Family Cantharidae — soldier beetles

In central Europe this family is represented by 103 species belonging to 9 genera; 41 species are found in the British Isles. The beetles have a rather thin and soft cuticle so that the body and elytra are much less rigid than is usual for beetles. Their vernacular name is taken from the red, black, blue or yellow elytra and pronotum characteristic of many species. In the summer they are to be found on bushes and flowers, often in large numbers. In general they prey on other insects, but they sometimes do damage by gnawing young oak shoots. The velvety larvae crawl about on the ground and live mainly on slugs and snails. They spend the winter under stones, or in fallen leaves and moss, but occasionally they come out of hiding and crawl on the snow. Adults have a relatively short life span and are to be found only in the warmer months.

1 *Podabrus alpinus, 11−14 mm (1 : 1)
Of the 2 central European species of this genus, the one depicted here is the more widely distributed and is generally the commoner. It has been recorded from every part of central Europe, but is rarer to the north. The beetles occur mainly in the mountains; in the lowlands of central Europe they are scattered and rare.

2 *Cantharis fusca, 11−15 mm (2 : 5)
There are 32 central European species of Cantharis of which 15 are to be found in the British Isles. The adult beetles are to be seen chiefly on bushes, flowers, grasses and cereal plants, although some favour leafy trees. C. fusca tends to be found in damp situations and is common over practically the whole of Europe and much of the British Isles.

3 *Cantharis livida, 9−13 mm (2 : 26)
This species is common throughout central Europe and also in Britain. Its colouring is rather variable and, as with other species of the genus, reliable determination may require examination of the genitalia.

4 Podistra pilosa, 7−10 mm (3 : 5)
Six species of this genus, previously known as Absidia, live in central Europe. The beetles are a uniform yellowish brown or brownish black colour and are often difficult to distinguish from one another, with the result that their areas of distribution are still somewhat uncertain. They are mostly mountain-dwellers and can be found on bushes. P. pilosa is widely distributed in central Europe, but its range to the north extends only to the edge of the German uplands; the only records from the plains of northern Germany are old and lack recent confirmation.

5 *Rhagonycha fulva, 7−10 mm (5 : 2)
The 16 species of Rhagonycha known from central Europe are likewise very often difficult to distinguish from one another, although the 7 species occurring in the British Isles present no serious identification problems. From the end of June through to August or even September R. fulva is the commonest soldier beetle in central Europe; the same is true of Britain where the species is sometimes colloquially known as the 'blood-sucker'. Adults are most often seen on the flowers of umbelliferous plants, frequently in numbers. The reason why mating pairs are so often found is that copulation takes a relatively long time.

6 *Silis ruficollis, 6−7.5 mm (7 : 2)
There are 2 species of this genus in central Europe; S. ruficollis (the only British species) occurs throughout central Europe and the southern part of northern Europe, although it is rarely found in large numbers. The species is to be found mostly at low altitudes, living on wet ground beside water or in damp, marshy meadows.

7 Malthinus biguttatus, 4.5−6 mm (8 : 9)
This genus has 10 species in central Europes, four of which are found in the British Isles. The beetles can be found at the edges of woods, in clearings and on hedges, trees and shrubs. M. biguttatus (formerly also termed biguttulus) occurs chiefly in the eastern part of central Europe, becoming rarer towards the west.

8 *Malthodes maurus, 3.5−4 mm (9 : 10)
The 33 species of this genus in central Europe (12 in the British Isles) are generally hard to tell apart. The beetles are to be found on trees and bushes as well as in meadows; they are active mostly in the evening. The species shown here is widely distributed in northern and central Europe, where it is usually common. In Britain it is largely confined to the north and is infrequent.

9 *Malthodes minimus, 3.3−4 mm (9 : 12)
In central and northern Europe (including the British Isles) this is generally the commonest species of Malthodes; it also occurs in the north of the Balkan Peninsula, but is absent from the Alps.

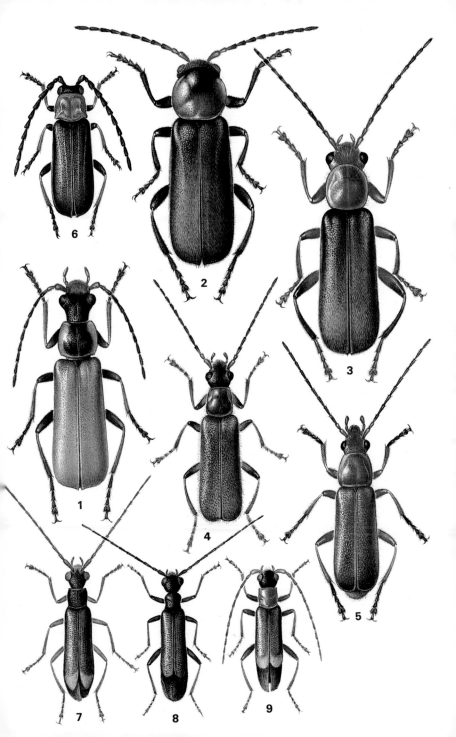

Family Drilidae

In central Europe, this family is represented by two not very common species belonging to the genus *Drilus*. The males have fully developed wings and elytra, while the females are like larvae – wingless, with short legs and antennae and a small head. The males frequent flowers, but the females prefer damp, hidden spots, or hide under stones and snail shells. The larvae eat slugs and snails.

1 *Drilus flavescens* – male, 4–8 mm (1 : 2)

This is the commoner of the two *Drilus* species found in central Europe and the only one occurring in Britain. It prefers warm and dry situations and in such places can be fairly common. Further north and east it becomes rarer or is absent altogether. In Britain it is confined to the south-east where it is rare and more or less restricted to chalky hillsides.

2 *Drilus flavescens* – female, 13–15 mm

The larviform females climb up blades of grass during the day, making it easier for males to find them.

Family Malachiidae

Some 15 species of this group (often regarded as a subfamily of Melyridae – see p. 164) are found in the British Isles, but the central European fauna is much more extensive, including 50 species belonging to 14 genera. The beetles have a soft cuticle, are usually brightly coloured and are often easy to recognize by the presence of pouches which can be inflated and then protrude from the sides of their thorax or abdomen. The larvae are predacious, but the adults live mainly on pollen, although occasionally they may turn carnivorous. They are to be found chiefly on flowers, shrubs and grasses.

3 *Troglops albicans*, 2.75–3 mm (1 : 1)

Two species of this genus live in central Europe. The beetles, which have unusually large heads, frequent blossoming trees and shrubs. *T. albicans*, the commoner of the two, occurs in the southern, south-eastern and middle part of central Europe, while in the north-west it is rare.

4 *Hypebaeus flavipes*, 1.5 mm (3 : 1)

This is the commonest of the 3 species of this genus found in central Europe and the only one to be found in Britain, where it is very rare. In central Europe it is to be found chiefly on hornbeams and is usually fairly common, except in the north-west and north-east, where it is rare or absent.

5 *Charopus flavipes*, 2.25 mm (4 : 1)

The 3 central European members of this genus are small and of a uniform black colour. The males have narrow elytra, while those of females are much broader and bulging. The beetles are to be found on flowering grasses, especially in the shade. *C. flavipes* is abundant in most parts of central Europe.

6 *Malachius bipustulatus*, 5.5–6 mm (6 : 7)

This genus has 16 species in central Europe (6 in the British Isles). The beetles are very variably coloured. The adults are found on flowering grasses and blossoms, while the larvae are to be found mostly beneath bark, and in decaying wood, although a few also frequent the nests of solitary wasps. *M. bipustulatus* is very common everywhere in central Europe, and is also the commonest species of the genus in Britain.

7 *Anthocomus rufus*, 4.25–5 mm (7 : 1)

3 species of this genus are found in central Europe, of which 2 also occur in Britain. *A. rufus* lives in marshy areas on late-flowering sedges, where it can be found in abundance from August to October. The larvae of *Anthocomus* species are predacious, feeding on the larvae of wood-boring beetles; they therefore occasionally occur in houses and in the winter may be seen crawling on window-panes.

8 *Ebaeus thoracicus*, 2.25–2.5 mm (12 : 2)

The 9 species of this genus are known in central Europe, but none is known with any certainty to occur in Britain. The adult beetles are found on flowers, while it is thought that the larvae usually develop in the nests of solitary bees. *E. thoracicus* is locally common in central Europe but otherwise generally rare.

9 *Axinotarsus pulicarius*, 3–3.5 mm (14 : 2)

Of the 3 species of this genus known to occur in central Europe and the British Isles, *A. pulicarius* is generally the most abundant. In Britain it is a local species found only in the south-east. The beetles are to be found on flowering grasses.

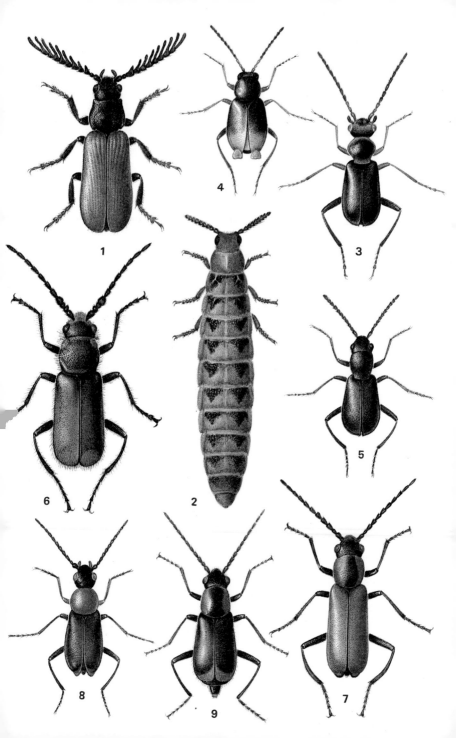

Family Cleridae — chequered beetles

Although some chequered beetles are of a uniform metallic colour, many earn their name, as they have variegated patterning, especially of the elytra. In central Europe there are 27 species, only 9 of which are known to occur with any certainty in Britain. Both adults and larvae are predacious. Some species are to be found on flowers or wood, while one group of species occurs on old bones and carrion.

1 *Tillus elongatus*, 6−10 mm   (2 : 1)
This is the only species of the genus to occur in central Europe and since it is apparently active only at night it is seldom seen. The larvae specialise in preying on the larvae of various Anobiidae (woodworms); from May to July adults can occasionally be seen on the trunks of old deciduous trees, especially beech.

2 *Opilo domesticus*, 7−12 mm   (6 : 3)
This genus has 3 species in central Europe, of which only one − *O. mollis* − occurs in Britain. The larvae live in old wood, where they prey on other insect larvae. *O. domesticus* lives mainly in buildings, where it is an effective nocturnal predator of pests such as woodworms and the House Longhorn.

3 *Thanasimus formicarius* − Ant Beetle, 7−10 mm   (7 : 1)
The 3 species of this genus live in central Europe (2 in Britain). The adult beetles may be seen on warm days, running about on tree stumps and timber stacks, chasing other insects; the larvae, which are found under the bark of logs and stumps, are also predators. *T. formicarius* occurs in conifer woods everywhere in central Europe, where its favourite prey is the bark beetle *Tomicus piniperda*. However, it is not confined to conifers and, in Britain, is also to be found in oak, beech and other woodlands.

4 *Trichodes apiarius* − Bee-eating Beetle, 9−16 mm   (9 : 1)
Adults of the 4 species of this genus occurring in central Europe are to be found in the summer on umbelliferous flowers, while the predacious larvae live in the nests of aculeate Hymenoptera. The larvae of the species shown here live with honey-bees and wild bees. In some parts of central Europe, especially in the north and east, the species has become rare or has disappeared altogether during the present century.

5 *Korynetes caeruleus*, 3.5−7 mm   (13 : 1)
Two species of this genus (formerly thought to be a single species) live in central Europe. The beetles are to be found both indoors and out. They prey on other insects, especially woodworms.

6 *Necrobia violacea*, 4−5 mm   (14 : 2)
There are 3 *Necrobia* species in central Europe and the British Isles, of which one − *N. violacea* − is cosmopolitan. In central Europe the beetles are common everywhere; they are predators who inhabit dry carrion and other decomposing animal matter.

Family Derodontidae

This family has only 2 species, belonging to 2 genera, in central Europe, one of which also occurs in Britain. The adult beetles are notable for the presence of 2 ocelli (simple auxiliary eyes) on the top of their head.

7 *Laricobius erichsoni*, 2−2.5 mm   (2 : 1)
This beetle used to be a rare inhabitant of mountain forests, but in the past few decades it has multiplied and spread and, as well as establishing itself in countries to the north, including Britain, it is now abundant in conifer woods everywhere in central Europe. Both adults and larvae are voracious predators of the harmful woolly aphids on firs. It has been introduced into America as a biological control agent, with some success.

Family Lymexylidae

The 3 species of this family in central Europe (2, both very local, in the British Isles) belong to 2 genera comprising long soft-bodied beetles which run about on felled wood; the larvae live in the wood.

8 *Hylecoetus dermestoides*, 6−18 mm   (1 : 1)
Of the 2 species of this genus found in central Europe, only *H. dermestoides* is at all widespread and common. The males are normally black and the females light brown (but not always). The larvae bore tunnels in felled wood and eat fungi which grow in them.

9 *Lymexylon navale*, 7−16 mm   (2 : 1)
The males of this species are remarkable for their curious tufted maxillary palps. The beetles can be found on standing but damaged deciduous trees and on felled wood, especially oak.

170

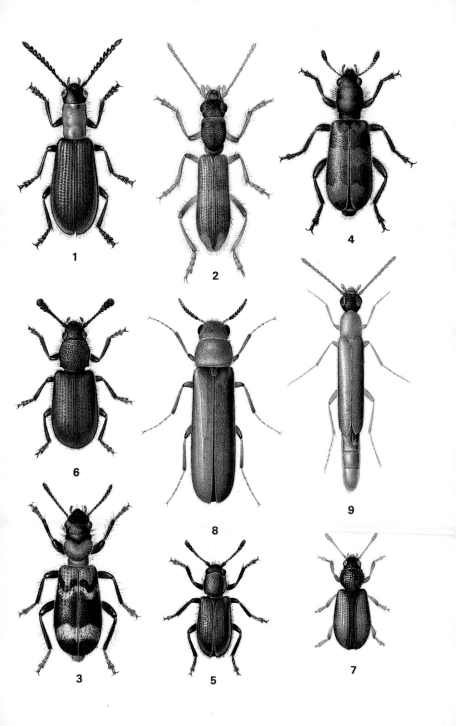

Elateridae — click beetles

The click beetle family is represented in central Europe by 50 genera with a total of 168 species (69 in Britain). The beetles are familiar to everybody because of the characteristic spring device between their first and middle thoracic segments. Click beetle larvae are very characteristic, with their long, thin body, and are known to us all as 'wireworms'. Some eat roots and can do serious damage in fields and gardens, while others are omnivorous and others again are carnivorous and are even capable of turning cannibal.

1 *Ampedus sanguineus, 12—17.5 mm (1 : 15)

Formerly termed *Elater*, the genus *Ampedus* has 27 species in central Europe (14 in Britain). The predacious larvae live in rotting wood. *A. sanguineus* is a common species found chiefly in conifer wood (mainly pine), but also in beech and oak.

2 *Ampedus pomorum, 9—12 mm (1 : 19)

In older works this species is named *Elater ferrugatus*. It is the commonest member of the genus in central Europe. The beetles are to be found the whole year round, as one generation of adults lives until July and the next generation appears in August. They develop in the wood of conifers and deciduous trees attacked by red rot.

3 *Sericus brunneus, 8—9 mm (8 : 1)

Of the 2 species of this genus found in central Europe, the one shown here is not uncommon. It occurs everywhere, though chiefly on sandy ground, and ascends in the Alps to altitudes of up to 2,500 m. The larvae live under moss and eat roots. The beetles complete their development in midsummer, remain in the soil until the following spring and then appear on low plants and bushes.

4 *Dalopius marginatus, 6—7.5 mm (9 : 1)

This only species of the genus found in central and northern Europe closely resembles *Agriotes* species; in earlier works the genus was named *Dolopius*. The beetles appear everywere in abundance from April to July. The larvae live in forest soil, where they evidently chiefly eat insect larvae, supplemented by roots.

5 *Agriotes lineatus, 7.5—10.5 mm (10 : 9)

This genus has 15 species in central Europe, 6 of which occur in Britain, and all have a light brown to black back. The larvae develop in the soil and eat roots; they are among the most serious of field and garden pests. This species is common everywhere in central Europe.

6 *Synaptus filiformis, 9—12 mm (13 : 1)

The only species of *Synaptus* found in central Europe, this beetle looks like an elongate *Agriotes*. Its range extends from Europe to western Asia; in central Europe it is common in the south and rarer in the north. The beetles are to be found from May to July, chiefly on shrub willows. The larvae probably lead a predacious existence in the soil of damp meadows.

7 *Adrastus pallens, 4.2—5.2 mm (15 : 4)

All 6 central European species of this genus are small and measure less than 7 mm; the majority have yellowish brown elytra with a dark suture line. Two species of *Adrastus* occur in Britain. The beetles can often be found on shrub willows, or on other vegetation, not infrequently in large numbers. The larvae live in the soil of damp meadows. The species illustrated here is the commonest member of the genus.

8 *Melanotus erythropus, 12—18 mm (16 : 2)

The 6 species of this genus occurring in central Europe (2 in the British Isles) have an elongate, black or black-brown body and all look very much alike. The beetles are to be found on flowers and bushes or on wood, in which the larvae develop; the latter also eat roots, however. *M. erythropus* is common everywhere in central Europe. The larvae develop in hardwood attacked by red rot; after emergence from the pupa the adult beetle remains in the wood to hibernate.

9 *Agrypnus murinus, 12—17 mm (19 : 1)

The sole central European member of this genus has a very characteristic form and colouring and can hardly be mistaken for any other beetle. In earlier works it goes under other generic names, such as *Lacon, Brachylacon* or *Adelocera*. This species is one of the commonest click beetles in central Europe. The beetles can be found on plants or under stones, from the spring until well into the summer. The larvae, which live in the soil and eat roots, can sometimes be a nuisance.

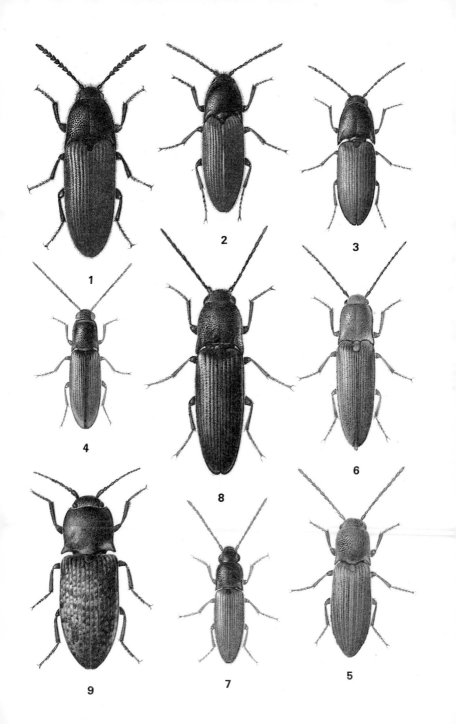

1 *Ctenicera pectinicornis, 16−18 mm (22 : 3)
Until recently, this genus − which has 4 species in central Europe − was known as *Corymbites*. The males have conspicuously pectinate antennae, while those of females, from the third segment onwards, are only serrate. The larvae develop in the soil or in rotting wood. The beetles can be seen in the spring on low vegetation, especially flowering grasses and bushes. This species is fairly common in damp meadows everywhere in central Europe from the end of May until June.

2 *Actenicerus sjaelandicus, 12−15 mm (24 : 1)
The only species of *Actenicerus* found in central Europe is listed in earlier works as *Corymbites* (*Actenicerus*) *tessellatus*. The males do not possess pectinate antennae but, like the females, have antennae which are serrate from the 3rd segment onwards. In central Europe the beetles can be seen from April to August in damp meadows and on the outskirts of woods. The larvae, which live in the soil, can be a pest in both field and forest.

3 *Prosternon tessellatum, 10−12 mm (25 : 1)
The 2 species of this genus found in central Europe are characterized by whorled patterns of pubescence on their elytra and pronotum. From April to August this species, the only one found in Britain, abounds on conifer wood and low vegetation everywhere in central Europe. The larvae develop in conifer stumps and humus.

4 *Selatosomus aeneus, 10−16 mm (29 : 5)
The 9 members of this genus occurring in central Europe (7 in the British Isles) are wide-bodied beetles which are generally to be found crawling on the ground or hiding under stones, but sometimes on low vegetation. The larvae eat roots, but are also facultative predators. *S. aeneus* is common in fields and open country everywhere from the spring to the summer. The larvae are sometimes a pest of agriculture.

5 *Denticollis linearis, 9−12.5 mm (33 : 4)
The most distinctive feature of the 4 species of this genus in central Europe is their small, humped pronotum, which is narrower than their elytra. The beetles are to be found on bushes and trees; the larvae, which are predacious, live in rotting wood. The species shown here, the only member of the genus found in Britain, is common everywhere in central Europe.

6 *Cidnopus aeruginosus, 8−12 mm (34 : 2)
In earlier works, this genus, which has 5 species in central Europe, two of which are found in Britain, was called *Limonius*. The beetles' basal antennal segments can be tucked into a groove on the underside of the prothorax. The larvae feed on grass roots and the adult beetles are found mainly on grasses, but on other plants also. *C. aeruginosus* occurs in France, ranging eastwards across central Europe into Asia. In central Europe the beetles are particularly abundant in low-lying country.

7 *Athous haemorrhoidalis, 9.5−15 mm (41 : 1)
Thirteen members of this genus are known in central Europe, 6 of which are also found in the British Isles. The males are generally rather narrow, the females somewhat wider, with a bulging pronotum. The species shown here is one of the commonest click beetles in both central Europe and Britain, and the adults can be found everywhere in large numbers on trees and bushes, especially at the margins of woods. The larvae develop on the roots of plants and sometimes do damage.

8 *Hypnoidus riparius, 5.3−6.8 mm (43 : 1)
The 3 central European species of this genus have thickset, domed bodies. This species, the only one found in Britain, occurs over a large part of Europe and Siberia (in the west and south only at high altitudes). The larvae develop in the soil. The beetles occur beside rivers and in damp localities in flat country, but chiefly in the mountains.

9 *Fleutiauxellus quadripustulatus, 3−3.8 mm (44 : 2)
The 2 central European and British members of this genus used to be included in the genus *Hypnoidus*. The beetles − none of which measures more than 5 mm − develop in sandy or gravelly soil; the adults are to be found mostly under stones or on low vegetation. The species illustrated here is to be seen in June and July in central Europe, where it is most abundant in the north and east.

174

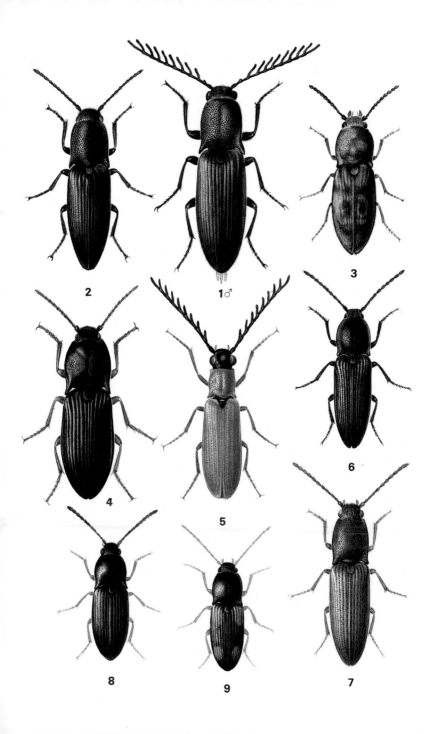

1 *Zorochrus minimus, 2.5−3.8 mm　　　　　　　　　　　　　　　　　　(47 : 4)

Earlier authors regarded this genus (which has 7 species in central Europe but only one in Britain) as a subgenus of *Hypnoidus*. The beetles live chiefly in sand on the banks of rivers and streams, where they can often be found in large numbers. This species (referred to as *dermestoides* in many works) is distributed over most of central Europe; it is absent in very low, flat country, but is otherwise abundant.

2 *Cardiophorus vestigialis, 7−8.5 mm　　　　　　　　　　　　　　　　(49 : 7)

The 12 central European species of this genus have a rounded, somewhat heart-shaped pronotum; only two species are known with any certainty to occur in Britain. In central Europe the beetles can be found on low vegetation, especially where it is warm, but are absent in very low country and in the mountains. The larvae live predaciously in the soil, at the foot of old trees and in tree stumps.

3 *Dicronychus equiseti, 7−9 mm　　　　　　　　　　　　　　　　　　(50 : 4)

This genus (formerly known as *Platynychus*, a subgenus of *Cardiophorus*) has 4 species in central Europe, all very similar. The species shown here, the only *Dicronychus* in the British Isles, can be found in May and June on bushes and on the ground, especially in sandy areas; it is not very common, however.

Family Cerophytidae

This family is represented by only one genus in central Europe.

4 Cerophytum elateroides, 6−7.5 mm　　　　　　　　　　　　　　　　　(1 : 1)

Only the males of this species have long, pectinate antennae; those of the females are serrate. The species is known to occur only in central Europe and immediately neighbouring countries. They can be seen from April to June in dead wood on old deciduous trees and on tree trunks. They are now rare everywhere.

Family Eucnemidae − false click beetles

The family Eucnemidae is represented by 15 genera, with a total of 25 species, in central Europe, but only 6 species in the British Isles. They are related to and resemble Elateridae. The larvae live in rotting or splitting wood, not infrequently on trees which are still standing.

5 *Melasis buprestoides, 6−9 mm　　　　　　　　　　　　　　　　　　(1 : 1)

The only species of *Melasis* found in central Europe, this beetle is to be found in deciduous woods in June, but sporadically and rarely. It has a preference for beeches, hornbeams and elms.

6 *Eucnemis capucina, 4.3−6.5 mm　　　　　　　　　　　　　　　　　　(3 : 1)

Likewise the only member of its genus in central Europe, this is the commonest eucnemid there, although it is rare in Britain. The beetles can be found on diseased deciduous trees and in tree fungi.

7 *Dirhagus pygmaeus, 3.5−6 mm　　　　　　　　　　　　　　　　　　(8 : 2)

This genus, which has 4 species in central Europe and one of them is found in Britain, is termed *Dirrhagus* or *Microrhagus* in older works. The males have particularly long processes on the segments of their antennae. *D. pygmaeus* is the commonest species of the genus in central Europe. The beetles are to be found on dead hardwood and, on warm summer days, on low vegetation.

8 *Hylis olexai, 3−5 mm　　　　　　　　　　　　　　　　　　　　　(11 : 1)

Four members of this genus, known as *Hypocoelus* in many works, live in central Europe (2 in Britain). They closely resemble *Dirhagus* species. *H. olexai* is the commonest, but in central Europe it occurs only in long established woodland. Although it has not been recorded from the north-east, it is probably present everywhere. The larvae live chiefly in damp and rotting wood − mainly of beech, but also of poplar and fir.

Family Throscidae

This family, termed Trixagidae in older works, has 2 genera. One of them (*Drapetes*) is today included in the Eucnemidae; the other (*Trixagus*) is referred to as *Throscus* in many works. In central Europe there are 6 species of *Trixagus* (5 in Britain), none of which is able to jump very well. The beetles can be found by sieving ground litter, or can be caught by sweeping the low vegetation layer.

9 *Trixagus dermestoides, 2.8−3.3 mm　　　　　　　　　　　　　　　　(1 : 2)

This species is a native of practically the whole of Europe and in central Europe it is the commonest species of the genus.

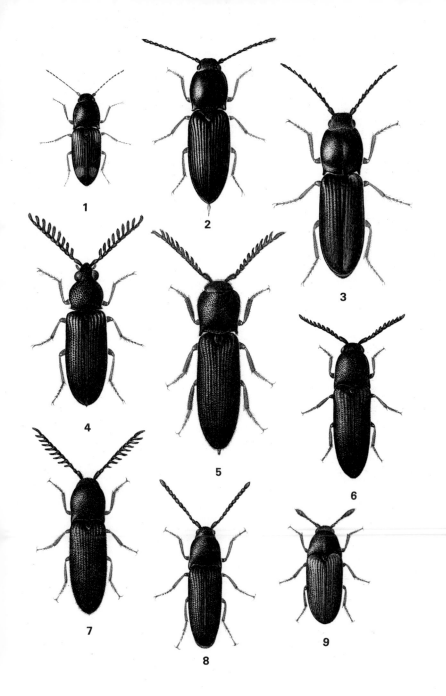

Family Buprestidae — jewel beetles

In central Europe this family is represented by 25 genera with a total of 118 species. By comparison the British fauna is depauperate with only 12 species, some of which may now be extinct, and none of which are common. In fact, most buprestid species avoid the Atlantic climate of extreme western Europe, and no species are known to occur in Ireland. The larvae develop chiefly in wood or the stems of plants; a few are leaf-miners. The beetles are to be found mainly when the sun shines, sitting on the flowers of their larval host plants or on other, generally yellow flowers.

1 *Acmaeodera degener,* 8−12 mm (1 : 2)
A whole series of species of this genus live in the Mediterranean region, but only 2 have been recorded from central Europe. The beetles are characterized by the absence of a scutellum and by fused elytra. They can be found on flowers − mostly those which are yellow in colour. This species has an eastern race stretching from southern Europe to Austria and Silesia, and a western race extending to northern Baden in south-west Germany. The beetles are to be found from June to August on oak trees and on flowers, but they are not abundant. The larvae develop in oak.

2 *Chalcophora mariana* − Pine-borer, 24−33 mm (2 : 1)
This only species of the genus found in central Europe is noted for its size and for its minute scutellum. It avoids the regions bordering the Atlantic and is completely absent in north-west Germany. The beetles are to be found in pine-woods from May to July. The larvae bore tunnels deep in felled or diseased wood.

3 *Capnodis tenebrionis,* 10−27 mm (3 : 1)
Apart from this characteristic species there are 2 other rather similar but larger southern European species of *Capnodis* which have been recorded from central Europe; there are old records for both from Moravia. *C. tenebrionis* is also a south European species, but has been found in the Czech Republic, Slovakia and Austria. Old reports of its presence in Switzerland and Bavaria are dubious. The larvae live in the roots of cultivated fruit trees and wild *Prunus*; the adult beetles may be found on their larval hosts.

4 *Perotis lugubris,* 15−30 mm (4 : 1)
The only species of this genus known to occur in central Europe likewise comes to the region as a rare immigrant from the south-east; all records of its occurrence in Austria and Germany are uncertain. The larvae live in the roots of fruit-trees.

5 *Ptosima flavoguttata,* 7−13 mm (5 : 1)
The only species of *Ptosima* recorded from central Europe formerly went under the name *P. undecimmaculata*. It ventures from south-eastern Europe into the southern Rhineland, but is found there only rarely and sporadically. The larvae live in various rosaceous plants, chiefly fruit-trees.

6 *Sphenoptera antiqua,* 13−17 mm (6 : 1)
There are old records for three species of this genus from the southern parts of central Europe, but no recent finds have been made. The larvae of the species shown here develop in the roots of milk-vetch, sainfoin and pinks; larval development takes 2 years.

7 *Dicerca alni,* 16−22 mm (7 : 3)
This genus is represented by 6 species in central Europe. The beetles' elytra are usually produced into a 'tail'. Their development takes 2−3 years. *D. alni* is rare and found in only a few places in central Europe, but becomes commoner to the east. The larvae live in dead alder wood and, occasionally, in the wood of other deciduous trees. The beetles are on the wing from June to August.

8 *Poecilonota variolosa,* 13−21 mm (8 : 1)
This species, the only member of *Poecilonota* found in central Europe, looks like a *Dicerca,* except that its elytra are less tapering. It is commonest in eastern and southern Europe and absent in the extreme west. In central Europe the beetles are rare and their incidence is sporadic; they are to be found from June to September on poplars, which (especially aspens) are their larval hosts.

9 *Lampra dives,* 10−15 mm (9 : 1)
The 3 native central European species of this genus are listed in older works as a subgenus (*Lampra*) of the genus *Poecilonota*. The species shown here develops only on willows. In central Europe it occurs mainly in the east, but only in a few places (e.g. near Munich and Vienna) and is rare. The beetles can be found from July to August.

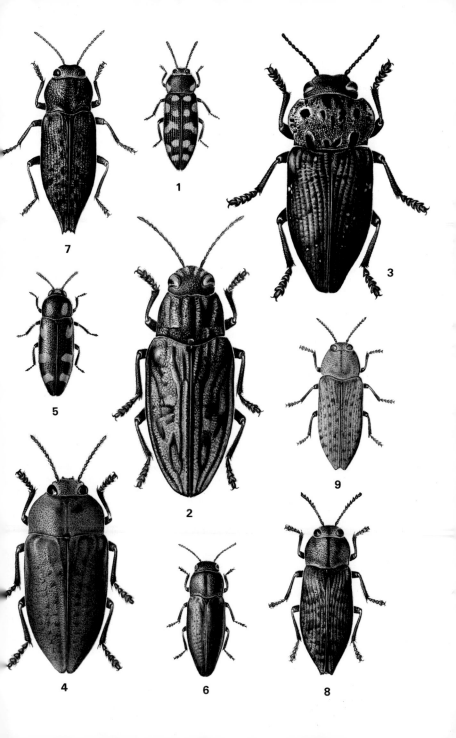

1 *Palmar festiva,* 6−12 mm (10 : 1)

This genus, only recently separated from the genus *Lampra,* is represented by one species in central Europe. The beetles have a metallic back with symmetrically arranged dark spots. This species ranges from the southern part of central Europe, across southern Europe, to north Africa. To the north it has been found only as far as Württemberg. The larvae develop under the bark of juniper trees, on which the beetles can be found from June to August.

2 *Eurythyrea austriaca,* 15−23 mm (11 : 1)

The 2 species of this genus found in central Europe resemble *Buprestis* species, but are mostly bright green in colour. The species shown here occurs locally in the Czech and Slovak Republics. Reports of its presence in Germany are all old and new finds are hardly to be expected. The larvae develop in the wood of firs.

3 *Buprestis rustica,* 12−20 mm (12 : 2)

The 5 members of this genus found in central Europe all have a very small scutellum. The one shown here is a boreomontane species inhabiting central and northern Europe, the northern part of southern Europe, the Caucasus and southern Siberia. It avoids the most westerly parts of Europe. Larval development takes 2 years, in dead spruce, fir and pine wood. From June to September the adult beetles can be seen on conifers in the hot midday sun, often in quite large numbers. When approached they do not immediately fly away.

4 *Buprestis octoguttata,* 9−18 mm (12 : 5)

Two of the *Buprestis* species found in central Europe have yellow spots. The one shown here is rare in the east and also very rare towards the west. It occurs chiefly in bogs on bog-pines, the trees in which the larvae develop. The beetles are on the wing from May to August.

5 **Melanophila acuminata,* 8−11 mm (13 : 2)

Of the 2 species of this genus known to occur in central Europe, this one is noted for its habit of appearing on freshly charred, sometimes still warm wood, after forest fires. The larvae develop beneath the bark of fire-damaged trees − mainly conifers, but also deciduous trees. This species occurs almost throughout the holarctic region, but in central Europe it is usually found only singly, from May to September. When the sun shines the beetles are very restless and hard to catch.

6 *Phaenops cyanea,* 7−12 mm (14 : 1)

The 3 species of *Phaenops* found in central Europe closely resemble those of the preceding genus. *P. cyanea* may be blue, green or black. It is rare towards the west and becomes more abundant towards the east. The adult beetles can be found from May to July on dead pine (occasionally spruce) wood, where the larvae develop beneath the bark. The beetles seem never to settle when the sun shines.

7 *Anthaxia quadripunctata,* 4.5−8 mm (15 : 23)

This genus has 24 species in central Europe, only one of which is found in Britain. The generally small beetles are flat-bodied and may be either a plain dark colour or quite brightly coloured. The larvae develop under the bark of deciduous trees and conifers and many pupate deep in the wood. The beetles are found chiefly on yellow flowers, not infrequently in large numbers. The species shown here is the commonest member of the genus in central Europe, and occurs throughout the palaearctic region. The adult beetles can be seen from May to September; the larvae develop between the inner bark and sap-wood of firs, spruces and larches.

8 **Anthaxia nitidula,* male, 5−7.5 mm (15 : 15)

This *Anthaxia* species is absent in the north-west parts of central Europe and becomes more abundant towards the south. There are a few records, none very recent, for southern England. The beetles are to be found on flowers from May to August; the larvae develop under the bark of fruit-trees and blackthorn. The males are a uniform green colour with only the elytral tip sometimes of a slightly different metallic hue.

9 **Anthaxia nitidula,* female, 5−7.5 mm

The females of this species have a different appearance from the males − a rare phenomenon in Buprestidae. Their head and pronotum are gold-green or brassy while their elytra are entirely bluish green.

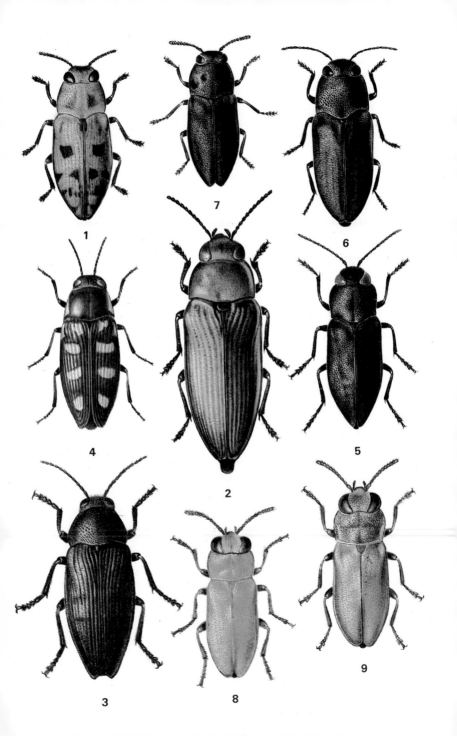

1 *Chrysobothris affinis,* 10.5−15 mm (16 : 2)
There are 3 species of this genus in central Europe. Their larvae develop in trees, beneath the bark and in the wood. This species can be found from May to July everywhere in central Europe, except for the north-west, usually in reasonable numbers, and sometimes large numbers may be seen on the trunks of deciduous trees; they never settle for long in the sunshine. The polyphagous larvae develop in hardwood.

2 *Coroebus elatus,* 4.5−7.2 mm (17 : 4)
The 4 members of this genus known from central Europe resemble *Agrilus* species, but their pronotum has a single (rather than double) margin; they are also more convex in general form. The species depicted here occurs mainly in the eastern part of central Europe and is rarely found in the west. The adult beetles can be seen from May to August, chiefly in rockrose flowers; the larvae develop in the roots of rosaceous plants.

3 **Agrilus angustulus,* 4−6.5 mm (20 : 6)
With 39 species, this is the largest genus of Buprestidae in central Europe. The mostly small and elongate beetles have a double-margined pronotum. They are not always easy to identify (especially the females) as differences between the species are small and there is considerable variation within species. The larvae develop solely in leafy plants, on which the beetles can often be seen in large numbers. The species shown here is the commonest member of the genus in central Europe and is probably the commonest buprestid in Britain. The beetles are to be found from May to August − chiefly on oaks, but also on beeches, hornbeams and hazels.

4 **Agrilus pannonicus* − Two-spot Wood-borer, 8−13 mm (20 : 3)
This relatively large *Agrilus* species, referred to as *A. biguttatus* in many works, has a characteristic white streak behind the middle of each elytron. The beetles vary in colour (green, gold-green or blue), but the males are always all one colour, while the females have a gold-green pronotum. The beetles, which become rarer towards the north, can be found from May to June. The larvae develop in thick oak bark.

5 **Agrilus sinuatus,* 4.5−10 mm (20 : 29)
This species appears from May to July, mostly only in the south-western part of central Europe and seldom or never in the north and east. The larvae develop in rosaceous trees, particularly hawthorn, but can be a pest on fruit-trees.

6 *Cylindromorphus filum,* 3.2−5 mm (22 : 1)
Both central European members of this genus have a long, narrow, cylindrical body. *C. filum* can be found from June to August on dry, warm, grassy hillsides. Its principal area of distribution lies to the south-east of central Europe. The larvae probably develop in grasses.

7 **Aphanisticus pusillus,* 2.2−3 mm (23 : 3)
This genus has 3 species in central Europe (2 in Britain). The one illustrated here becomes rarer towards the north. The adult beetles appear from July to September, hibernate and reappear in April and May. The larvae develop in rushes and sedge.

8 *Habroloma nana,* 2−3 mm (24 : 1)
The single species of *Habroloma* found in central Europe resembles a *Trachys* species; it has a short, thick-set body, and a distinctive fine ridge down its elytra. It is absent in the north-west of central Europe and otherwise occurs only in dry and warm localities, where, however, it may sometimes be fairly abundant. The beetles hibernate and come out of hiding in May. The larvae develop in cranesbill, where they are leaf-miners.

9 **Trachys minuta,* 2.8−3.5 mm (25 : 1)
There are 6 species of this genus in central Europe (3 in Britain). The larvae tunnel mines in the leaves of various plants. Mine entrances are marked by black spots, showing where the egg was originally concealed. This species is fairly common everywhere in central Europe. The larvae develop in the leaves of many deciduous trees, but prefer those with downy leaves.

182

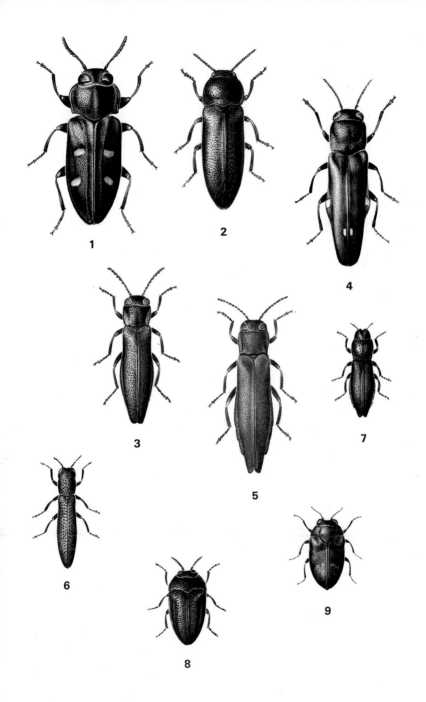

Family Dascillidae

This family has only one species in central Europe.

1 *Dascillus cervinus*, 9−11.5 mm   (1 : 1)
This species is rare or absent in the north-western part of central Europe; in montane regions it is commoner, and although very local it is common in certain places in Britain. The adult beetles appear in the spring on flowers and bushes, persisting until summer in mountain areas. The larvae feed on roots.

Family Scirtidae

In central Europe there are 25 species of this family, widely called Helodidae, belonging to 6 genera. The oval or round-bodied, weakly chitinized beetles are to be found near water, in which the larvae − which rather resemble woodlice − develop. Pupation generally takes place on the land.

2 *Microcara testacea*, 3.2−6 mm   (2 : 1)
The only member of the genus found in central Europe, this beetle resembles *Helodes* and *Cyphon* species. It is to be found from May to July in the vicinity of shaded stagnant water. It is common in the British Isles.

3 *Cyphon palustris*, 3.2−3.4 mm   (3 : 2)
The larvae of the 12 species of this genus in central Europe live in shallow water; the beetles are to be found on waterside plants and in débris and (in the winter) in moss, under bark or in the stems of rushes. This species is abundant everywhere in central Europe, and is widely distributed in the British Isles.

4 *Scirtes hemisphaericus*, 3−3.6 mm   (6 : 1)
The 2 central European and British species of this genus are distinguished chiefly by their broad hind femora and the long, sharp spines at the end of their hind tibiae, which are used for jumping. The species shown here is to be found from May to August on plants in the vicinity of water, sometimes in large numbers.

Family Dryopidae

This family has 12 genera, with a total of 42 species, in central Europe (21 in Britain). They form 2 groups, which are often regarded as separate families. The 2 groups − dryopids proper and elmids − have one particular feature in common: strikingly long limbs with 2 large claws, which give the beetles a firm hold on objects (stones, wood) under water. The beetles spend most of their life under water and the larvae of elmids, which live on algae, moss and detritus, never leave it.

5 *Dryops similaris*, 4.2−4.6 mm   (2 : 5)
This genus has 13 species in central Europe (8 in Britain). Air is carried under water by the close-set hairs covering the beetle's body. The species depicted here is common everywhere in central Europe; the beetles can be found on the muddy banks of both stagnant and flowing water.

6 *Elmis aenea*, 1.9−2.2 mm   (5 : 4)
The 6 central European members of this genus (known in older works as *Helmis*) are to be found chiefly under stones and in moss in fast mountain streams. *E. aenea* (formerly considered to be a variety of *E. maugetii*) is very common in streams in northern and central Europe. It is the only member of the genus found in the British Isles, where it is one of the commonest of the Elmidae.

7 *Esolus angustatus*, 1.8−2 mm   (6 : 3)
The beetles of the 3 species of this genus found in central Europe live in running water under stones. The species shown here occurs in mountain brooks, which are cold even in the summer, and in forest streams; it is absent at very low and very high altitudes. In its favourite haunts in can be fairly abundant.

8 *Oulimnius tuberculatus*, 1.7−1.9 mm   (7 : 1)
This genus, which has 2 species in central Europe (4 in Britain), used to be known as *Limnius*. The species shown here is widely distributed in central Europe; in flat country and at low altitudes in the mountains it is abundant. It can be found in moss and other vegetation in streams and rivers and at the edges of lakes.

9 *Limnius volckmari*, 2.8−3.2 mm   (9 : 2)
In old works, this genus, which has 5 species in central Europe, was termed *Latelmis* or *Lathelmis*. The beetles live in running water. The species depicted here, the only member of the genus found in Britain, is common everywhere in central Europe. The beetles can be found on stones and among plants in streams in flat country and in the mountains at low altitudes.

184

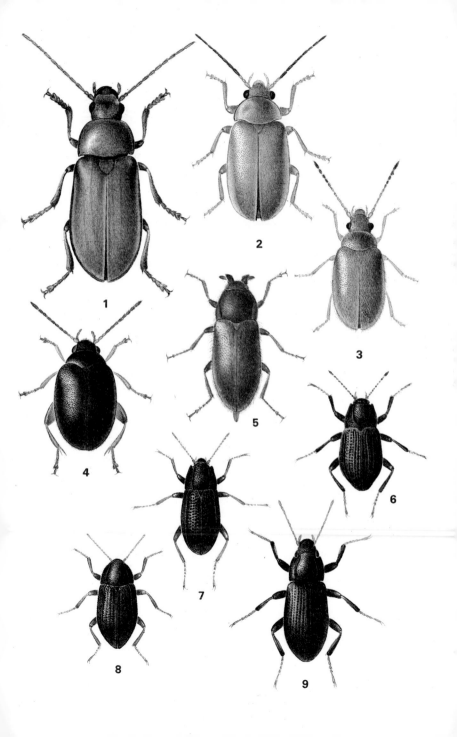

Family Heteroceridae
In central Europe this family is represented by 15 species belonging to 2 genera. Eight species occur in Britain. Both adults and larvae live gregariously in burrows, which they excavate in ground beside water.

1 *Heterocerus fenestratus, 3−4.5 mm   (2 : 6)
This genus comprises 14 of the 15 species of the family. In all of them the markings on the elytra have the same basic pattern − 3 light, toothed cross bands and a light spot near the scutellum. This species is the commonest member of the genus in central Europe, and is widely distributed in the British Isles.

Family Dermestidae − carpet beetles, hide beetles
Many of the 48 species (belonging to 12 genera) of this family in central Europe are serious household pests. 30 of them occur in Britain. Whereas the larvae subsist almost entirely on matter of animal origin, the adults of some species also feed on pollen and are frequently found on flowers.

2 *Dermestes lardarius − Larder Beetle, 7−9.5 mm   (1 : 17)
There are 18 species of this genus in central Europe (9 in Britain). The larvae may be found in birds' nests as well as on dry cadavers and other animal matter; many live in houses. The species illustrated here attacks various products of animal origin in homes and warehouses.

3 *Attagenus pellio, 3.5−6 mm   (2 : 3)
The 5 species of this genus found in central Europe resemble *Dermestes* species. *A. pellio* is seldom found in the open, but is common everywhere indoors. The larvae can do severe damage to furs and carpets.

4 *Trogoderma granarium − Khapra Beetle, 1.7−3 mm   (3 : 3)
The 4 members of this genus found in central Europe are all oval. This species lives only in warm buildings. Regular importation of the beetle in consignments of grain make it a dangerous pest of stored products, especially the malt silos of breweries.

5 *Anthrenus verbasci, 1.7−3.5 mm   (8 : 7)
The 10 central European members of this genus are small and round. The larvae subsist on materials containing chitin and keratin, while the adults also feed on pollen. In buildings they can do damage to woollen textiles (Carpet Beetle) and to zoological collections (Museum Beetle). In central Europe *A. verbasci* is the commonest pest in insect collections.

Family Nosodendridae
Only one species of this family lives in central Europe.

6 Nosodendron fasciculare, 4−4.5 mm   (1 : 1)
Somewhat resembling pill beetles, adults of this species are to be found on escaping sap, where they probably live on fly larvae. This species occurs in only some parts of central Europe, chiefly in the south.

Family Byrrhidae − pill beetles
The 39 species in central Europe belong to 14 (15) genera. Only 12 species occur in Britain. Pill beetles have oval or rounded, convex bodies. In many cases their appendages can be completely withdrawn, leaving no part exposed to an enemy. The larvae live mostly on the ground, feeding on moss roots.

7 *Simplocaria semistriata, 2.5−3 mm   (4 : 2)
The 5 central European species of this genus live on moss. The species shown here, the only member of the genus found in Britain, occurs everywhere, often in large numbers.

8 *Cytilus sericeus, 4.5−5.5 mm   (10 : 1)
Both of the *Cytilus* species found in central Europe live in wet, mossy meadows and in marshes. The larvae, which look like woodlice, are the only byrrhid larvae which run about in the open. This species is common everywhere in central Europe. In the British Isles it is mostly found on heaths and moorland.

9 *Byrrhus pilula − Pill Beetle, 6.7−9.3 mm   (11 : 2)
The 10 members of this genus found in central Europe, 4 of which occur in Britain, tuck their legs into grooves in their body and feign death when disturbed. *B. pilula* is the most widely distributed species in Britain but is found mostly on well-drained soils.

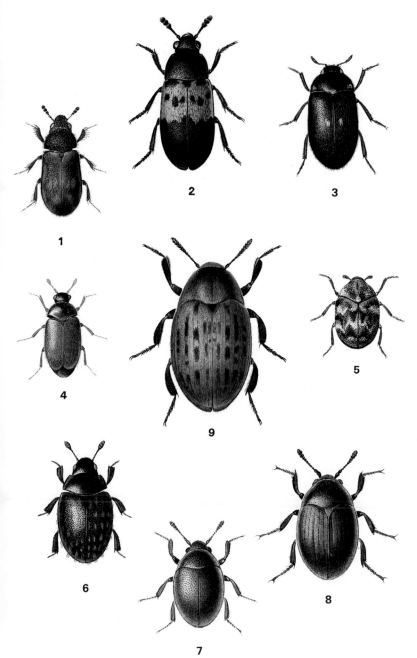

Family Trogossitidae

In central Europe this family, often split into 2 families — the Trogossitidae proper and the Peltidae — is represented by 10 species belonging to 9 genera, which are evidently the remains of what were once much larger groups. The species are of varied form; 4 of them occur in Britain. The larvae and adults of most species live on wood attacked by fungi, but some species are predacious on bark beetles and a few are pests of stored products.

1 *Tenebrioides mauritanicus*, 6—11 mm   (3 : 1)

Two species of this genus live in central Europe. *T. mauritanicus,* the only species found in Britain, has a cosmopolitan distribution and is a pest of cereal products, rice, sugar and other stored foodstuffs.

Family Byturidae

In central Europe and the British Isles there are only 2, very similar, species of this family, whose larvae live in ripe raspberries and the fruit of other *Rubus* species. The adult beetles are to be found in flowers.

2 *Byturus tomentosus* — Raspberry Beetle, 3.2—4 mm   (1 : 1)

The hairy yellowish or greyish beetles eat pollen; the larvae develop in raspberries and blackberries. Quite recently it was demostrated that the related species *B. ochraceus* develops only in herb bennet and not in raspberries. Both species are very common in central Europe.

Family Nitidulidae — sap-beetles

This family is represented in central Europe by 22 genera with a total of 146 species, most of them very small; 95 species are found in Britain. Their form varies, but the majority are oval or ovoid. Their modes of life vary considerably.

3 *Kateretes pedicularius*, 1.6—3 mm   (1 : 1)

3 species of this genus are found in central Europe and the British Isles. The larvae probably live on rushes, sedge and reed-grass, since that is where the beetles are most likely to be found; they can also be caught on flowers and bushes in damp localities, however. This species is common everywhere in central Europe.

4 *Heterhelus scutellaris*, 1.9—2.7 mm   (2 : 1)

Of the 2 species of this genus known to occur in central Europe, the one depicted here occurs in the centre and south, where it is common in the mountains and their foothills; in the north it is found only sporadically or is completely absent.

5 *Brachypterus urticae*, 1.5—2.3 mm   (3 : 1)

The larvae of the 4 species of this genus found in central Europe, 2 of which are found (commonly) in Britain, develop in flowering stinging-nettles and pupate in the ground. This species is abundant everywhere.

6 *Brachypterolus pulicarius*, 2—3 mm   (5 : 1)

This genus, formerly termed *Heterostomus,* has 3 species in central Europe (4 in Britain). The larvae develop in the flowers of toadflax and snapdragons and also pupate in the ground. This species occurs everywhere in central Europe, usually in abundance.

7 *Carpophilus hemipterus*, 2—4 mm   (6 : 4)

The 9 central European species of this genus have short elytra, but the exposed part of their abdomen is shorter than their pronotum. *C. hemipterus* is a cosmopolitan species which has become established in central Europe, where it has been widely recorded but occurs rather sporadically.

8 *Pria dulcamarae*, 1.6—1.8 mm   (7 : 1)

The larvae of the single species of this genus found in central Europe develop in woody nightshade. The adult beetles, which are also usually found on the larval host plant, are generally quite common.

9 *Meligethes aeneus* — Pollen Beetle, 1.5—2.7 mm   (8 : 14)

This genus is represented in central Europe by 60, and in the British Isles by 33, species, most of which closely resemble one another. The larvae, which are quite often host-specific, and the adult beetles, which are less choosy, are found in flowers, where they mostly eat the pollen, but sometimes gnaw and damage the pistil and ovary. The adult beetles hibernate and then often appear in vast numbers. The species depicted here is common everywhere in central and northern Europe. The beetles live on various Cruciferae. By nibbling the flowers they can deform the pods, and are often a pest of such crops as oilseed rape.

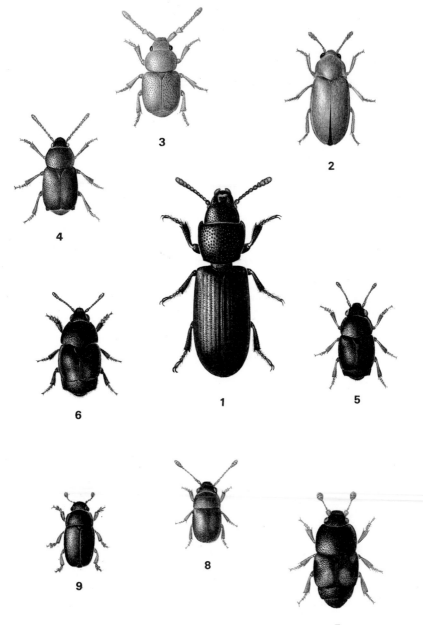

1 *Epuraea aestiva*, 2.5–3.5 mm (9 : 33)

Although this genus is represented by 37 species in central Europe (22 in Britain), relatively little is known of the biology of the individual species. The larvae are to be found mostly in the passages of bark beetles, on escaping sap or on fungi, but it is not known definitely whether they are predacious. The adults of several species may be found on flowers. The species are sometimes hard to tell apart, and for exact identification the sex organs often need to be examined. This species occurs over much of the palaearctic region and also in Alaska. In central and northern Europe it is one of the commonest members of the genus and is found in large numbers everywhere. At least some larvae develop in the nests of bumble-bees. In the winter the beetles can sometimes be found in moles' nests.

2 *Omosita colon*, 2–3.6 mm (10 : 3)

The 3 central European and British species of this genus are to be found on bones, dry carrion and similar material (e. g. old skins). *O. colon* occurs throughout the holarctic region; in central Europe it is the commonest of the 3 species and is to be found there everywhere.

3 *Nitidula rufipes*, 2–4.6 mm (11 : 3)

The 4 species of this genus found in central Europe and Britain all live on carrion, bones and skins. *N. rufipes* occurs throughout the holarctic region; it is distributed over the whole of central Europe, but the beetles are rarer in the east than in the west.

4 *Amphotis marginata*, 4–4.5 mm (12 :1)

The only species of this genus found in central Europe may be recognized by the particularly wide first segment of its antennae and the thick ribs on its elytra. The beetles live in the nests of the ant *Lasius fuliginosus*, occur throughout the whole of Europe except the very north, and can be encountered everywhere in central Europe, where they are commonest in the south.

5 *Pocadius ferrugineus*, 2.6–4.6 mm (15 : 1)

Also the only member of its genus found in central Europe, this beetle resembles the preceding species, but has a prominent fringe of long hairs on its pronotum and elytra. The larvae and adults live in puff-balls. The beetles occur everywhere in central Europe, usually in quite large numbers.

6 *Thalycra fervida*, 3–5 mm (17 : 1)

This broad-bodied beetle is the only member of the genus found in central Europe. The larvae probably live in truffles, earth-balls and other related fungi. The beetles can be caught towards the evening on grasses and flowers, especially in forest clearings. They occur everywhere in central Europe, but are more abundant in mountainous regions.

7 *Cychramus luteus*, 3–5.6 mm (19 : 2)

The 2 members of this genus found in central Europe have a short, wide, but convex body. They probably live on fungi. The species shown here, the only *Cychramus* species found in Britain, is common everywhere in central Europe, where the beetles can be found on flowers.

8 *Glischrochilus quadripunctatus*, 3–6.5 mm (21 : 3)

This genus has 3 species in central and northern Europe; it used to be divided into 2 genera, but these are now regarded as at most subgenera. The elongate oval, black-bodied beetles have 2 yellow or reddish spots on each of their elytra. They are to be found at escaping sap and in the passages of bark beetles or other beetles living in wood. This species is also referred to as *G. quadripustulatus* in earlier works. It is abundant everywhere in central Europe, but less so in the west.

9 *Pityophagus ferrugineus*, 4–6 mm (22 : 1)

This genus is represented in central Europe by 3 species with long, parallel-sided, reddish brown bodies. In the species shown here the head, the top of the pronotum and the tip of the elytra are usually darker. *P. ferrugineus*, the only British species of the genus, is to be found under the bark of coniferous trees; it occurs everywhere in central Europe, is generally quite abundant, but is commoner in the mountains than in the plains.

190

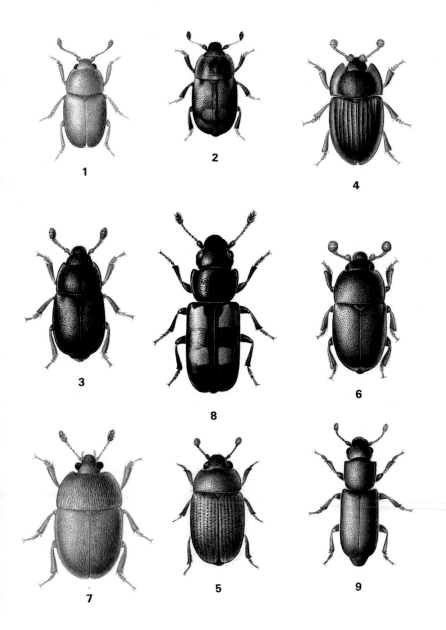

Family Cybocephalidae

The 5 central European species belong to a genus which is sometimes regarded as a separate family, but often referred to the Nitidulidae as a subfamily or tribe. Unlike other Nitidulidae they are predacious, however, and appear to live on scale-insects. Cybocephalids can hardly be mistaken for any other beetle because of their characteristic wide, triangular scutellum, their large, sloping head and their ability to roll up into a ball. None of them occur in the British Isles.

1 *Cybocephalus politus,* 1.3−1.6 mm (1 : 4)
This is the commonest cybocephalid in central Europe. It is distributed over practically the whole of Europe except the Mediterranean region, and in central Europe it is to be found everywhere.

Fmily Rhizophagidae

This family includes the genus *Rhizophagus,* with 14 central European species, and also, in most modern works, the genus *Monotoma* (see below). The long-bodied species of *Rhizophagus,* 12 of which occur in Britain, measure 2.5−5.5 mm in length and mostly live beneath bark, where they hunt down bark beetles.

2 *Rhizophagus bipustulatus,* 2.3−3.5 mm (1 : 9)
This species is the commonest member of the family in central and northern Europe. The beetles are to be found mainly under the bark of deciduous trees.

Family Cucujidae

Some 19 genera of this family, with a total of 49 species (including *Monotoma* and those sometimes referred to the Silvanidae) are known in central Europe. 30 species occur in Britain. The mostly very flat-bodied beetles have widely differing modes of life, but many live under bark.

3 *Monotoma picipes,* 1.9−2.5 mm (1 : 5)
There are 9 species of this genus found in central Europe and the British Isles. They are often referred to the Rhizophagidae or a separate family − Monotomidae. The beetles live in compost heaps and under rotting vegetation, often in large numbers; a few species live with ants. This species is the commonest member of the genus in central and northern Europe.

4 *Ahasverus advena,* 2−2.6 mm (5 : 1)
This only species of this genus found in central Europe has been carried all over the world in consignments of rice and similar goods. It is now well established in central and northern Europe, where the beetles are also to be found in the open under piles of mouldy grass, as well as in barns and food-stores.

5 *Oryzaephilus surinamensis* − Saw-toothed Grain Beetle, 2.5−3.5 mm (6 : 1)
Two members of this genus live in central Europe. The one shown here has been spread with grain and flour all over the globe. In central Europe it is sometimes found in the open, as well as in grain stores and flour mills.

6 *Silvanus unidentatus,* 2.4−2.8 mm (7 : 2)
Two species of this genus occur in central and northern Europe. They resemble the preceding species, but their pronotum is not toothed at the sides and only the anterior corners are produced into points. The species illustrated lives under the bark of deciduous trees.

7 *Psammoecus bipunctatus,* 2.3−2.8 mm (11 : 1)
The only member of the genus found in central and northern Europe, this beetle is clearly distinguishable from related species by its colouring. It is common everywhere in central Europe except the Alps. The beetles are to be found in marshes on reeds and under reed debris.

8 *Pediacus depressus,* 3.5−4.5 mm (15 : 1)
The beetles of the 2 species of this genus found in central and northern Europe live under the bark of various deciduous trees. This species is fairly common on dry, dying wood of deciduous trees and is occasionally found on conifers.

9 *Cryptolestes ferrugineus,* 1.6−2.2 mm (17 : 10)
This genus is represented by 18 species in central Europe. Many species are found under bark, while others are associated with stored products. The beetle shown here is cosmopolitan, and in central Europe it is the commonest species living in the company of man, in grain, flour and flour products and in dried fruit; it is seldom encountered in the open.

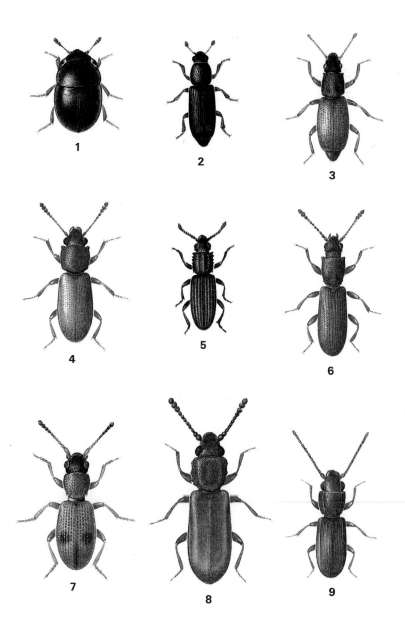

1

2

3

4

5

6

7

8

9

Family Erotylidae

This family has 19 species belonging to 7 genera in central Europe (7 species in Britain). They somewhat resemble cryptophagids and on occasion have been grouped together with them in a single family. Both larvae and adults live in wood fungi.

1 *Tritoma bipustulata*, 3.5−4 mm   (1 : 1)

Both the central European species of this genus are a blunter oval shape than the other members of the family. This species, the only member of the genus found in Britain, is abundant on wood fungi in central Europe the whole year round; its black and red colouring is somewhat variable.

2 *Triplax russica*, 5−6.5 mm   (2 :3)

This génus is represented by 9 species in central Europe (4 in Britain). The beetles always have a red or yellow pronotum and legs. Both larvae and adults live in wood fungi, often in large numbers. The species shown here is common everywhere in central Europe; the beetles can be found in fungi on deciduous trees, especially beeches.

3 *Dacne bipustulata*, 2.5−3.3 mm   (3 : 4)

The 4 species of this genus living in central Europe resemble those of the preceding genus, but are smaller. The species shown here is abundant everywhere in central Europe and is also common in Britain; it occurs chiefly on fungi on deciduous trees, even when they are quite dry.

Family Cryptophagidae

In central Europe there are 134 species of this family belonging to 16 genera; 100 species occur in the British Isles. They are mostly very small, elongate (rarely rounded) beetles seldom measuring more than 3.5 mm and never more than 5.5 mm. They live chiefly in rotting and mouldy vegetable matter and less often in hollow trees, fungi or animals' nests. A number of species live in the company of man, in cowsheds, stores and cellars.

4 *Telmatophilus typhae*, 1.5−2.6 mm   (1 : 4)

The 5 members of this genus found in central Europe and the British Isles resemble *Cryptophagus* species. They often congregate on flowering bur-reeds and bulrushes, while the larvae develop in the seeds; in the winter the beetles can be found sheltering in the leaf sheaths. This species is by far the commonest in central Europe.

5 *Cryptophagus pseudodentatus*, 2−2.7 mm   (8 : 28)

As far as we know, all the 56 members of this genus found in central Europe live on fungi, particularly moulds; 42 species are recorded from Britain. The beetles can be found among decaying leaves, on other mouldy vegetable matter, in animals' nests, in hollow trees and often in the vicinity of man − in cowsheds and cellars, but especially in straw and hay debris in barns. The species illustrated here is abundant everywhere in central Europe, particularly on flowers and in mouldy hay.

6 *Antherophagus pallens*, 3.5−5 mm   (11 : 3)

Adults of the 3 species of this genus occurring in central Europe and Britain are to be found on flowers (chiefly white Labiatae). They are carried by flower-visiting bumble-bees into the latter's nests, where the beetles' larvae develop. The species shown here is the commonest and most widely distributed species in central Europe.

7 *Caenoscelis subdeplanata*, 2−2.4 mm   (12 : 1)

In central Europe this genus is represented by 3 species, 2 of which also occur in the British Isles. The one depicted here lives on fungus-infested wood, but is also found in compost and other decaying matter.

8 *Atomaria fuscata*, 1.4−1.9 mm   (14 : 14)

There are 54 species of this genus in central Europe (43 in Britain), all of them only 1−2.5 mm long, and very often difficult to distinguish from one another. The beetles live chiefly in mouldy material, but also in waterside débris, dung and fungi. *A. fuscata* is very common everywhere in central and northern Europe.

9 *Ephistemus globulus*, 0.8−1.3 mm   (16 : 1)

The 2 species of this genus known in central Europe are found mostly under decaying vegetation. The one shown here, the only British species of the genus, is abundant in manure and decomposing matter everywhere.

194

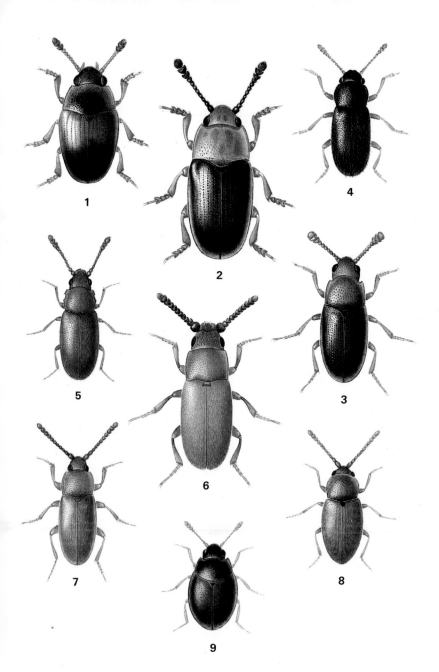

Family Phalacridae

In central Europe this family is represented by 22 species (16 in Britain) belonging to 3 genera. The beetles are small, with a shiny, convex body, and are to be found mostly in flowers.

1 *Phalacrus corruscus, 1.5−3 mm   (1 : 1)
In older works this species is referred to as *P. fimetarius,* and it is probably the commonest of the 7 species of *Phalacrus* occurring in central Europe. The beetles live on rusts and smuts which are parasitic on sedge and grasses. The species shown here is fairly abundant on blighted cereals.

2 *Olibrus millefolii, 1.5−1.8 mm   (2 : 3)
The 12 members of this genus in central Europe (7 in Britain) develop in the flower heads of Compositae. *O. millefolii* is common on milfoil (yarrow) everywhere.

3 *Stilbus testaceus, 1.8−2.3 mm   (3 : 1)
Although all 3 central European and British species of this genus are relatively common, nothing is known as yet of the beetles' development. *S. testaceus,* which lives mainly on dry grass, is rare in the Alps, but abundant everywhere else.

Family Lathridiidae − mould beetles

The members of this family, which in central Europe number 67 species belonging to 9 genera, live on the mycelia and spores of all kinds of fungi, especially moulds; 51 species are found in the British Isles. Since fungi occur in every possible situation, lathridiids occur wherever it is damp or something is decomposing. They are also found in stables and cowsheds, sometimes in quite large numbers, but from man's point of view they are absolutely harmless.

4 *Aridius nodifer, 1.5−2 mm   (3 : 10)
The 3 species of this genus found in central Europe and Britain are notable for the thick ribs on their elytra. They were formerly included in the genus *Lathridius.* As mould-feeders they are to be found on bark, wood and leaves, in hay and straw débris and occasionally on mildewy wallpaper in damp houses. The species depicted here is virtually cosmopolitan and is common everywhere in central Europe and the British Isles.

5 *Lathridius minutus, 1.2−2.4 mm   (4 : 5)
There are 8 species of this genus, formerly known as *Enicmus,* in central Europe (4 in Britain). The beetles resemble *Aridius,* but the ribs on their elytra are not so obvious. They are found in similar situations to species of *Aridius. L. minutus* is a cosmopolitan and is one of the commonest members of the genus in central Europe.

6 *Dienerella elongata, 1.3−1.8 mm   (5 : 1)
The 7 species of this genus found in central Europe and the British Isles are small, narrow, and flat-bodied, with 2 ribs down each of their elytra. Several of the species are not truly established in central Europe, but are regularly imported from other regions. *D. elongata* is established in central and northern Europe where it is found in dry powdered wood, birds' nests and hen-houses and on mildewy wallpaper in houses.

7 *Corticaria pubescens, 2−2.8 mm   (7 : 1)
23 species of this genus are known to occur in central Europe (14 in Britain). The sides of the beetles' pronotum are generally distinctly notched or serrated. Some species are associated with dead wood, and others with mildewed grass or reeds. The species illustrated here is absent in the north and north-west of central Europe, but is otherwise generally abundant.

8 *Cortinicara gibbosa, 1−1.6 mm   (8 : 1)
The single species of this genus (placed in *Corticarina* in most works) living in central Europe has large eyes. Its habits resemble those of the preceding genus, but the beetles also frequent flowering shrubs in large numbers. *C. gibbosa* is reputedly cosmopolitan and is common everywhere in central and northern Europe, including the British Isles.

9 *Melanophthalma transversalis, 1.3−2 mm   (9 : 1)
Two members of this genus are found in central Europe and the British Isles. The one illustrated here is common in central Europe but much less so in Britain. It occurs throughout the palaearctic region and is found in similar situations to species of *Corticaria.*

196

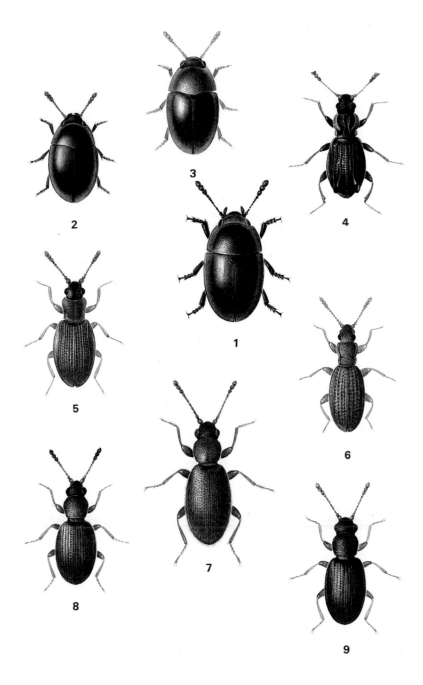

Family Mycetophagidae

This family is represented by 5 genera and 14 species in central Europe (11 species in Britain). All of the species live on or in fungi of one sort or another; a few live under mouldy straw.

1 *Litargus connexus, 2.4−2.8 mm   (3 : 1)
The only member of the genus found in central and northern Europe, this beetle lives on wood fungi and beneath fungus-infested bark. It occurs throughout the palaearctic region and is generally common.

2 *Mycetophagus quadripustulatus, 5−8 mm   (4 : 1)
In central Europe there are 10 species of this genus, 7 of which also occur in Britain; all of them live in wood fungi or fungus-infested wood. The yellowish red elytral spots of this species are rather variable in size and occasionally altogether lacking. The beetle is common everywhere, including the British Isles.

3 *Typhaea stercorea, 2.5−3 mm   (5 : 1)
The single species of this genus found in central Europe has a cosmopolitan distribution. It is found in the open as well as on mouldy plant debris in barns and cellars, where the beetles are always abundant.

Family Colydiidae

The 39 species of the 21 genera of this family in central Europe are very variable in shape. They live under bark, in rotting wood, on tree trunks and lichens and under fallen leaves. Several of the genera are to be found deep under stones and wood. Several of the genera are often referred to a separate family − Cerylonidae.

4 *Myrmechixenus subterraneus, 1.3−1.6 mm   (1 : 1)
Two species of this genus occur in central Europe. Both of them also occur in the British Isles but are rare. In central Europe the species depicted here is quite often to be found in the nests of Formica species (especially Formica pratensis).

5 *Bitoma crenata, 2.6−3 mm   (16 : 1)
The only species of the genus (sometimes spelled Ditoma) in central Europe can be identified from the ridges down its pronotum and elytra, as well as by its colour. The beetles can be found on dead bark, and both they and the larvae prey on other insects. The species is common everywhere in central Europe.

6 *Cerylon histeroides, 1.8−2.2 mm   (24 : 4)
With their compact form and smooth, glabrous back, the 7 central European members of this genus somewhat resemble narrow-bodied Histeridae; 3 species occur in Britain. The beetles live under loose bark or in mouldy wood and feed chiefly on bark beetles. The species shown here is abundant under the bark of deciduous and coniferous trees everywhere.

Family Endomychidae

In central Europe there are 23 species of this family belonging to 12 genera. However, only 6 species occur in Britain. Most of them are fairly broad and convex in form; they resemble− and are related to − ladybirds. Both the adult beetles and their larvae live on fungi, in particular puff-balls and moulds.

7 Sphaerosoma pilosum, 1.4−1.6 mm   (1 : 7)
Sometimes referred to a separate family − Sphaerosomatidae − the 8 minute species of this genus found in central Europe have an almost hemispherical form. The beetles live in ground litter, under moss or in brushwood interspersed with fungal mycelia. This is the commonest and most widely distributed species in central Europe and is the only member of the genus found in Britain.

8 *Mycetaea hirta, 1.5−1.8 mm   (2 : 1)
This is the only member of the genus Mycetaea found in central and northern Europe. The yellowish brown beetles live mostly in cellars (chiefly on the fungus Merulius lacrymans) and in barns, stables and cowsheds. M. hirta abounds everywhere in central Europe and although it is less commonly seen in the open it can sometimes be found in hollow trees.

9 *Endomychus coccineus, 4−6 mm   (13 : 1)
This only species of this genus occurring in central and northern Europe has very characteristic colouring. The larvae are also brightly coloured and crawl about openly on wood fungi. In central Europe the beetles are fairly abundant everywhere on fungi and on fungus-infested wood.

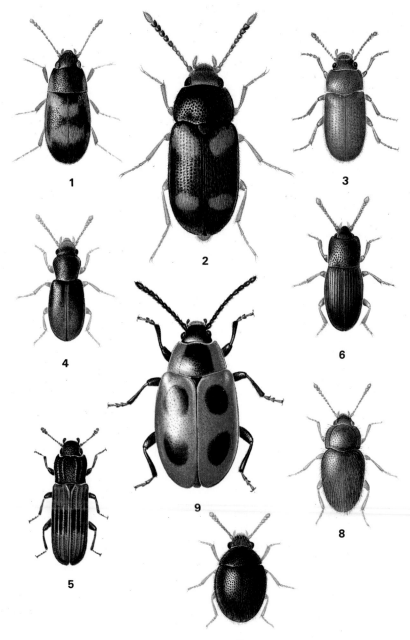

Family Coccinellidae — ladybirds

This family is represented in central Europe by 35 genera with a total of 88 species, 43 of which occur in the British Isles. Most ladybirds — both as larva and as adult — are helpful to the gardener, farmer and forester by eating plant-sucking bugs, especially aphids; only a few species are vegetarian or feed on mildew. When in danger ladybirds feign death and many release a defensive malodorous fluid from an opening between femur and tibia. Their identification can, in some cases, be surprisingly difficult because of the variability within many species, especially in colouring.

1 *Subcoccinella vigintiquatuorpunctata, 3—4 mm (3 : 1)

This is the only member of the genus in central Europe and is one of the few vegetarian ladybirds. Both adults and larvae frequent a wide variety of plants and can do considerable damage to them. This species is common everywhere in central Europe, especially in dry meadows.

2 Cynegetis impunctata, 3—4.5 mm (4 : 1)

The sole member of this genus in central Europe resembles the preceding one, but its ground colour is less red and more ochre. While the previous species varies from unspotted to black, in this species unspotted specimens are commoner and black ones practically non-existent. They are also plant-feeders and in central Europe the beetles can be found chiefly in damp meadows and woods, sometimes in large numbers.

3 *Coccidula rufa, 2.5—3 mm (5 : 2)

There are 2 species of this genus in central Europe and the British Isles. For ladybirds the beetles have a very long body, with almost parallel sides. They live on marsh and aquatic plants, in particular rushes, which they rid of aphids. They are common everywhere in central Europe and Britain, where they hibernate among rushes.

4 Rhizobius chrysomeloides, 2.5—3.5 mm (6 : 2)

The 2 species of this genus in central Europe likewise have a rather elongate, oval body. The beetles and the larvae live on a variety of plants, where they eat aphids. The beetles can be caught in the summer on vegetation, and in winter they can be found in moss, at plant-roots, and under bark. The species shown here is the commoner of the two in the middle and eastern part of Germany; near water it is generally quite abundant. The beetles are to be found chiefly on pine-trees and shrubs. The second species — R. litura — is common in most parts of the British Isles where it is found chiefly on low vegetation.

5 Scymnus abietis, 2.2—3 mm (8 : 6)

The 27 species of this genus in central Europe (8 in the British Isles) comprise small, hairy beetles with short antennae, whose larvae feed on woolly aphids and other bugs. This species can be caught by beating the branches of spruces (they are generally plentiful near the top). It is commoner in the south of central Europe than in the north.

6 *Stethorus punctillum, 1.2—1.5 mm (9 : 1)

In earlier works this genus was regarded as a subgenus of Scymnus; in central Europe and the British Isles there is one species, which feeds on plant mites ('red spiders') and is thus very useful. The beetles live mainly on shrubs and deciduous trees. They particularly favour the under side of lime leaves, where they hunt a Tetranychus species. In central Europe the species is generally common.

7 *Chilocorus bipustulatus, 2.7—4 mm (12 : 1)

There are 2 species of this genus in central and northern Europe. The one shown here occurs throughout the palaearctic region. Both the adult beetles and the larvae eat aphids and scale-insects and are fairly common. In Britain it is found most commonly on heathland.

8 *Exochomus quadripustulatus — Four-spot Ladybird, 3—5 mm (13 : 1)

The beetles of the 2 central European species of this genus resemble the preceding species, but have a completely hairless back. They chiefly frequent conifers, but can also be found on hawthorn, maple and buckthorn. They eat aphids and scale-insects and are thus very useful.

9 *Adonia variegata, 3—5.5 mm (16 : 1)

The single species of Adonia found in central and northern Europe has extremely variable colouring, especially as regards the number of spots. The beetles are often common, especially in coastal areas, where they may occur in large numbers at the edge of the water. They feed on aphids.

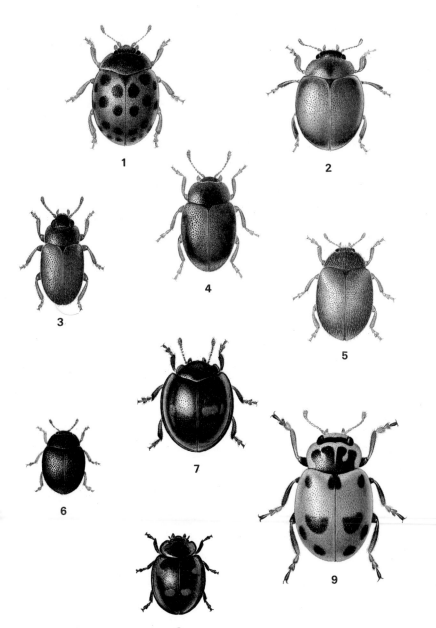

1 *Aphidecta obliterata,* 3.3−5 mm (17 : 1)
The only member of the genus in central and northern Europe, this beetle has a dingy yellow to brownish back. Its elytral markings are rather variable and quite often altogether lacking. It is a fairly common species everywhere in central Europe and lives on conifers, where it preys on conifer aphids.

2 *Hippodamia tredecimpunctata* − 13-spot Ladybird, 4.5−7 mm (18 : 1)
This genus has 2 species in central Europe. Although there are usually numerous black spots on the beetle's red elytra, the markings vary so that, at one extreme, the beetle can be entirely red or, at the other, completely black. The beetles are to be found in marshy meadows on bur-reed, rushes, sedge, reed-grass and willows; they also occur on *Prunus* species, where they feed on aphids. *H. tredecimpunctata* is the only species found in Britain, where it is rare.

3 *Anisosticta novemdecimpunctata* − 19-spot Ladybird, 3−4 mm (19 : 1)
This is probably the only species of the genus in central Europe, since a second, circumpolar relative found in the far north hardly ventures into central Europe and is absent from the British Isles. The yellow, longish, black-spotted beetles abound on aquatic and waterside plants.

4 *Tytthaspis sedecimpunctata* − 16-spot Ladybird, 2.5−3 mm (22 : 1)
The only central and north European species of *Tytthaspis* is distinguished by its extremely small scutellum. The black spots on the beetle's convex yellow elytra sometimes merge. This species is found most commonly in damp situations but is also sometimes abundant near the coast. In the mountains it is not found above about 500 m.

5 *Adalia decempunctata* − Ten-spot Ladybird, 3.5−5 mm (23 : 2)
In earlier works, this genus − which has 4 species in central Europe (2 in Britain) − was included in the genus *Coccinella.* Although the beetles' markings are very variable, their position is still a good guide to the insect's identity. The species shown here occurs throughout the palaearctic region. In central and northern Europe, including the British Isles, it can be found on deciduous trees and in meadows, and is common almost everywhere.

6 *Adalia bipunctata* − Two-spot Ladybird, 3.5−5.5 mm (23 : 3)
This species occurs throughout the holarctic region and in central and northern Europe it is abundant everywhere. Adults are often to be found overwintering in houses, especially in the corners of window-frames and other niches. If we find such a beetle in a warm room during the winter we should remove it to a cooler spot, such as an unheated loft. Frost does not harm them, but if they pass the winter in the warmth they do not revive in the spring. They are important predators of aphids.

7 *Adalia bipunctata* − Two-spot Ladybird
This species has particularly variable colouring. Generally the commonest form is that with red elytra and a black spot on each, but the form illustrated here is also fairly common. The differences are determined both genetically and by environmental factors. Red forms survive the winter better, while black forms reproduce more actively.

8 *Coccinella septempunctata* − Seven-spot Ladybird, 5.2−8 mm (25 : 3)
The 7 central European species of this genus, 5 of which also occur in the British Isles, comprise beetles with red or yellow elytra and variable black markings. The Seven-spot is one of the best known ladybirds and it varies very little in its colour-pattern. The adult beetles and the larvae prey on aphids. The species is common everywhere in central and northern Europe, including the British Isles.

9 *Coccinella quinquepunctata* − Five-spot Ladybird, 3−5 mm (25 : 5)
This species is rather similar to the preceding one, but is smaller. The black spots on its elytra are also more variable in size and shape. The Five-spot is widely distributed in the palaearctic region. It is fairly common everywhere in central Europe and is especially abundant near water, but is also to be found on dry hillsides. In the British Isles it is much more local; although not uncommon in parts of Scotland it is very rarely found further to the south.

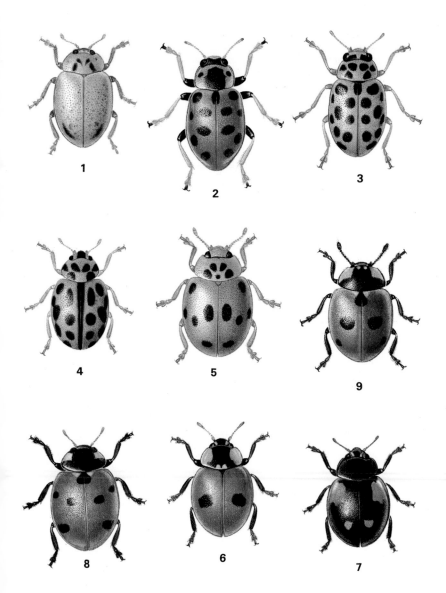

1 *Synharmonia conglobata,* 3.5−5 mm (27 : 3)

The 3 species of this genus found in central Europe used to be included in the genus *Coccinella*. None of them occur in the British Isles. The species shown here, whose black spots may be much enlarged, is generally common everywhere in central Europe, especially on *Prunus* species and poplars.

2 *Harmonia quadripunctata,* 5.5−6 mm (28 : 1)

The only species of this genus found in central and northern Europe used likewise to be included in the genus *Coccinella*. It occurs in the southern part of northern Europe, including England, and in southern and central Europe, where the beetles are comparatively abundant on pines. In the winter they are to be found under loose pieces of bark.

3 *Myrrha octodecimguttata,* 3.5−6 mm (29 : 1)

Earlier authors considered this genus − which is represented by one species in central Europe − to be a subgenus of *Halyzia*. The species' area of distribution stretches across Europe and the Mediterranean region to beyond the Balkans. In central Europe the beetles are fairly common on conifers and they are particularly numerous on bog-pines in the highland moors of Upper Bavaria.

4 *Calvia quatuordecimguttata,* 4.5−6 mm (31 : 2)

This genus − with 4 species in central Europe (2 in Britain) − also used to be regarded as a subgenus of *Halyzia*. This species, which is characterized by a row of 3 light yellow spots across each of the elytra, just before the middle, occurs in Europe, Siberia and North America. In central Europe the beetles are common everywhere. They can be caught in the spring by tapping flowering plants and deciduous trees and in the winter by sieving leaves and moss.

5 *Calvia quatuordecimpunctata,* 3.5−4.5 mm (32 : 1)

In most works this species is referred to the genus *Propylea*. Its colouring is rather variable and it may be confused with *Synharmonia conglobata* (this plate, No. 1). *Calvia 14-punctata* is one of the commonest ladybirds in central and northern Europe, including the British Isles. It preys on many kinds of plant-lice.

6 *Neomysia oblongoguttata,* 7−9 mm (33 : 1)

The single species of this genus in central Europe is to be found in older works under the genus *Paramysia*. The adult beetles are among the largest of European ladybirds, and are easily identifiable because of their distinctive colouring. In conifer woods they are often common, especially on pines.

7 *Anatis ocellata* − Eyed Ladybird, 8−9 mm (34 : 1)

Typical specimens of this single central European member of the genus are unmistakable, but the black centres of the pale patches on its elytra are of variable size, and sometimes missing altogether. The pronotum is always black and yellow, however. This is the largest ladybird found in central and northern Europe. It is to be found on coniferous trees, where it feeds on plant-lice.

8 *Halyzia sedecimguttata,* 5−7 mm (35 : 1)

The only member of this genus found in central Europe generally has 8 light spots on each of its elytra, although the hindmost spots are sometimes missing. In central Europe the beetles are fairly common in deciduous woods, but can sometimes also be found on conifers. In Britain the species is very local and usually rare.

9 *Psyllobora vigintiduopunctata,* 3−4.5 mm (37 : 1)

This genus (often referred to as *Thea*) has 1 species in central Europe. The lemon yellow, black-spotted beetles have a distinctive colour-pattern which varies very little. They occur throughout the palaearctic region, and are generally common in central and northern Europe, including Britain. They live on mildew.

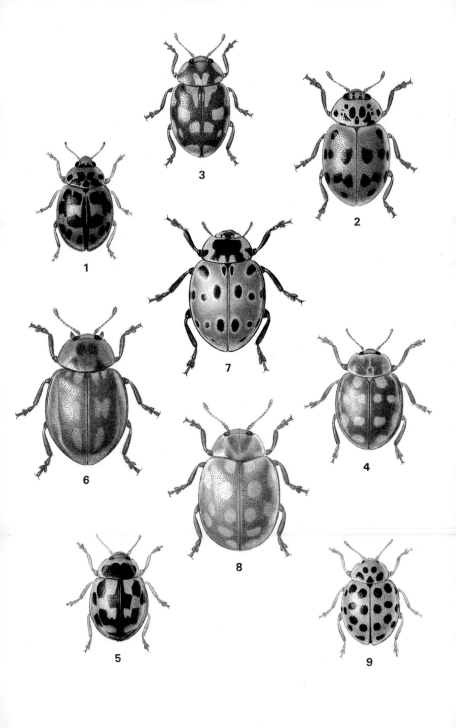

Family Sphindidae

This family is represented in central Europe by a single genus and species.

1 *Sphindus dubius, 1.8−2 mm (1 : 1)

The longish, approximately cylindrical beetles live on slime moulds (Myxomycetes). They are fairly common at low altitudes in central Europe, but are of very local occurrence in Britain. A somewhat larger species (3 mm) is known in the Balkans.

Family Aspidiphoridae

This family is represented in central Europe by 2 species, both of which belong to the same genus. *Aspidiphorus* is often included in the Sphindidae.

2 *Aspidiphorus orbiculatus, 1.2−1.5 mm (1 : 1)

Adults of *Aspidiphorus* are round and capable of rolling partially into a ball. This species, the only member of the genus found in Britain, often occurs together with *Sphindus dubius* in central Europe, but in general it is commoner. The beetles, which also live on slime moulds, swarm in the evening.

Family Cisidae

The 45 species of this family found in central Europe are brown or black, with a cylindrical body, and mostly look very much alike. The beetles can be found on tree fungi, including very hard bracket fungi, often in large numbers; they tend to be most abundant at the height of summer, but they can be caught the whole year round. 22 species occur in Britain.

3 *Octotemnus glabriculus, 1.5−1.8 mm (1 : 1)

The typical feature of these elongate oval beetles is their antennae, which have only 8 segments, the last 3 of which form a club. Of the 2 species of this genus in central Europe the one depicted here (the only British species) is widely distributed and is common in hard tree fungi everywhere.

4 *Rhopalodontus perforatus, 1.8−2.2 mm (3 : 1)

The 2 species of this genus in central Europe are remarkable for the rounded, widened tips, with comb-like teeth, of their tibiae. The species illustrated here, the only member of the genus found in Britain, lives gregariously in bracket fungi of the genus *Fomes;* it is widely distributed, but is not common.

5 *Sulcacis affinis, 1−1.3 mm (5 : 1)

The 4 central European species of this genus were formerly included in the genera *Ennearthron* or *Entypus*. Two of the species are found in Britain. Their legs somewhat resemble those of the preceding species in form. *S. affinis* is widely distributed in Europe and Siberia. In central Europe, the beetles abound in tree fungi everywhere.

6 *Cis boleti, 2.8−4 mm (6 : 11)

This genus has 28 species in central Europe (17 in Britain), i. e. more than half the entire family. The antennae have 10 segments, the last 3 forming a club; the tibiae are simple in form. The beetles are mostly brown to blackish brown, but usually have reddish yellow antennae and legs; they live in tree fungi. This species is distributed over the whole of the palaearctic region. In the southern part of central Europe it is common in tree fungi everywhere, but in the north it is often rarer than other members of the genus. It is widely distributed and common in Britain.

7 *Cis jacquemarti, 1.5−2 mm (6 : 3)

This species is common chiefly in fungi growing on beeches; it used often to be regarded as a variety of *C. nitidus*. It occurs in both northern and central Europe, where it is generally common.

8 *Cis hispidus, 2−2.4 mm (6 : 7)

This rather narrow species occurs chiefly in dry tree fungi. It is abundant everywhere in central Europe and not uncommon in many parts of Britain.

9 *Ennearthron cornutum, 1.4−2 mm (7 : 2)

The 5 central European species of this genus are closely related to the species of *Cis*. They are to be found mostly in tree fungi, but a few live in the passages of bark beetles (*Cryphalus* species) in thin branches. The species shown here, the only British representative of the genus, is widely distributed in central Europe, but is usually not very common.

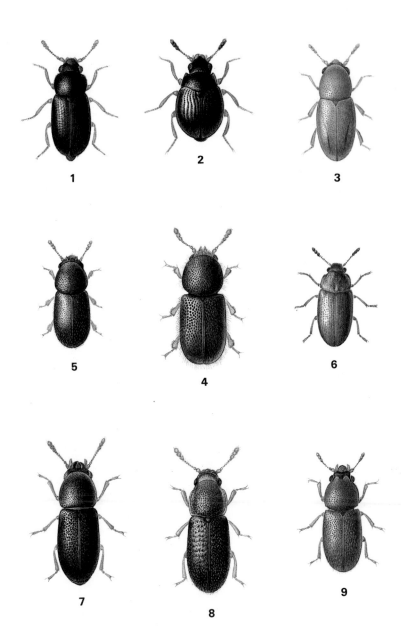

Family Lyctidae — powder-post beetles

There are 4 species of this family, belonging to 2 genera, in central Europe and 5 in Britain. The females have very long ovipositors, with which they deposit their eggs in cracks in wood. The larvae eat dry sap-wood and destroy it in the same way as Death-watch Beetles.

1 *Lyctus brunneus* – Common Powder-post Beetle, 2.5−8 mm (mostly 4−5 mm)   (2 : 1)

This genus has 3 species in central and northern Europe. The one shown here is virtually cosmopolitan; it is constantly being imported into central Europe and is now naturalized there. It is a serious pest of seasoned wood and is to be found chiefly in wood-yards, carpenter's workshops and houses.

Family Bostrychidae — false powder-post beetles

In central Europe there are 13 genera of this family, with a total of 18 species. The beetles have a cylindrical body and often resemble bark beetles, but have a quite different antennal structure. Their pronotum covers their head like a hood. A number of species are regularly imported to central Europe in wood from other parts of the world. The native species in central Europe are mostly warmth-loving or are primaeval forest relics. In Britain only one species of Bostrychidae is native, and this is probably now extinct. The beetles tunnel in wood and can live to a fair age.

2 *Stephanopachys substriatus*, 3.5−6.5 mm   (3 : 1)

Two species of this genus, both with boreoalpine distribution, are known in central Europe. As the beetles age, the bristles and rasp-like teeth on their body wear away. They are to be found chiefly on conifers, especially pines. *S. substriatus* has been found in Britain but is doubtfully established.

3 *Rhizopertha dominica*, 2−3 mm   (4 : 1)

The only species of the genus found in central Europe is of tropical origin and is constantly being imported in plant products, grain and cow-cake. It cannot be regarded as naturalized, however, since the beetles can survive only in warm buildings in the company of man.

4 *Dinoderus minutus*, 2.4−3.8 mm   (5 : 4)

In central Europe this genus is represented by 5 species, of which the one depicted here is the commonest and most widely distributed. All 5 species tunnel in bamboo canes, so that their incidence in central Europe has increased with the growing popularity of this material. The species shown here originates from tropical and subtropical regions and is a special nuisance because it also attacks sugar cane, corn and maize.

5 *Bostrychus capucinus*, 6−15 mm   (8 : 1)

The single species of this genus in central Europe is very distinctively coloured. The beetles are found chiefly in warm localities and develop in oak sap-wood and the wood of fruit-trees; they particularly favour dry roots and withered vines. Although native to the British Isles, *B. capucinus* appears to be now extinct in the old English forests where it was once found.

6 *Heterobostrychus brunneus*, 5−11 mm   (11 : 1)

This genus has 6 tropical species which are all pests and are often carried to other parts of the world. *H. brunneus* is the species most frequently imported to Europe.

7 *Bostrychoplites cornutus*, 7−18 mm   (12 : 1)

This genus has 15 species living in Africa and Arabia. The adult beetles bear highly distinctive horns on their pronotum. The species depicted here is often imported to central Europe in timber.

8 *Sinoxylon perforans*, 5−8 mm   (13 : 2)

Roughly 50 species of this genus are known to occur in Africa and Asia. This species has been recorded from vine wood in Germany but the specimens were probably imported.

9 *Xylopertha retusa*, 3−6 mm   (14 : 1)

Known in earlier works as *Xylonites,* this genus is represented by only one species in central Europe. The beetles are to be found only in warm localities in dry wood of oaks and vines; they are never very common and are often rare.

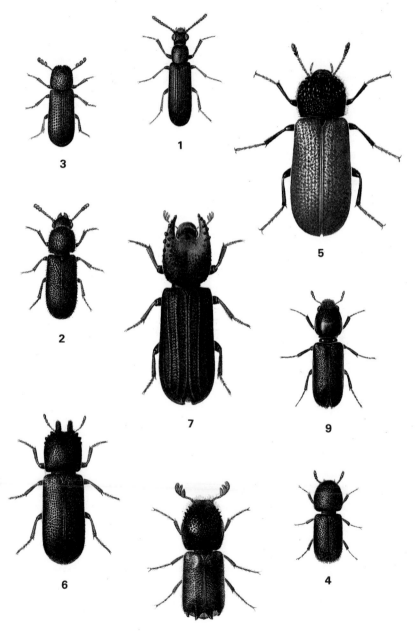

Family Anobiidae

This family is represented in central Europe by 76 species belonging to 23 genera; 28 species of the family occur in Britain. The beetles have a cylindrical body and their head is usually hidden by their pronotum. As a rule the beetles tunnel in dead wood or in other firm material like tree fungi and pine cones. A few are pests of stored products, however, while others live in dry dung or in puff-balls. The digestive tract of many species has been shown to contain microorganisms which help or enable the beetles to digest and metabolize wood.

1 *Hedobia pubescens*, 5−7.5 mm (1 :1)
Three species of this genus are natives of central Europe. Unlike most other Anobiidae the tips of their antennae are not enlarged. The beetles live in dead wood, in particular thin branches of deciduous trees. This species occurs only in warm localities in the southern part of central Europe and is very rare (no new finds have been made for some time). They develop in mistletoe.

2 **Hedobia imperialis*, 3.1−5.2 mm (1 : 2)
This species, the only member of the genus found in Britain, is fairly abundant everywhere in central Europe. The beetles can be found in spring on flowering shrubs, especially hawthorn; later they can be shaken from deciduous brushwood. The beetles swarm in the evening.

3 **Grynobius planus*, 4−6 mm (2 : 1)
Formerly known as *Priobium*, this genus is represented by only one species in central and northern Europe. This is so variable that it has been described as several species, under the names *tricolor, excavatum* and *eichhoffi*. It is one of the largest European anobiids, lives in dry wood on deciduous trees and in the evening runs about on tree stumps and trunks.

4 **Dryophilus pusillus*, 1.7−2.5 mm (3 : 3)
Of the 2 species of this genus found in central Europe and Britain, the one shown here is the commonest. The beetles can be found in the spring on conifers.

5 **Ochina ptinoides*, 2.5−3.8 mm (4 : 2)
The 2 members of this genus found in central Europe have serrate antennae. This species, the only member of the genus found in Britain, is not evenly distributed; there are large areas where it is completely absent, while elsewhere, especially in warm places, it can be common. The beetles are to be found on dry ivy.

6 **Xestobium rufovillosum* − Death-watch Beetle, 5−9 mm (5 : 2)
This genus is represented by 3 species in central Europe (but only one in Britain). In the spring it can be found on flowers. It develops in oaks and willows, whose wood may be completely riddled by its passages; it can also severely damage woodwork in buildings. In Britain it is well-known for the damage it causes to the woodwork of old churches.

7 *Episernus striatellus*, 2−3 mm (6 : 3)
The 5 members of this genus in central Europe, none of which occur in the British Isles, resemble those of the next genus. They live on conifer wood. The species depicted here is found in the south-west of central Europe, where its incidence is sporadic and rare.

8 **Ernobius mollis*, 2.8−6.2 mm (7 : 12)
Ten species of this genus live in central Europe (5 in Britain). Marked size and sex-related differences make examination of the sex organs necessary when determining the species. The beetles develop in fir and pine cones and in the pith of conifer twigs. The species shown here is the only common one in central Europe, and is also the commonest species of the genus in Britain. It does not occur only in the open, but also in de-barked timber in houses, where it can be a pest.

9 *Oligomerus brunneus*, 5−6.5 mm (8 : 2)
The two native central European members of this genus, neither of them found in Britain, resemble *Anobium* species, but have no protuberance on their pronotum. The species shown here is to be found in low-lying country, in the wood of hollow deciduous trees; it is rarer in the north and west.

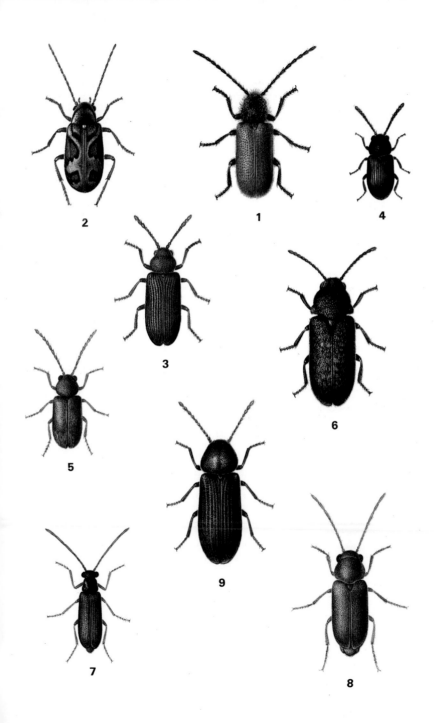

2

1

4

3

5

6

7

9

8

1 *Stegobium paniceum* – Bread Beetle, 2–4 mm   (9 : 1)
This genus, referred to as *Sitodrepa* in older works, is represented by only one species in central Europe. It has a cosmopolitan distribution, and although it develops in bread and products made with flour (hence its name *paniceum*), it also infests a great variety of other plant and animal products, even hot spices and drugs. This makes it one of the very worst of stored products pests. It occurs in houses, stores and warehouses everywhere in central and northern Europe, sometimes in very large numbers.

2 *Gastrallus immarginatus*, 2–2.5 mm   (10 : 2)
This genus is represented by 2 species in central Europe, only one of which is found in Britain. The species shown here (referred to as *G. laevigatus* in many works) is rare to very rare in central Europe. It lives on mistletoe and only exceptionally on old deciduous trees.

3 *Nicobium castaneum*, 4–6 mm   (11 : 1)
The single species of this genus found in central Europe is actually a native of southern and western Europe. Records for central Europe, like those for Britain, probably relate to imported individuals.

4 *Anobium punctatum* – Woodworm or Furniture Beetle, 2.5–5 mm   12 : 1)
There are 12 species of this genus in central Europe (5 in Britain). The one depicted here, termed *striatum* in older works, is relatively rare in the open, where it is found on dry wood of deciduous and coniferous trees and displays a liking for ivy. However, the beetles are serious pests of structural timber in buildings and in old furniture, where their larvae, the well-known 'woodworms', can be exceedingly destructive.

5 *Anobium emarginatum*, 3.5–4.5 mm   (12 : 10)
This species occurs in the southern part of northern Europe as well as in central Europe, where it is very rare in the plains and lately seems to have disappeared in many places altogether. In the mountains in the middle and southern part of central Europe the beetles live chiefly on dry spruces; they are commoner in the east than in the west.

6 *Anobium pertinax*, 4.5–6 mm   (12 : 12)
The males of this species can be heard as they knock their head and thorax on the floor of their burrows and make ticking sounds to attract a mate. This species occurs chiefly in the open; it used to be present everywhere in central Europe, and in some areas was quite abundant, but lately it has become markedly scarcer. The beetles are to be found indoors less often than outdoors, but they sometimes attack worked timber (chiefly that of conifers and only exceptionally hardwood).

7 *Priobium carpini*, 3–5 mm   (13 : 1)
This genus – known as *Trypopitys* in older works – has only 1 species in central Europe. It is widely distributed and is to be found in worked conifer wood, though not in large numbers. In the open the beetles can be seen from May to August on the trunks of dry deciduous and coniferous trees, where they are rarer still.

8 *Ptilinus pectinicornis*, 3.5–5.5 mm   (14 : 1)
Both the central European species of this genus are remarkable for the long pectinate antennae of the male; female antennae are merely serrate. *P. pectinicornis*, the only British species, is fairly common on deciduous hardwoods (especially beeches) from May to July everywhere in central Europe. In houses it sometimes attacks woodwork and can do considerable damage to furniture.

9 *Ptilinus fuscus*, 3–5.5 mm   (14 : 2)
This differs from the preceding species chiefly in respect of its more granulate back and the shorter processes on the male's antennae. In central Europe the beetles are to be found in the open from May to June on deciduous trees with soft wood (chiefly willows and poplars), in places devoid of bark. In the plains they are fairly abundant.

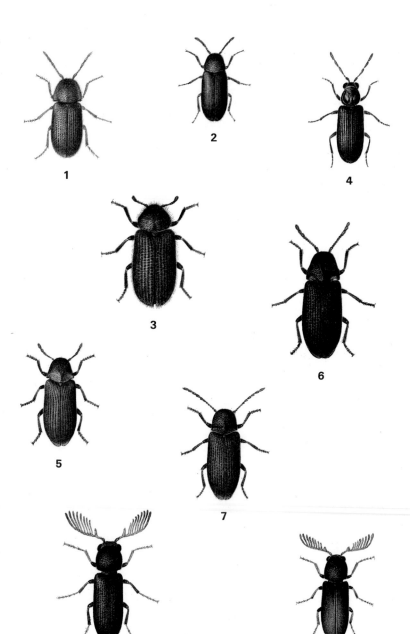

1 *Pseudoptilinus fissicollis,* 5−7 mm (15 : 1)

The single member of this genus found in central Europe used to be included in the genus *Ptilinus,* but the processes on the males' antennae are shorter and the pronotum has a longitudinal groove in the midline. The insects develop in fallen lime branches. The species has been recorded from only a few scattered localities in central Europe.

2 *Xyletinus laticollis,* 4 mm (16 : 3)

There are 10 species of this genus in central Europe, only one of which is found in Britain. Both sexes have stout, distinctly serrate antennae of 11 segments. The beetles can tuck their head almost completely into their thorax so that they have an unbroken contour like a pill beetle. They develop in dry wood and bark on deciduous trees; a few larvae also live in dung. The biology of some species is still unknown. The beetles are to be seen mostly from the middle of May to the beginning of July. This species occurs chiefly in the southern part of central Europe, but is not very common; in the coastal region of north Germany it is found occasionally on dry dung.

3 *Xyletinus pectinatus,* 3.5−5 mm (16 : 6)

This species occurs everywhere in central Europe, but is in general rare. The beetles are active at night and live on dry wood, particularly oak.

4 **Xyletinus longitarsis,* 2.6−4 mm (16 : 5)

This species, listed in many works as *X. ater,* is the commonest member of the genus in central Europe. The beetles are to be found chiefly on oak trunks and undergrowth.

5 **Lasioderma serricorne,* 2−2.7 mm (17 : 1)

Four species of this genus are known to occur in central Europe. The round or oval beetles have serrate antennae; they can bend their head a long way under their thorax and curl themselves up into a ball. They develop in the stems of herbaceous plants. The species shown here is cosmopolitan and has been carried all over the world in merchandise; the beetles display a special fondness for tobacco. This species can not be said to have become an established member of the central European fauna, as it can live only in warm buildings, i. e. in the company of man; it is by no means rare, however.

6 *Mesocoelopus niger,* 1.8−4.2 (19 : 1)

This species, the only member of the genus in central Europe, has a bluntly oval and regularly domed body. It is very widespread, although there are regions from which it has not yet been recorded. The beetles live on ivy.

7 **Dorcatoma flavicornis,* 1.5−2.4 mm (22: : 1)

The 7 species of this genus found in central Europe (4 in Britain) comprise oval, black (seldom brown), rather shiny beetles with a convex body. The last 3 segments of their antennae are large and serrated. The beetles, most of which look very much alike, live in hard tree fungi or in wood containing the mycelia of such fungi. This species is quite common in the north and east of central Europe and becomes rarer towards the south and west. The beetles are to be found mainly in fungi on deciduous trees (preferably oaks).

8 **Caenocara bovistae,* 1.6−2.5 mm (23 : 1)

The 3 central European species of this genus resemble those of the preceding genus, but have a round body. The beetles live in puff-balls, but in the summer they can also be caught on low vegetation. The species shown here is widespread in central Europe, but occurs only in some places and usually in small numbers; it is rare in Britain.

9 **Anitys rubens,* 2.2−2.8 mm (24 : 1)

This is the only species of the genus found in central Europe and the British Isles. It resembles the 2 preceding species, but is reddish brown. The beetles are widely distributed in central Europe, but are not common, and in the south and west there are areas where they are completely absent. They are very rare in Britain. They live in red-rotten wood in hollow deciduous trees (chiefly oaks); they seldom leave their breeding places.

214

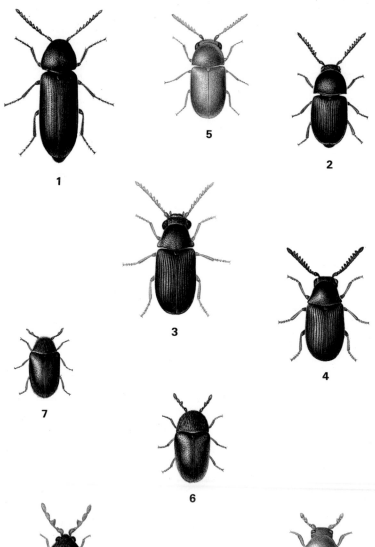

Family Ptinidae — spider beetles

In central Europe there are 23 species of spider beetles belonging to 4 genera. About 20 species are of regular occurrence in Britain. Many of them are cosmopolitan species which owe their wide range to their ability to exploit man-made habitats. New species are constantly being brought to central Europe from other faunal regions and many of them have settled there. A few species can be real pests, but the majority are no more than nuisances in our homes. The adult beetles frequently live on dry substances, while the larvae develop chiefly in grain, cereal products and dried plant material; when about to pupate they bore a tunnel in harder material. The beetles are active at night.

1 *Gibbium psylloides*, 2−3.2 mm (1 : 1)
This is the only member of the genus found in central Europe. It is both cosmopolitan and synanthropic and although its incidence is very sporadic it can occur in large numbers. The beetles have very long legs and can live to the age of 18 months. The larvae often develop between the floor boards of old houses, where they live on the insulating chaff filling; they are also to be found in warehouses, bakeries and compost heaps. When ready to pupate they bore a hole in wood, but do not eat the wood itself.

2 *Mezium affine*, 1.9−3.3 mm (2 : 1)
This and one other species of the same genus repeatedly find their way to central Europe from southern Europe and Africa, but have not yet settled there. Their habits are similar to those of the preceding species.

3 *Trigonogenius globulus*, 3 mm (3 : 1)
This is an American species which is frequently imported into Europe. It is found regularly in the coastal towns of Germany, Denmark and Holland. It is an established species indoors in parts of Britain.

4 *Sphaericus gibboides*, 1.3−2.7 mm (4 : 1)
This is another species that is frequently brought to Germany, Holland and France, but is not truly established in Europe. The adult beetles and larvae live on seeds and dry plants.

5 *Niptus hololeucus*, 2.6−4.6 mm (5 : 1)
This beetle is completely covered with golden yellow hairs. In 1838 it was introduced to England from the south of Russia and since then it has spread all over the world. In central Europe it is to be found everywhere − in homes and warehouses − often in large numbers. The larvae develop mainly in starchy materials, such as the remains of grain in chaff filling the space between floorboards. To pupate they bore holes in harder material and can thereby do considerable damage, especially to textiles.

6 *Tipnus unicolor*, 1.7−3.1 mm (6 : 1)
The sole species of this genus found in central Europe is less hairy than *N. hololeucus* and has hairs that are more greyish brown in colour. It is found mostly in barns and outbuildings, but also occurs in marmot and mouse burrows and bumble-bee nests. It is rather local and rarely found in large numbers.

7 *Paraniptus globulus*, 2 mm (7 : 1)
This species also resembles *Niptus hololeucus*, but is far less hairy. It originates from south-western Europe and north Africa and although it has been imported to north-west Germany it has not yet settled there.

8 *Ptinus fur* − male, 2.6−4.3 mm (8 : 5)
There are 20 species of this genus found in central Europe, about 12 of which also occur in Britain. In this species, which is distributed throughout the holarctic region, sexual dimorphism is particularly marked. In central Europe it occurs everywhere, often in large numbers, but in southern Europe it is rare. In the open the beetles can be found in birds' nests and in old trees, but they are mainly synanthropic, living on all kinds of substances of both plant and animal origin. Occasionally they do damage in grain stores.

9 *Ptinus fur* − female
Not only are the females a different shape from the males, but they also have different markings.

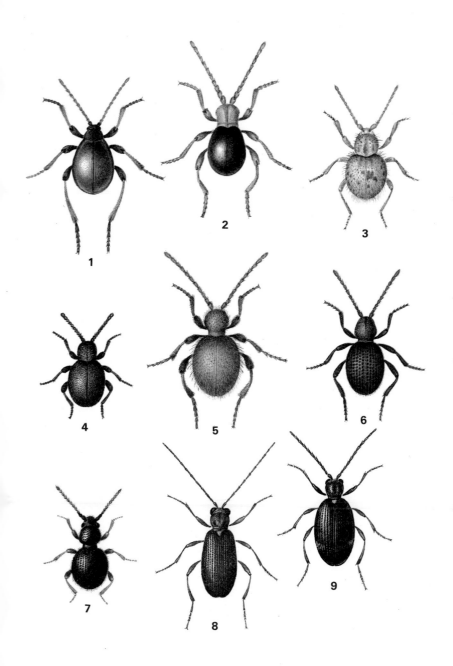

Family Oedemeridae

This family is represented in central Europe by 30 species from 10 genera. The adult beetles are weakly chitinised and therefore have a very soft cuticle. Their antennae are generally long and thin and their ribbed elytra often taper to a point. The adult beetles can be found on flowers, where they eat pollen; the larvae develop in rotting wood and in dry stems of herbaceous plants. Only 9 species of the family occur in Britain.

1 *Nacerda ustulata*, 8—12 mm   (4 : 3)
Seven species of this genus inhabit central Europe, all of them resembling longhorn beetles. Only one — *N. melanura* — is found in Britain. In the summer the one shown here is fairly abundant on flowers everywhere.

2 *Chrysanthia nigricornis*, 5—8 mm   (6 : 2)
The beetles of the 2 species of this genus found in central Europe are mostly a metallic blue, green or copper colour. Their long, narrow, tapering elytra, each with 4 longitudinal ribs, are separated by a gap at the tip. The species depicted here is found everywhere in central Europe, but becomes rarer towards the south, and is rare in Britain.

3 *Ischnomera coerulea*, 6—10 mm   (7 : 2)
There are 3 species of this genus (formerly known as *Asclera*) in central Europe and the British Isles. *I. coerulea* is abundant everywhere in central Europe except at high altitudes, where it is rare.

4 *Oncomera femorata*, 8—10 mm   (10 : 5)
 This genus has 11 species in central Europe. The elytra taper off sharply towards the tip and consequently are separated by a wide gap. The females have legs of normal shape, but the males' hind femora are often abnormally thick. The larvae develop in dry stems and the upper parts of the roots of various herbaceous plants. The beetles, which are able to fly very well, are to be found chiefly in sunshine on the outskirts of woods, on flowering shrubs, meadow flowers and grasses. The species shown here occurs everywhere in central Europe and in some places is abundant, especially in the south.

5 *Oedemera lurida*, 5—7 mm   (10 : 11)
In exceptional cases this species can measure up to 9 mm. It is distributed over the whole of the palaearctic region, and in central Europe it is common everywhere.

Family Pythidae

In central Europe this family is represented by 8 genera with a total of 18 species (12 in Britain), the majority of which are placed by many authors in the family Salpingidae. The beetles' heads are sometimes produced into a short rostrum. Both the adult beetles and larvae live under the bark of deciduous and coniferous trees or in the passages of bark beetles, where they prey on other insects.

6 *Lissodema cursor*, 2.5—3.6 mm   (2 : 1)
The 2 species of this genus found in central Europe and Britain live in dry branches on various deciduous trees. The species shown here is fairly common and widely distributed in central Europe, but rarer in Britain.

7 *Salpingus castaneus*, 3—3.3 mm   (5 : 1)
This genus, which has 5 species in central Europe (3 in Britain), is termed *Sphaeriestes* in earlier works. The beetles do not have their heads produced into a rostrum. The species depicted here is fairly common everywhere in central Europe. The adult beetles are to be found under the bark of conifers, where, like the larvae, they hunt bark beetles.

8 *Vincenzellus ruficollis*, 2.5—3.5 mm   (6 : 1)
The only central European and British species of this genus is referred to as *viridipennis* in older works, with *Vincenzellus* regarded as a subgenus of *Rhinosimus*. The beetle's head bears a short rostrum. In central Europe *V. ruficollis* is fairly common everywhere and can be found under loose bark on various deciduous trees.

9 *Rhinosimus ruficollis*, 3.3—4.5 mm   (7 : 3)
Adults of the 3 central European species of this genus are notable for the long rostrum on their heads. This species is common in crumbling wood on deciduous trees attacked by bark beetles.

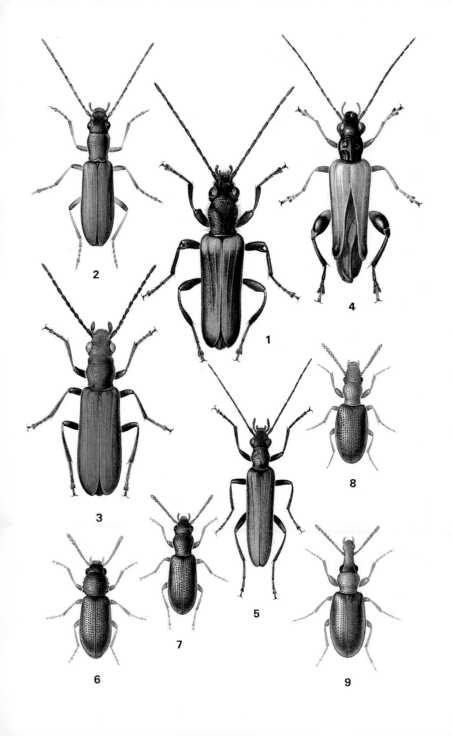

Family Pyrochroidae — cardinal beetles

Represented in central Europe and Britain by only 2 genera and 3 species, and notable mainly for the red elytra. The larvae live under the dry bark of deciduous trees, where they eat other insects or, if none are available, devour each other. The adult beetles are found on flowering shrubs or felled tree trunks.

1 *Pyrochroa coccinea* — Cardinal Beetle, 14—18 mm   (1 : 1)
P. coccinea is the larger of the 2 central European species of this genus. In central Europe it is common everywhere, but it is less common than *P. serraticornis* in Britain. The beetles are to be found chiefly on flowers at the edges of woods; the larvae live under the bark of dead trees.

2 *Schizotus pectinicornis*, 8—9 mm   (2 : 1)
In older works this genus is treated as a subgenus of *Pyrochroa*. The only species of the genus found in central Europe is widely distributed, especially in mountainous country, but is nowhere common.

Family Scraptiidae

In earlier works, this family was regarded as a subfamily of Mordellidae. The larvae of the single central European genus develop in rotting wood, while the adult beetles are to be found chiefly on trees, bushes and flowering shrubs on the outskirts of woods. Adults and larvae of the genus *Anaspis* (see p. 222) have similar habits and are referred to the Scraptiidae (rather than Mordellidae) by many authors.

3 *Scraptia fuscula*, 2.3—2.8 mm   (1 : 3)
Two species of *Scraptia* occur in central and northern Europe. *S. fuscula* is widely distributed in central Europe, although generally rare.

Family Aderidae

The 2 central European genera of this family, with 9 species, were formerly placed in the Hylophilinae (or Xylophilinae), a subfamily of Anthicidae. The various species live at the foot of old trees, in powdered wood under loose bark, under straw and hay and on shrubs and herbaceous plants.

4 *Aderus nigrinus*, 1.6—2.5 mm   (2 : 1)
This genus, termed *Hylophilus* or *Xylophilus* in earlier works, has 6 representatives in central Europe, and 3 in the British Isles. *A. nigrinus* is one of the commonest species in central Europe.

Family Anthicidae

In central Europe there are 32 species of this family (13 in Britain) belonging to 5 genera. The beetles are small and with their narrow pronotum they resemble ants. The pronotum generally tapers strongly towards the back, the legs are long and thin with only the femora relatively stout. Most of the species live in decaying vegetable matter and subsist chiefly on dead beetles.

5 *Notoxus monoceros*, 3.7—5.5 mm   (1 : 3)
The 5 species of this genus in central Europe are characterized by the presence of a long forward-projecting horn on their rounded pronotum; the sides of the horn are dentated. The species illustrated here, the only member of the genus found in Britain, is widely distributed and common everywhere in central Europe.

6 *Mecynotarsus serricornis*, 1.5—2.2 mm   (2 : 1)
The only species of this genus found in central Europe also possesses a pronotal horn. The beetles can be found in fine-grained sand beside water and in sand dunes.

7 *Formicomus pedestris*, 3.5—5 mm   (3 : 1)
This species, the only one of its genus found in central Europe, looks remarkably like an ant. It is fairly common in parts of Lower Austria and western Hungary, but is really abundant only in southern Europe.

8 *Anthicus flavipes*, 2—2.5 mm   (4 : 14)
Some 24 species of this genus have been recorded from central Europe (12 from Britain). *A. flavipes* is common, particularly in the north and east. Found on dry, sandy soil beside rivers and lakes.

9 *Anthicus floralis*   (4 : 19)
This species is virtually cosmopolitan in distribution. In central Europe it is present everywhere, usually in abundance, and it is also common in the British Isles.

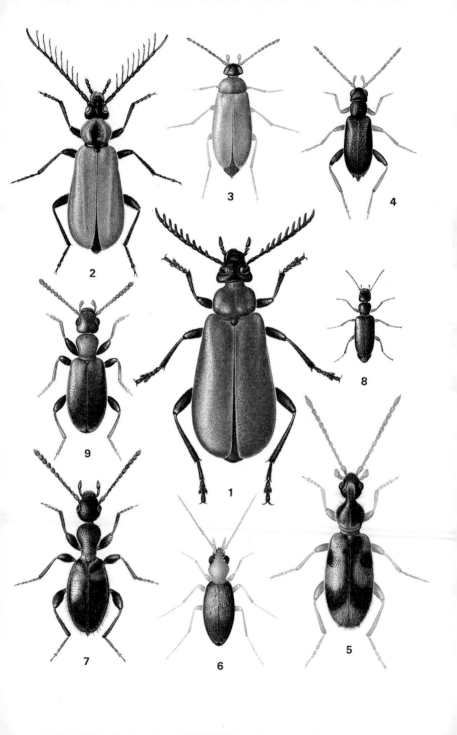

Family Meloidae — oil beetles, blister beetles

This family is represented in central Europe by 12 genera with a total of 33 species. The majority like dry, warm places and are therefore to be found mostly on southerly slopes, on dry grass, and in warm spots on the outskirts of woods. The adults live chiefly on leaves, pollen or nectar. However, the development of the immature stages is of an unusual type. The larvae of some species are parasites of burrowing bees, while others feed on grasshopper egg pods in the ground. Nine species occur in Britain, but none is common.

1 *Lytta vesicatoria* – Spanish Fly, 9–21 mm   (3 : 1)
This genus has only one representative in central Europe, which is primarily a southern European species. In central Europe, as in Britain, it is a rare and sporadic visitor. However, it can sometimes appear suddenly in considerable numbers, when it is to be found mainly on ash trees, lilac and privet. The pulverized beetles, which contain the toxin cantharidin, were once sold as an aphrodisiac.

2 *Cerocoma muehlfeldi*, 11–13 mm   (6 : 2)
The 3 species of this genus found in central Europe are noted for the curiously formed antennae of the males. The range of the species shown here extends into Austria and Hungary from the eastern part of the Mediterranean region.

3 *Meloe proscarabaeus* – Oil Beetle, 11–35 mm   (7 : 1)
In central Europe there are 13 species of this genus (7 in Britain). The females in particular have a long, stout, swollen abdomen. This species is the commonest member of the genus in central Europe, where in low-lying, flat country it can be fairly abundant. It is also the commonest meloid in Britain.

4 *Meloe rugosus* – Oil Beetle, 6–18 mm   (7 : 13)
This beetle is fairly common in central Europe in plains and the foothills of mountains. The beetles can be found in warm localities in the early spring and the autumn.

5 *Apalus muralis*, 8–10 mm   (10 : 1)
The form of its elytra renders the only species of this genus found in central Europe quite unmistakable. In central Europe it is rare and can be found only sporadically in the late summer and early autumn. In Britain it has not been seen in recent years, and may now be extinct. The larvae live parasitically with mason bees.

Family Rhipiphoridae

This family is represented by only 4 genera and 5 species in central Europe, only one of which is found in Britain. All are rare and the majority are very rare. The larvae live parasitically with various insects.

6 *Metoecus paradoxus*, 8–12 mm   (3 : 1)
The only species of the genus found in central Europe is very variably coloured. The beetles, which can be found everywhere from August to October, live underground in wasps' nests (*Vespula vulgaris*).

Family Mordellidae — tumbling flower beetles

This family is represented in central Europe by 118 species (24 in Britain) belonging to 16 genera. The abdomen of many species tapers off to a horny point. The larvae of most genera develop in galls or the stems of herbaceous plants, while those of *Anaspis* (referred by many authors to the Scraptiidae) live in rotten wood. Many species are thermophilic. The beetles are to be found mostly in flowers. They fly away quickly, are very lively and 'turn somersaults' if one tries to catch them.

7 *Mordella brachyura*, 5.8–6.5 mm   (3 : 7)
There are 8 species of this genus in central Europe, 2 of which occur in Britain. In central Europe the species illustrated is very common everywhere.

8 *Mordellistena brevicauda*, 4–5.5 mm   (11 : 29)
The 62 species of this genus currently recognised as occurring in central Europe are mostly confusingly alike. Only 7 species occur with any certainty in Britain. This one, which is very common everywhere in central Europe, is associated with cypress spurge (*Euphorbia cyparissias*).

9 *Anaspis frontalis*, 2.8–4 mm   (16 : 9)
The 29 members of this genus found in central Europe (14 in Britain) do not have a long pointed tip to their abdomen. The species shown here occurs in most parts of the palaearctic region and is the commonest member of the genus in central Europe.

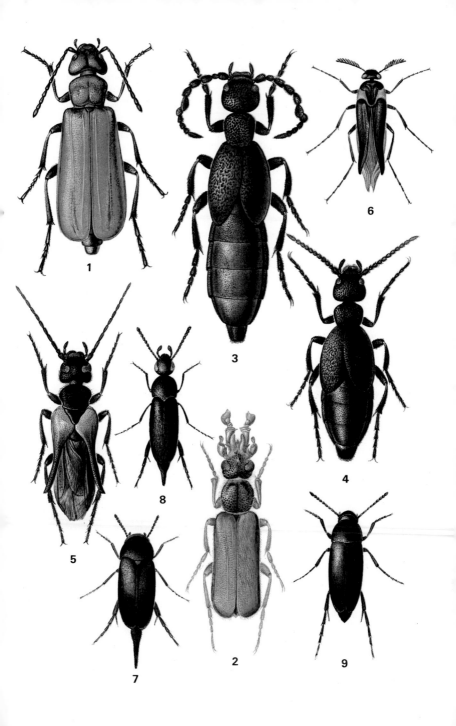

Family Melandryidae — false darkling beetles

This family, which in some works is listed under the name Serropalpidae, has 18 genera and 41 species in central Europe. The adult beetles mostly remain hidden behind loose bark on old trees, in tree fungi and in rotten wood and only a few appear in the open on flowering plants and shrubs. Eighteen species occur in the British Isles.

1 *Eustrophus dermestoides*, 4−5 mm (3 : 1)
This is the only species of the genus found in central Europe. The adult beetles can be found in reasonable numbers on fungus-infested oaks and willows, from the late spring until well into the summer.

2 *Orchesia micans, 4−5 mm (5 : 2)
There are 8 species of this genus in central Europe; 3 are found in Britain. The beetles somewhat resemble mordellids and possess a long spur at the end of their hind tibiae which enables them to somersault in a similar manner. The species shown here is widespread and fairly common in central Europe. From the spring to July, and sometimes into the autumn, the beetles can be found on fungi growing on deciduous trees or behind fungus-infested bark.

3 *Serropalpus barbatus*, 8−18 mm (12 : 1)
This boreomontane species is the only member of the genus found in central Europe. The larvae tunnel vertical passages deep in diseased or freshly felled firs and spruces. Since their development takes a long time, they can do serious damage when present in large numbers.

4 **Melandrya caraboides*, 10−16 mm (16 : 1)
The 3 members of this genus in central Europe have powerful legs. If one attempts to pick them up, they turn violent 'somersaults'. The species depicted here is fairly common in central Europe on fungus-infested, rotting wood of deciduous trees.

5 **Conopalpus testaceus*, 5−7 mm (18 : 1)
Two species of this genus live in central Europe. The one shown here is widespread in Europe (except the north) and is the only member of the genus found in Britain; in parts of central Europe it is quite abundant. The beetles are found chiefly on deciduous trees (preferably oak and beech) in old forests.

Family Lagriidae

This family, often regarded as a subfamily of Tenebrionidae, has only 3 species (2 in Britain) belonging to 2 genera in central Europe. The beetles mostly have a thick hairy coat. The larvae inhabit leaf litter, while the relatively short-lived adult beetles are to be found mainly on flowers or the foliage of various plants.

6 *Lagria hirta, 7−10 mm (1 : 1)
Of the 2 species of this genus found in central Europe the one shown here is the more widely distributed, and in the summer occurs everywhere in abundance.

Family Alleculidae

This family, often regarded as a subfamily of Tenebrionidae, has 11 genera, with a total of 33 species, in central Europe (8 species in Britain). The beetles lead varied lives, some being active at night, others liking warmth and sunshine. They are to be found in tree fungi, in fungus-infested wood, under loose bark and on flowers and trees. The larvae develop in tree fungi, in rotting wood or in the soil, among roots.

7 *Allecula morio*, 6−8 mm (1 : 2)
The 3 central European members of this genus are mostly black or brown. This one is to be found everywhere in rotting wood and in powdered wood in hollow trees, generally in comparative abundance.

8 *Prionychus ater, 12−14 mm (3 : 1)
There are 2 species of this genus in central Europe and the British Isles. The species shown here is widely distributed in central Europe. The adult beetles, which are nocturnally active, are mostly found under loose bark on deciduous trees.

9 *Gonodera luperus, 6.5−9 mm (6 : 1)
The only member of this genus in central Europe and Britain, this species is to be found everywhere in large numbers on flowering bushes at the margin of woods.

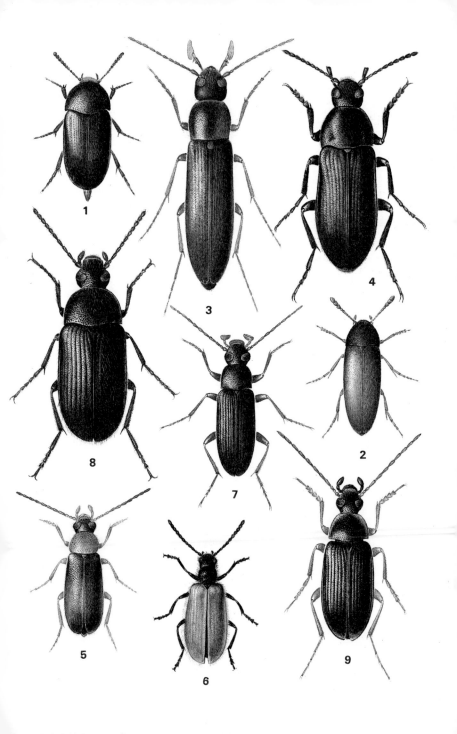

Family Tenebrionidae — darkling beetles

In central Europe this family (excluding Alleculinae and Lagriinae) is represented by 37 genera with a total of 74 species. Some 34 species are known to occur in Britain. Such a variety of form is exhibited by various tenebrionids that there is scarcely another beetle family to which some resemblance cannot be found. 'Darkling' is an appropriate name for many central European species, although not so apposite for the majority of tropical forms. Their habits are also very diverse; the various species can be found in decaying or rotten parts of plants, in tree fungi and fungus-infested wood, under loose bark, under fallen leaves, straw and hay, in cellars and cow-sheds and in birds' and mammals' nests; a number of species, several of them pests of stored products, are found in houses and other buildings.

1 *Blaps mortisaga* — Cellar or Churchyard Beetle, 20−31 mm   (3 : 2)
This genus contains 6 species which live in central Europe (3 in Britain). The beetles, the largest of central European Tenebrionidae, live in dark places, usually under boards and stones in the vicinity of houses. The species shown here is to be found in old cellars, sheds and barns, often in large numbers.

2 *Phylan gibbus*, 7.5−8.5 mm   (5 : 1)
This species, the only member of the genus occurring in central and northern Europe, is found only on the coast. It inhabits sandy shores on the coast of western Europe and the southern part of northern Europe; on the coasts of the North Sea and the Baltic the beetles are fairly common.

3 *Pedinus femoralis*, 7−9 mm   (6 : 3)
There are 2 species of this genus in central Europe. They have curious eyes, which are completely divided into an upper and a lower half. *P. femoralis* is a characteristic species of dry, warm, grassy 'steppes'. The beetles live on roots, and in years of abundance (chiefly in the east) they can do considerable damage to crops.

4 *Opatrum sabulosum*, 7−10 mm   (8 : 2)
In central Europe this genus is represented by 2 species. The beetles are mostly to be found under stones or at the roots of plants on dry, sandy or waste ground. The species depicted here is common everywhere in central Europe. It is the only species of the genus found in Britain, where it is of very local occurrence.

5 *Melanimon tibialis*, 3−4 mm   (9 : 1)
This single species of *Melanimon* found in central Europe has a similar form to *Opatrum*, but the first pair of tibiae are much wider and better adapted for digging. In central Europe this is a common species in sandy localities, while in Britain it is mostly found in sandy places on the coast.

6 *Phaleria cadaverina*, 5.5−7 mm   (12 : 1)
The only species of this genus found in central and northern Europe has rather variable but generally very light colouring for a darkling beetle. It is found only in the vicinity of salt water, on the Atlantic and North Sea coasts and on the west coast of the Baltic. The beetles occur in sandy localities and live mainly on carrion, but can also be found in seaweed and occasionally bury themselves deep in sand. In their central European haunts they are fairly abundant.

7 *Crypticus quisquilius*, 4.5−6 mm   (13 : 1)
This is the only species of the genus in central and northern Europe. The oval-bodied beetles somewhat resemble ground beetles of the genera *Amara* and *Harpalus* and can also run very fast. The hard-bodied, cylindrical larvae are reminiscent of elaterid larvae (wire-worms). Both the beetles and the larvae live in dry, sandy places under plants and stones. In central Europe the beetles are generally abundant. In Britain the species is found mostly in sandy coastal localities.

8 *Eledona agricola*, 2.2−2.5 mm   (16 : 1)
The single central and northern European species of *Eledona* has a very characteristic body structure. The tiny beetles live in tree fungi (chiefly *Polyporus sulphureus*) on various deciduous trees, especially willows. They are not rare in central Europe and, when found, usually occur in large numbers.

9 *Diaperis boleti*, 6−8 mm   (17 : 1)
Likewise the only member of its genus found in central Europe, this beetle has a convex, bluntly ovoid body. It lives in various tree fungi, and is to be found everywhere in central Europe, where it is generally quite common. In Britain it is one of the rarest of Tenebrionidae.

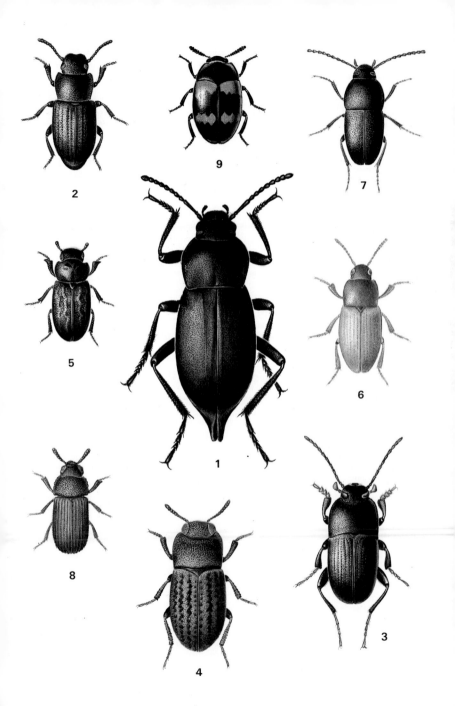

2

9

7

5

1

6

8

4

3

1 *Scaphidema metallicum, 4−5 mm   (19 : 1)
This is the only species of *Scaphidema* found in central and northern Europe. The larvae develop in tree fungi; the adult beetles are generally common and may be found in and on the branches of fungus-infested and rotting deciduous trees.

2 *Alphitophagus bifasciatus, 2.2−2.5 mm   (21 : 1)
The single central European species of this genus is virtually cosmopolitan in distribution. In central Europe the species may be found in the open in old, rotten deciduous trees or under mouldy, decaying vegetation, though not in large numbers. Its wide distribution is due to the fact that it is able to exploit a variety of stored products. The larvae live in damp cornflour, mouldy grain or chaff, and *A. bifasciatus* is therefore a regular inhabitant of cargoes; in central Europe it is also quite common in stables and cow-sheds.

3 *Corticeus linearis, 2.5−2.8 mm   (23 : 9)
This genus, often referred to as *Hypophloeus,* is represented by 10 species in central Europe (4 in Britain). The adult beetles and larvae live under the bark of trees attacked by bark beetles. This species is widely distributed in central Europe, but is only sporadically plentiful. The beetles can be found in pine branches attacked by *Pityogenes* species, particularly near the top.

4 *Palorus ratzeburgi, 2.8−3 mm   (24 : 3)
Three species of this genus are known to occur in central Europe; they live partly in the open, but chiefly in large numbers in stored flour and cereals, where they can do considerable damage. The beetles can sometimes be found under the crumbling bark of old deciduous trees, particularly beeches. In central Europe this species is strictly synanthropic and lives in stored grain, flour and bran.

5 *Tribolium confusum, 3.5 mm   (25 : 4)
Four species of this genus occur in central Europe. Single beetles are occasionally found in the open, e. g. in powdered wood in old hollow trees, but normally they are confined to stores of grain or flour. They seldom attack intact grains of corn, but are secondary pests on crushed or otherwise damaged seeds. They may be serious pests of stored flour. The species shown here is widespread and common everywhere in central Europe.

6 *Alphitobius diaperinus, 5.5−6 mm   (26 : 1)
In central Europe there are 2 species of this genus. *A. diaperinus,* known as *A. piceus* in earlier works, is the commoner of the 2 species. The beetles are found only in the company of man, in stored flour and other cereal products. They cannot be regarded as primary pests, as they generally infest only mouldy or otherwise damaged goods.

7 *Gnatocerus cornutus, 3.5−4 mm   (28 : 1)
This beetle − the only member of the genus found regularly in central Europe − has a highly characteristic head. It is a frequent pest in flour-mills, grain stores and bakeries. Both adult beetles and larvae live on cereals and cereal products.

8 *Tenebrio molitor − Meal-worm, 12−18 mm   (33 : 3)
Of the 3 *Tenebrio* species found in central Europe (2 in Britain), this is the commonest. It is not uncommon in the open, where it can be found in old hollow trees and birds' nests. Otherwise it is a pest of cereals, flour and flour products. Single individuals found in the house are likely to have flown in through the window, since in the evening they are attracted by lights. If present in numbers, however, their breeding-place is probably in the house and should be tracked down. The larvae, which are easy to rear, are bred as food for various small animals.

9 Stenomax aeneus, 12−16 mm   (39 : 1)
There are 2 species of this genus in central Europe. In earlier works they were included in the genus *Helops* or *Cylindronotus* and the species depicted here is sometimes also named *S. incurvus.* It is to be found mainly in the southern part of central Europe and is absent in northern Germany. The beetles are sometimes quite plentiful on fungus-infested branches or under loose bark on deciduous trees.

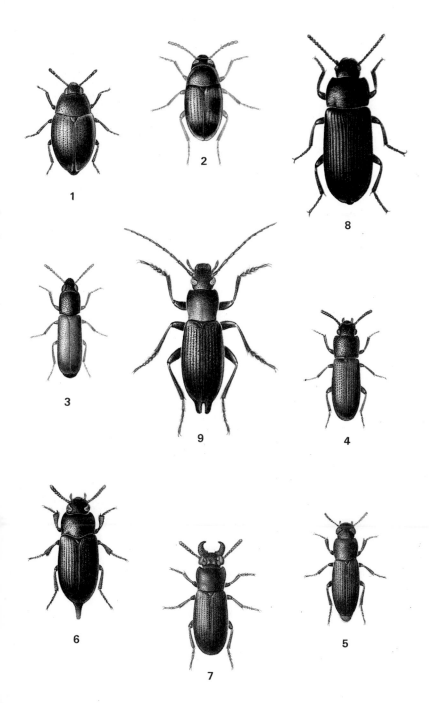

Family Scarabaeidae — chafers, dung beetles, etc.

This family is represented in central Europe by 49 genera with a total of 218 species, 89 of which occur in the British Isles. The distal 3 segments of the beetles' antennae are widened on one side to form a characteristic lamellate club. The beetles mostly have short, powerful legs; the first pair of tibiae are toothed along the outer margin and are often adapted for digging. The larvae (grubs) develop in soil where they live on roots, or are found in dung and other decaying organic matter.

1 *Trox sabulosus, 8—9 mm (1 : 2)

The beetles of the 7 central European species of this genus, often placed in a separate family — Trogidae — can make chirping sounds by rubbing their abdomen on their elytra. They live on dry materials of animal origin such as skins, hooves, feathers, bones, cadavers, etc. The species shown here is fairly common in sandy regions.

2 *Trox scaber, 5—8 mm (1 : 4)

This species is distributed over practically the whole globe. In central Europe it is fairly common at low altitudes, but is encountered only sporadically in the Alps. This species lives and develops in birds' nests.

3 *Odontaeus armiger, 7—10 mm (3 : 1)

The only member of the genus in central and northern Europe, this beetle has a short, convex body. On their head the males have a long, narrow horn which is movable at its base; the females have a short transverse ridge and 2 bosses. In central Europe the beetles, which are associated with truffles, are generally uncommon. In Britain the species is distinctly rare.

4 *Typhaeus typhoeus — male, 15—24 mm (5 : 1)

In the only central and northern European member of this genus the difference between the sexes is particularly great. The larger the male beetle, the more pronounced are its male characters; very small beetles have only small horns. This species can be found on sandy heaths and in open pinewoods, but only sporadically and in small numbers.

5 *Typhaeus typhoeus — female

Some 1—1.5 mm deep in the ground the beetles dig a gallery with several side-tunnels leading from it. In these they place dung; rabbit droppings are preferred, but other kinds of dung may also be used. The females do not lay the eggs on the actual dung, but some way away in the soil, so that the larvae have to make an effort to reach their first meal.

6 *Geotrupes stercorarius — Dor Beetle, 16—25 mm (6 : 4)

Seven species of this genus, often placed, with Odontaeus and Typhaeus, in the separate family Geotrupidae, live in central Europe. The beetles can produce chirping sounds by rubbing their hind coxae together. They swarm on still evenings, almost skimming the ground with a deep hum. Directly below a pile of dung, they excavate burrows in the ground, and carry dung into a chamber widened at the end where they lay their eggs. The species depicted here often occurs in large numbers in central Europe, but not in mountainous regions, and is fairly common in Britain.

7 *Geotrupes stercorosus — Dor Beetle, 12—19 mm (6 : 5)

This species — also termed G. silvaticus in older works — is generally an inhabitant of woodlands. The beetles are generally abundant in central Europe. They breed in the spring and rear their brood on dung, decaying fungi or other decomposing plant material.

8 Geotrupes vernalis — Dor Beetle, 12—20 mm (6 : 7)

This species has very variable colouring. In central Europe the beetles occur everywhere, generally in large numbers, although lately they have become rarer. The brood galleries are 7—8 cm deep and slope into the ground; at the bottom there are side-tunnels supplied with dung. The insect's development takes about 10 months.

9 Lethrus apterus, 15—24 mm (7 : 1)

With its large head and pronotum, this beetle — the only member of the genus in central Europe — is quite unmistakable. The beetles live on dry, sandy ground in the south-eastern part of central Europe. They carry fresh leaves into their passages, which are about 40 cm deep, and when fermented the leaves provide food for both the beetles and the larvae. The beetles also bite off young vine leaves, however, and are thus a pest in vineyards.

1 *Gymnopleurus mopsus,* 10−15 mm (9 : 2)

Three species of *Gymnopleurus* occur in central Europe. All three have a generally southern distribution and the genus is not represented in northern Europe. The wide, rather flat-bodied beetles resemble the Sacred Scarab, a member of the genus *Scarabaeus,* which is not represented in central Europe. Like the other 2 species, *G. mopsus* constructs small balls out of cow dung and buries them for its brood. In hot sunshine the beetles are very restless; they fly very fast with their elytra closed.

2 *Sisyphus schaefferi,* 6.5−12 mm (10 : 1)

The single central European species of *Sisyphus* may be recognised by its long, slender middle and hind legs; it also flies with its elytra closed. It occurs locally in places with chalky soil and is comparatively rare. It makes balls chiefly out of sheep dung, which it rolls away and buries; each ball is placed in a separate brood chamber.

3 *Oniticellus fulvus,* 7−12 mm (11 : 1)

The 2 members of this genus found in central Europe resemble the beetles of the larger genus *Onthophagus,* but have a longer body with more parallel sides. Neither species occurs in Britain. The species shown here is the commoner of the two, but even so is generally very rare. The beetles live in horse and cow dung.

4 *Copris lunaris* − Horned Dung Beetle, 16−24 mm (12 : 1)

The male of the only species of the genus found in central and northern Europe can easily be recognised by the long, sharp horn on its head and the shape of its pronotum. The female has a short horn on its head and a raised boss in the middle of its pronotum. In central Europe this species is commoner in the south and becomes steadily rarer towards the north. The beetles are to be found chiefly under fresh cow dung (less often under horse or sheep dung). The male and female excavate the brood chambers together and construct 7 or 8 and sometimes more dung masses for the brood; the female tends both the eggs and the larvae.

5 *Caccobius schreberi,* 4−7 mm (13 : 1)

This genus is represented by several species in southern Europe and the Mediterranean area, but only one of them extends at all far into central Europe. In central Europe *C. schreberi* is confined to warm localities. It is commoner in the east, but is known to occur as far west as the upper Rhine and the Main basin. The beetles can be found in horse manure and cow dung from April to August.

6 *Onthophagus taurus* − male, 6−11.5 mm (14 : 3)

There are 19 species of this genus in central Europe, six of which are also found in Britain. The main difference in the appearance of the sexes is that the males generally have a horned or embossed head-plate (clypeus), while the head of females bears only 1 or 2 transverse ridges. Pairs of beetles combine to dig branching galleries ending in brood chambers, in each of which they place dung on which the female lays an egg. Most of the work is done by the female, assisted by the male. This species is fairly common in central Europe south of the Main; further north it is rare and of sporadic occurrence.

7 *Onthophagus nuchicornis,* 6−9 mm (14 : 14)

This species is common in the north and east of central Europe and rarer in the west and south-west. The beetles have a preference for cow dung.

8 *Ochodaeus chrysomeloides,* 4−6 mm (16 : 1)

This is the only member of the genus found in central Europe. The beetles, which swarm in the evening, are commoner in the east. They live underground on fungi on warm, grassy hillsides, in riverside meadows and on the outskirts of woods; sometimes they are fairly abundant.

9 *Aegialia arenaria,* 5−6 mm (17 : 1)

The 3 central and northern European members of this genus resemble *Aphodius* species. The one depicted here lives on sandy coastlines in western and northern Europe. On the shores of the North Sea and the Baltic it is not uncommon and in some places it is actually abundant. The beetles are most easily found in sand dunes, crawling across bare patches of loose sand or at the roots of grasses.

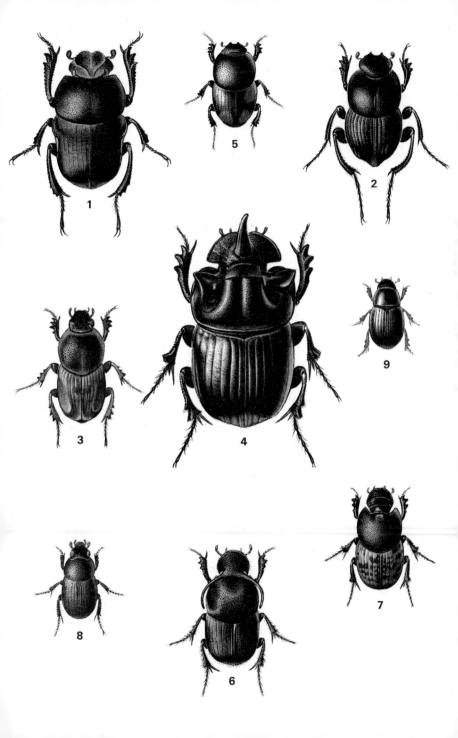

1 *Oxyomus sylvestris, 2.5–3.7 mm (18 : 1)
The single central and northern European species of this genus resembles an *Aphodius,* but its pronotum has a weak median groove and its elytra have very broad longitudinal furrows separated by narrow intervals. This species is common everywhere in central Europe. The beetles live in decomposing vegetable matter, compost, stable straw and dung, especially rabbit dung. Occasionally they are to be found in decaying mushrooms and tree fungi.

2 *Colobopterus erraticus, 6–7.5 mm (19 : 1)
Sometimes regarded as a subgenus of *Aphodius,* the genus *Colobopterus* is represented by 5 species in central Europe (4 in Britain). Its species have similar habits to those of *Aphodius* but may be distinguished from the latter by their particularly large scutellum. The species shown here occurs in all parts of the holarctic region except the north. In central Europe the beetles are generally fairly common in cow and horse dung; in the Alps they can be found at altitudes of up to 1,700 m.

3 *Colobopterus fossor, 10–13 mm (19 : 4)
This species is most commonly a uniform shining black but may also have reddish brown elytra. It is widely distributed in the northern parts of the palaearctic region and North America. It occurs everywhere in central Europe, but especially in wooded and mountainous regions, and is common in the British Isles. The beetles live mainly on fresh cow dung.

4 *Aphodius prodromus, 4–7 mm (19 : 44)
With 80 species this is by far the largest genus of Scarabaeidae in central Europe; 41 species occur in the British Isles. The small to medium-sized beetles have a characteristic general appearance and, except for short hairs on parts of the elytra in some species, are usually virtually devoid of pubescence above. In some instances related species are difficult to distinguish without recourse to examination of the male genitalia. Most of the species live in and feed on dung, although a few are to be found in other decaying organic matter. The adults do not excavate burrows for their brood, but lay the eggs directly in the substrate of their choice. This species occurs throughout the major part of the holarctic region and is common everywhere in central Europe and the British Isles. The beetles prefer horse manure, but can be found in all kinds of dung and rotting vegetation.

5 *Aphodius merdarius, 4.5 mm (19 : 55)
This species flies early in the spring. In central Europe it is to be found everywhere, but very sporadically, and is common only locally. The beetles live chiefly in fresh cow dung, but also frequent horse manure and human excrement. They are sometimes attracted to artificial light.

6 *Aphodius fimetarius, 5–8 mm (19 : 60)
This species with red elytra inhabits practically the whole of the holarctic region and is one of the commonest species of the genus in central Europe and the British Isles. It is even to be found at high altitudes in Switzerland and Bavaria, where it forms a special subspecies, *monticola,* which is more heavily and closely punctured than the type form.

7 *Aphodius ater, 3–5.5 mm (19 : 66)
Although usually black the elytra and pronotum of this species may sometimes be reddish brown. It is fairly common in pastures, in sheep and cow dung.

8 *Aphodius rufus, 5–7 mm (19 : 76)
This is another species with very variable colouring. It is common everywhere in central Europe, where the beetles can be found chiefly in cow and horse dung, but are also found in the dung of sheep.

9 *Aphodius sus, 4–5 mm (20 : 4)
Sometimes regarded as a distinct genus, the subgenus *Heptaulacus* to which this species belongs may be distinguished from other *Aphodius* by the smaller number of elytral striae – 7 to 9 rather than 10. Otherwise they resemble typical *Aphodius* and have similar habits. This is the most widely distributed member of the subgenus in central Europe, but it occurs sporadically and is hard to find, despite the fact that it is not confined to one type of habitat or one type of dung.

234

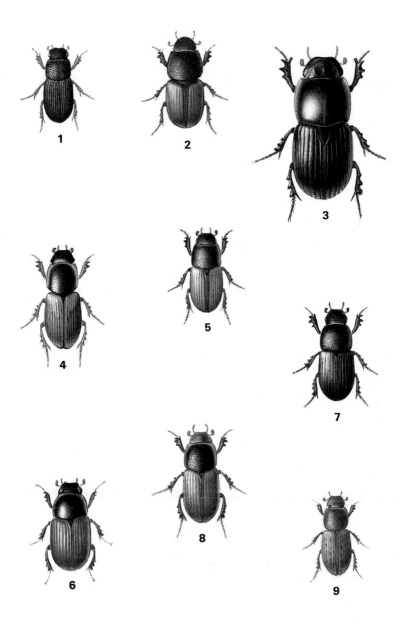

1 *Psammodius asper*, 2.6−4 mm   (21 : 2)
The adult beetles of the 2 species of this genus found in central Europe have a domed body which widens towards the rear. The pronotum bears a series of transverse ridges and grooves. The species shown here occurs locally on warm, sandy ground, but is not abundant.

2 **Rhyssemus germanus*, 2.5−3.5 mm   (22 : 1)
The 2 central European species of this genus resemble those of the preceding one, but have a more elongate body. This species is found only here and there in central Europe and is always more or less rare; it is especially rare in Britain. The beetles live on grass roots, under decaying leaf rosettes, under stones in rotting vegetation, in compost, under halophilic plants on salty ground and in mole, fox and rodent burrows.

3 **Diastictus vulneratus*, 2.8−3.5 mm   (23 : 1)
Of the 2 species of this genus found in central Europe, this one is the most widely distributed, although generally rare. The beetles are to be found together with the ant *Formica fusca* on sandy ground, on sandy river banks, in decaying vegetation and in moss. In Britain the species is known only from the Breckland area of West Suffolk.

4 **Pleurophorus caesus*, 2.5−3.2 mm   (24 : 1)
The 2 members of this genus which occur in central Europe have distributions which are centred on the Black Sea and Mediterranean but extend, in places, further to the north and west. The species illustrated here, which can still be quite common in parts of upper Austria, is elsewhere sporadic and rare and lives only where it is warm; it is extremely rare in Britain. The beetles are to be found chiefly under dry cow dung and decaying vegetation.

5 **Serica brunnea*, 8−10 mm   (25 : 1)
The only species of *Serica* found in central and northern Europe resembles a small cockchafer, but is more parallel-sided. It is fairly common and sometimes abundant in hilly and mountainous country. The beetles are active in the evening and at night and are attracted to artificial light. In the daytime they can be found hiding under moss and stones. The development of the larvae takes 2 years; they live on roots and can do damage in tree nurseries.

6 *Maladera holoserica*, 6−9 mm   (26 : 1)
The single central European species of this genus closely resembles the preceding species, but is usually darker. The beetles are to be found in dry, sandy areas; they avoid the region along the Atlantic coast and are absent on chalky and clayey ground. In general they are found singly and infrequently.

7 **Omaloplia ruricola*, 5−7.5 mm   (27 : 3)
There are 3 species of this genus in central Europe. The beetles swarm low over grasses and herbaceous plants in the daytime. This species, the only member of the genus found in Britain, occurs on dry, warm hillsides and in some places is quite common. The beetles fly in the morning and the middle of the day in June and July (occasionally also in May and in August and September).

8 *Miltotrogus aequinoctialis*, 13−18 mm   (29 : 2)
Four species of this genus occur in central Europe, but none of them are found in the British Isles or other parts of northern Europe. The range of this species extends to the south-eastern part of central Europe, and isolated finds have been reported in south-east Germany. The beetles appear at the beginning of April and fly during the afternoon. Their development takes 3 years.

9 **Amphimallon solstitiale* − Summer Chafer, 14−18 mm   (30 : 1)
Several species related to the Common Cockchafer are known as 'Summer Chafers', especially the 7 native central European species of this genus, which is often regarded as a subgenus of *Rhizotrogus*. Like the Common Cockchafer, the species illustrated here, the only member of the genus found in Britain, flies after dusk. The beetles are generally abundant, especially on loose soil, but are usually absent in mountains. Their development takes 2 years.

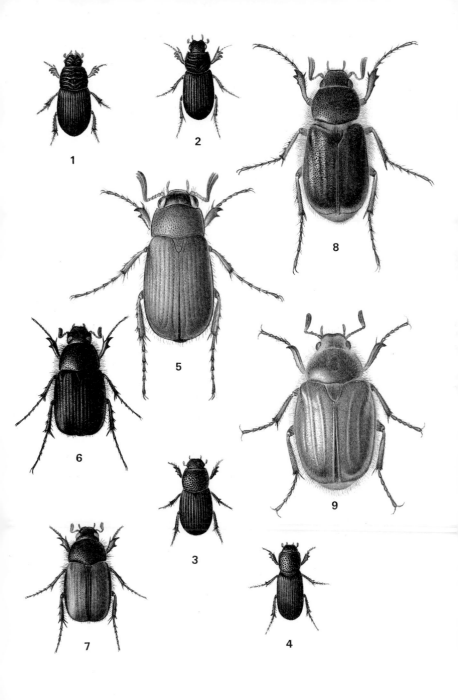

1 *Rhizotrogus aestivus,* 12−18 mm (31 : 3)
There are 4 species of this genus in central Europe, none of which occur in the British Isles. The grubs live in soil on uncultivated, sandy, grassy ground or in fallow fields. This species is widely distributed in central Europe, but is absent in the plains. The beetles can be locally abundant on dry, warm hillsides, especially on chalky ground. They fly after dusk.

2 *Anoxia villosa,* 23−29 mm (32 : 3)
The genus *Anoxia* is native to southern Europe and the Near East, where its species take the place of the May-beetle; 2 species extend into central Europe. The one shown here has been recorded the farthest north, in Hanau and Kehl (Germany) on the rivers Main and Rhine respectively. The beetles, which are to be found in sandy regions, fly after dusk. In central Europe they are rare, but in their native haunts they can do damage to fruit-trees and vines by eating the leaves.

3 *Melolontha hippocastani,* 22−26 mm (33 : 1)
The mame 'May-beetle' is applied to 3 central European species, one of which, *Melolontha pectoralis* (not found in Britain), is a very rare relic living in the south-west of central Europe. The grubs of the species shown here, whose development takes 3−4 years, eat roots and in years of particular abundance can do serious damage. The beetles eat the leaves of deciduous trees. The distinctive feature of this species is the nodose swelling at the end of its pygidium. In central Europe it lives chiefly on sandy heaths and in woods, while in Britain it is confined to the north.

4 *Melolontha melolontha* − Common Cockchafer or May-beetle, 20−30 mm (33 : 2)
The pygidium of this species is produced to a narrow, pointed process. In earlier works the beetle is referred to as *M. vulgaris.* It is the commonest member of the genus in central Europe and is absent only at altitudes of over 1,000 m.

5 *Polyphylla fullo* − Walker, 25−36 mm (34 : 1)
The only species of this genus found in central Europe is conspicuous and unmistakable as regards both its colouring and size. It is widely distributed in central Europe and the adjacent parts of southern Europe, but is not to be found everywhere and is generally rare. The beetles fly in the evening. They eat beetle grubs and their development takes 3−4 years.

6 *Euchlora dubia,* 12−15 mm (35 : 1)
The 2 members of this genus in central Europe can be found from May to August, according to the weather. This species, the only member of the genus occurring in Britain, is to be found everywhere in central Europe, especially in sandy regions, where it is often fairly common. In the south the beetles live chiefly on willows, in the north on birches, but they also live on other plants. The larvae eat roots and their development takes 2 years.

7 *Mimela aurata,* 16−22 mm (36 : 1)
The only species of *Mimela* found in central Europe is actually a native of southern Europe, but its range extends to the Alps and in some parts of Austria it is fairly common.

8 *Phyllopertha horticola* − Garden Chafer, 8.5−11 mm (37 : 1)
Likewise the only member of the genus in central Europe, this species is very common there. The beetles eat leaves and can do damage to fruit-trees and rose-bushes. The larvae live on grass, cereal and clover roots, but they are small and do little damage.

9 *Anisoplia villosa,* 10−11 mm (39 : 2)
The 10 species of this genus known to occur in central Europe live mainly on the anthers of cereal and grass flowers, while the grubs live in the ground and have a liking for grass roots. None of them are found in the British Isles or other parts of northern Europe. The beetles occur chiefly on warm, dry slopes with loose or sandy soil and can be found from the end of May to the middle of August on grasses and ears of corn.

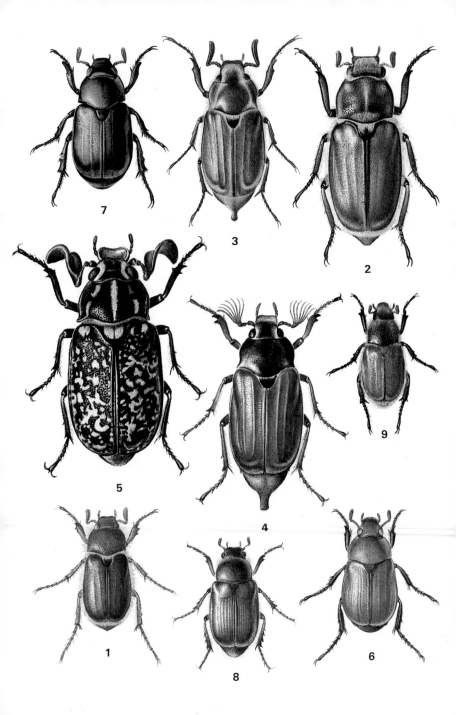

1 *Hoplia praticola,* 9−11 mm   (40 : 1)
This genus is represented by 11 species in central Europe. The beetles' short and generally flat-topped body
is partly or completely covered with coloured or metallic scales, sometimes interspersed with long hairs.
They also have very strong legs (especially the male's hind tibiae). The species depicted here is rare and
sporadic in central Europe and appears only locally and now and again in any abundance; in the north it is
absent altogether. The beetles can be found on May and June mornings on various shrubs or in grass; the
females are seldom seen, since after pairing they immediately retire underground.

2 *Hoplia philanthus,* 8−9 mm   (40 : 2)
In central Europe this species, the only *Hoplia* found in Britain, occurs chiefly in hilly or mountainous
country, where it can be found in meadows and on fruit-trees, young pines, blades of corn and flowers. The
beetles swarm in the afternoon from June to August; their development takes 2−3 years. They are
commoner in the west.

3 *Hoplia farinosa,* 9−11 mm   (40 : 5)
This species is covered with yellow, green or brown scales. It occurs in mountains and foothills in the
south-east of central Europe, and in Germany from Bavaria to Baden. It is generally common to very
common and can be found on flowers on the outskirts of woods and in meadows. The beetles fly from May to
July.

4 *Oryctes nasicornis* − European Rhinoceros Beetle, 20−40 mm   (41 : 1)
The only member of the genus found in central Europe is actually a native of southern Europe. It used to be
found chiefly in oak tanning bark, where the larvae found the necessary warmth, but the increasing use of
chemicals in tanneries caused a steady decline in its population. The beetles found compost, mouldy
sawdust, straw and the like to be a satisfactory substitute, however, and they now occur quite often, and
sometimes in large numbers, in central Europe, where they fly in June and July. The females have a smaller
horn on their head than the males.

5 *Pentodon idiota,* 14−22 mm   (42 : 2)
Like the preceding species, this beetle, which is also the only member of its genus found in central Europe,
can make shrill sounds by means of a stridulatory device on its propygidium. It is rare and occurs sporadically
in Slovakia and lower Austria.

6 *Tropinota hirta,* 8−11 mm   (43 : 1)
This genus belongs to the subfamily Cetoniinae (or rose chafers), which keep their elytra closed during
flight. The beetles fly in the sunshine or sit on flowers. This is a thermophilic species and in central Europe is
to be found mostly on dry, warm hillsides; it is absent from regions with an Atlantic climate. The beetles can
be found in May and June, eating pollen. The larvae live in the soil, where they consume humus and decaying
vegetable matter.

7 *Oxythyrea funesta,* 8−12 mm   (44 : 1)
This single species of this genus found in central Europe, where it is confined to the south, is very
characteristically coloured. The beetles are to be found sporadically, in warm places, from May to June,
sitting on flowers and blossoming shrubs.

8 *Cetonia aurata* − Rose Chafer, 14−20 mm   (45 : 1)
This species is very variably coloured; its back may be green or gold, dark or variegated, and even its white
markings are variable. The larvae develop in rotten wood and humus; the beetles fly from April to
September and are commonly found sitting in flowers. Towards the north the species becomes rarer.

9 *Cetonia lugubris,* 19−25 mm   (46 : 1)
This species, sometimes placed in the separate genus *Liocola,* closely resembles other rose chafers in
appearance and habits; in earlier works it is referred to as *C. marmorata.* It is local in occurrence and is not
common. The larvae develop in the wood-mould of old deciduous trees; adult beetles can be seen, usually
singly, in June and July on escaping sap and on flowers.

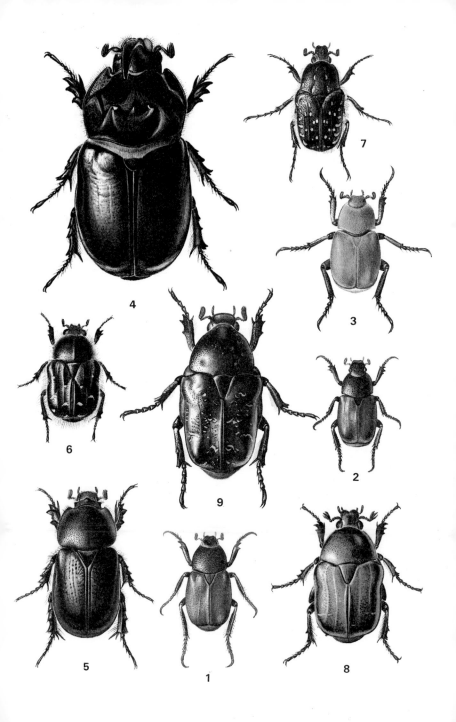

1 *Cetonia morio,* 17−20 mm (47 : 2)
This is one of 7 species belonging to the subgenus *Potosia* found in central Europe. All of them resemble the Rose Chafer, but may be distinguished by the form of the processes on the under side of their body. The species shown here is a native of south-western Europe and north Africa, but occurs as far north as Alsace in France. In June and July the beetles can often be found under stones, but also on ripe fruit.

2 *Cetonia aeruginosa,* 22−28 mm (47 : 3)
This, the largest member of the subgenus *Potosia,* is to be found only in the continental part of central Europe; it avoids the Atlantic coast and is thus commoner in the east than in the west. The larvae live in the wood-mould of old oaks, mainly in the crown and not near the bottom; their development takes 3 years. The beetles are to be found in May and June on flowering shrubs on the sunny side of woods.

3 **Cetonia cuprea,* 14−23 mm (47 : 6)
This is the commonest and most widespread species of the subgenus *Potosia* in central Europe. It is distributed from the north of Norway to the Mediterranean region, although in Britain it is absent from the south. From May to July the beetles are to be found everywhere in comparative abundance on flowers, escaping sap and ripe fruit; the larvae inhabit ants' nests, where they live on pieces of decaying wood.

4 *Valgus hemipterus* − male, 6−10 mm (48 : 1)
This beetle, the only member of the genus found in central Europe, has short elytra which leave part of its abdomen uncovered. It occurs in southern and central Europe, western north Africa, the Caucasus and Asia Minor and occurs as far north as Holland. The larvae develop for one year in the rotting wood of dead deciduous trees. The beetles hibernate in the pupal chamber and appear in May and June on flowers.

5 *Valgus hemipterus* − female
With its long, pointed pygidium, the female of this species is unmistakable.

6 *Osmoderma eremita* − Hermit Beetle, 24−30 mm (49 : 1)
The form, size and colouring of the only species of this genus found in central Europe make it unmistakable; it is also supposed to smell like Russian leather. It occurs in the southern part of northern Europe and in southern and central Europe, where the beetles can be found on flowers from June to September, but only in some places and somewhat rarely. The larvae live in the wood-mould of old deciduous trees and their development takes several years.

7 **Gnorimus nobilis,* 15−18 mm (50 : 1)
The 2 central European members of this genus strongly resemble rose chafers. The one shown here has very variable colouring. It occurs in the south of northern Europe, including southern England, and in central and southern Europe. In central Europe it is mostly found sporadically and rarely, but towards the south it becomes more frequent. The beetles, which fly from May to July, can be seen on flowers; the larvae live in the wood-mould of hollow trees.

8 **Gnorimus variabilis,* 17−22 mm (50 : 2)
In some works this species is also referred to as *G. octopunctatus,* a reference to its elytral markings, although the extent of the white spots varies markedly. The species has a similar life-history to *G. nobilis* and the ranges of the two species are also similar. The incidence of this species in central Europe is very sporadic and in the west and the north especially it is very rare. In Britain it has been found at only one locality: Windsor Forest.

9 **Trichius fasciatus,* 9−12 mm (51 : 1)
Of the 3 members of this genus found in central Europe, the one shown here is the most widely distributed and the most abundant. Except for the brightly and very variably coloured elytra, the beetle's back is covered with long, woolly hairs. In central Europe this species occurs in mountainous regions and the surrounding country and is generally fairly common, while in Britain it is confined to the north and west. The beetles can be found on flowers in June and July; the larvae develop in rotting hardwood.

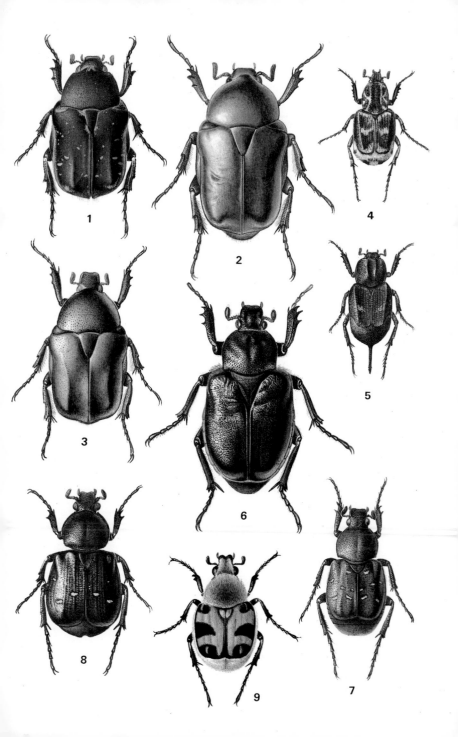

Family Lucanidae — stag beetles

In central Europe this family is represented by 7 species belonging to 6 genera, all of which are depicted here. The moderately large to large beetles have geniculate (elbowed) antennae, whose first segment is especially long and thin. As with scarabaeids, the more distal segments are frequently widened fan-wise on one side. The jaws are often exaggeratedly enlarged, especially in the males. Development from egg to beetle takes several years; the larvae pupate in a hard case made of particles of wood and earth.

1 *Lucanus cervus* — Stag Beetle, male, 25–75 mm   (1 : 1)
The male of the only species of *Lucanus* found in central Europe is the largest and most imposing beetle in the native fauna. In large specimens the antler-like mandibles are disproportionately huge, while small males have only short, spiked mandibles. The latter were once considered to be a separate species (*capreolus*). The larvae live in the root-stocks of deciduous tree stumps, less often of conifer stumps; their development takes at least 5 years. The Stag Beetle primarily inhabits oakwoods, where the adults like to lick escaping sap. It flies after dusk. Today, it has become rare in many parts of its range but is still locally common in southern England, including the London area.

2 *Lucanus cervus* — female, 30–45 mm
The female's mandibles are normally developed and their bite can be quite painful.

3 *Dorcus parallelipipedus* — Lesser Stag Beetle, male, 19–32 mm   (2 : 1)
The males have a particularly large, wide head. This is the only member of the genus in central and northern Europe, where it is widespread and often abundant. The larvae develop in the decayed, crumbling wood of deciduous trees.

4 *Platycerus caraboides*, 9–13 mm   (3 : 2)
This genus — also named *Systenocerus* in older works — has 2 species in central Europe. Since both species have a variably coloured back (mostly a metallic blue or green), they are not easy to distinguish and are consequently frequently mistaken for one another. *P. caraboides* is generally smaller, shorter and less robust than its fellow species. In central Europe the beetles are commonest at low altitudes and in flat country. The species has occurred in Britain in the past but is now extinct.

5 *Platycerus caprea*, 13–15 mm   (3 : 1)
In earlier works, this species, rather confusingly, is to be found under the name *P. caraboides*. The beetles, which are larger, more robust and longer than the preceding species, occur in the middle and southern part of central Europe, chiefly in the mountains.

6 *Ceruchus chrysomelinus*, 11–16 mm   (4 : 1)
The males of the only member of this genus found in central Europe have long mandibles. This species occurs in the southern part of central Europe, but is not common. The larvae, whose development takes 2–3 years, live in the wood of deciduous and coniferous trees with red rot.

7 *Sinodendron cylindricum* — male, 12–16 mm   (5 : 1)
The characteristic features of the only member of the genus in central Europe are its cylindrical body and the horn on its head. It is a local species which is rare and hard to find. Its development takes place in rotten, crumbling hardwoods (chiefly beech) and takes 3 years. The beetle hibernates in the pupal chamber before finally emerging.

8 *Sinodendron cylindricum* — female, 12–16 mm
The horn on the female's head is shorter and less robust than that of the male, and the depressions in its pronotum are also shallower.

9 *Aesalus scarabaeoides*, 5–7 mm   (6 : 1)
The single member of this genus found in central Europe differs from all other stag beetles in respect of its thickset, *Trox*-like scarabaeoid form. The beetles are rare; they occur in woods in low-lying country and the foothills of mountains. The larvae live in rotten oak stumps (less often beech). Their development probably takes 3 years.

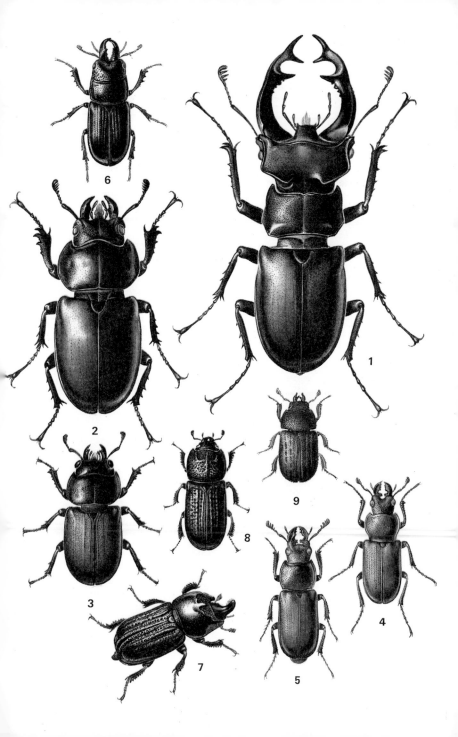

Family Cerambycidae — longhorn beetles

The Cerambycidae are represented in central Europe by 231 species belonging to 85 genera, of which only some 60 species occur in Britain. Their considerable average size and their handsome appearance have always made them popular with collectors. They are plant-eaters, and many of them visit flowers. The larvae of almost all species live either in wood or in herbaceous plants; only a few live in the soil and eat roots. Most longhorn beetles like sunshine, but some are active only in the evening or at night; few are attracted by lights.

1 *Parandra brunnea*, 10−24 mm (1 : 1)
Most members of this genus live in North and South America. The one depicted here was introduced to Dresden (Germany) in 1916 from North America and became established. The larvae develop in the bottom of the trunk of diseased lime-trees (less often poplars). The beetles are to be found in August and September.

2 *Megopis scabricornis*, 30−50 mm (2 : 1)
This genus, which has only one species in central Europe, is known in older works as *Aegosoma*. In central Europe the beetles are very rare. They fly after dusk in July and August and during the day they hide beneath the bark or in the larval passages of their host trees (chiefly willows and poplars).

3 *Ergates faber* − male, 25−60 mm (3 : 1)
Owing to its size and its robust form, the only species of this genus found in central Europe is unmistakable. The males can be distinguished from the females by their longer antennae and the structure of their pronotum. In central Europe the species becomes rarer towards the west. The beetles appear from July to September and are active at night; during the day they remain in hiding. The larvae, whose development takes several years, live in old pine trunks (less often those of spruce).

4 *Ergates faber* − female, 25−60 mm
The female's antennae stretch only about halfway down its body; the whole upper surface of its pronotum is wrinkled.

5 *Prionus coriarius*, 18−45 mm (4 : 1)
The male of this species is conspicuous for its stout, serrate antennae. The female's antennae are narrower and less obviously serrate. In central Europe the beetles are generally found singly, but the species is widely distributed and not usually rare. In July and August they swarm in the evening and are attracted to artificial light. The larvae develop in the roots of deciduous trees (less often of conifers).

6 *Tragosoma depsarium*, 15−30 mm (5 : 1)
This is the only species of *Tragosoma* found in central Europe, where it is very rare. The beetles, which live in the mountains, take to the wing on muggy July and August evenings, but stay concealed beneath loose bark on their host trees during the day. The larvae develop in damaged pine, fir and spruce trunks and stumps.

7 *Spondylis buprestoides*, 12−24 mm (6 : 1)
The only central European species of this genus is fairly common in pinewoods. The beetles may be found from June to September, but usually remain hidden away beneath loose bark, not emerging until after dusk. The larvae develop in dry pine (seldom spruce) stumps.

8 *Nothorhina punctata*, 7−15 mm (7 : 1)
Likewise the only member of its genus in central Europe, this species is referred to as *N. muricata* in earlier works. It is very rare. In June and July, the adult beetles are active during the warmest part of the day. Eggs are laid on healthy pines, usually those in an isolated position, and the larvae develop in pine bark.

9 *Arhopalus rusticus*, 10−30 mm (8 : 1)
In central and northern Europe there are 2 large, elongate, very similar species of this genus, referred to as *Criocephalus* in many works. The species shown here is generally fairly common, although scarce in Britain. The beetles fly from June to September in the evening and at night; during the day they remain in hiding. The larvae live first of all in the inner bark and then in the wood of damaged pines or − less often − of other conifers; their tunnels greatly diminish the value of the wood as timber.

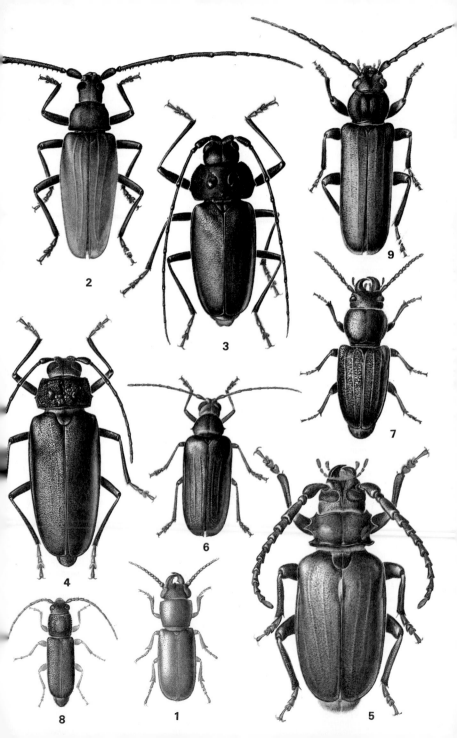

1 *Asemum striatum, 8−23 mm (9 : 1)

The only member of this genus found in central Europe is not always completely black; the elytra may also be reddish brown. It is a fairly common species and the adult beetles can be found from May to August. The larvae develop in damaged conifers (chiefly pines), where their burrows affect the value of the wood as timber. Adult beetles sometimes emerge from wood already used for construction.

2 *Tetropium castaneum, 9−18 mm (10 : 1)

There are 3 species of this genus in central Europe, of which only the present species is native to Britain. All of them have very variable colouring. The larvae live in the sap-wood of conifers, where they eat out wide, irregular passages; they pupate deep inside the wood at the end of a hook-shaped passage. They are the worst forest pests among the longhorn beetles, since they attack standing (though generally ailing) trees. After infestation by bark beetles or gale damage they can completely destroy whole stands within 3 years. The species depicted here is the commonest member of the genus. The beetles fly from May to July.

3 *Rhagium bifasciatum, 12−22 mm (11 : 1)

This genus has 4 species in central and northern Europe, three of which occur in Britain. The larvae of this species burrow in the trunks of spruces and other conifers. It occasionally also attacks deciduous trees. The beetles are fairly abundant from May to August; they can be found on flowers as well as on their host trees.

4 *Rhagium inquisitor, 10−21 mm (11 : 4)

This and the next 2 members of the genus were formerly included in the genus *Harpium* (today only a subgenus). *R. inquisitor* occurs throughout the whole of the palaearctic region and also in North America. The larvae live beneath the bark of conifers and from September the young beetles can already be found in the pupal chamber. From April to August the beetles can be found in abundance on flowers and on their tree hosts.

5 Rhagium sycophanta, 17−30 mm (11 : 2)

This is the largest species of the genus. The larvae develop under the bark of oak stumps (less commonly of other deciduous trees). The beetles can be found in fair numbers on oak stumps from May to July, although they can also be seen on flowers and on other types of wood.

6 *Rhagium mordax, 13−22 mm (11 : 3)

This species is common everywhere in central Europe. From May to August the beetles can be found on flowers and on the wood of its larval host, especially tree stumps. The larvae develop beneath the bark of deciduous trees (rarely conifers). The beetles spend the winter in the pupal chamber.

7 Rhamnusium bicolor, 15−23 mm (12 : 1)

This species is very variably coloured, but the beetles are mostly yellow or reddish brown, with the elytra − especially of the females − blackish blue. This is the only member of the genus found in central Europe, where it is not very common. The larvae develop in various deciduous trees (chiefly hollow willows, poplars and chestnuts). In June or July the adult beetles are also to be found on these trees, but only for a period of about 14 days.

8 Xylosteus spinolae, 14−16 mm (13 : 1)

The males of the only member of this genus in central Europe are slimly built; the females are broader. This species is a native of south-eastern Europe; from there its range extends into southern Carinthia (Austria), where it is rare. Larval development, in hazel wood, takes two years; the young beetle spends the winter in the pupal chamber.

9 Toxotus cursor, 16−30 mm (14 : 1)

In older works, this genus − which has only one species in central Europe − is named *Oxymirus*. The beetles have very variable colouring and alongside entirely black or russet insects we can find striped specimens. The larvae develop in old conifer wood (chiefly spruce stumps). From May to August the adult beetles are fairly abundant and can be found on flowering shrubs or on the wood of trees in which the larvae develop.

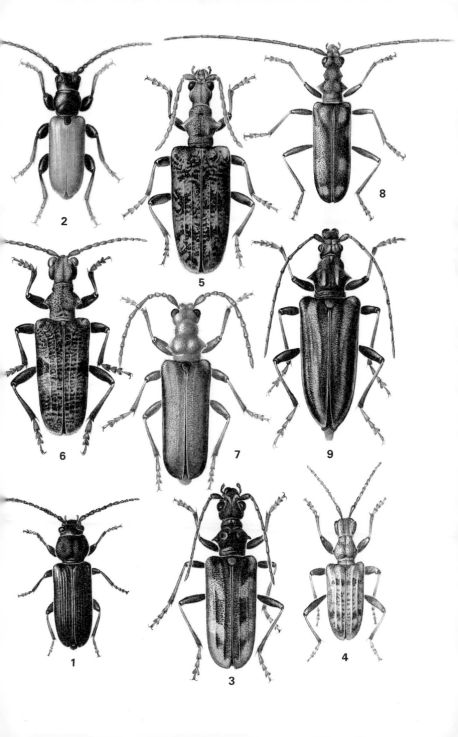

1 *Stenocorus meridianus, 15−25 mm (15 : 1)
The name of this genus used to be spelled *Stenochorus;* it has 2 species in central Europe. The beetles resemble *Toxotus,* but are somewhat slimmer. The larvae develop in the damaged wood of various deciduous trees, while the adult beetles are to be found on shrubs or flowers. The colouring of this species, the only member of the genus found in Britain, varies from black to yellowish, with all kinds of intermediate combinations. From May to June the beetles are quite plentiful on the outskirts of woods; the larvae live in diseased deciduous trees.

2 *Akimerus schaefferi,* 15−24 mm (16 : 1)
The single central European member of this genus is broader than the preceding species. The sexes are differently coloured, the males having plain reddish brown elytra and the females reddish brown to black elytra with a pale yellow band across the middle. In general the beetles are rare. In June and July they can be seen on flowering oaks and elms, almost always near the top. The larvae develop chiefly in old oaks, seldom in elms and hornbeams.

3 *Pachyta quadrimaculata,* 11−20 mm (17 : 1)
Of the 2 members of this genus found in central Europe, this one is a boreomontane species which ranges from central Europe as far east as the river Amur. The beetles can be seen in mountainous country from June to August, sitting on flowers; the larvae develop in conifer wood, especially that of spruce.

4 *Evodinus clathratus,* 10−12 mm (18 : 3)
There are 3 species of this genus in central Europe, all of them restricted to mountainous districts, where the beetles frequent flowers. The one shown here is the commonest species. The beetles can be found on flowers from May to July; nothing as yet is known of the development of the larvae.

5 *Gaurotes virginea,* 9−12 mm (19 : 1)
Two species of this genus occur in central Europe. This one lives in mountain forests, where the beetles can be found from May to July on flowers, often in large numbers. The larvae develop in oaks and possibly in other deciduous trees as well.

6 *Acmaeops collaris,* 7−9 mm (20 : 4)
This genus is represented by 4 species in central Europe. This, the only one found in Britain, resembles *Gaurotes* species. In central Europe it is generally fairly common, but towards the north and the north-west (e.g. in Britain), it grows rarer and in some regions it is absent. The beetles can be found on flowers from April to July; the larvae develop in oaks and also, perhaps, in other deciduous trees.

7 *Acmaeops pratensis,* 6−10 mm (20 : 2)
This beetle may be bicoloured or completely black. It is a boreomontane species found, in central Europe, in mountain forests in June and July on flowers (especially Umbelliferae). The larvae develop in spruce over a period of several years.

8 *Pidonia lurida,* 9−11 mm (21 : 1)
The sole species of this genus found in central Europe is fairly common in the south. In June and July the adult beetles are to be found on flowers, chiefly in glades in mountain forests. Further north the species becomes rare and its incidence more sporadic. The larvae develop in conifer wood.

9 *Cortodera femorata,* 8−11 mm (22 : 1)
The 5 members of this genus found in central Europe, none of which occur in Britain, look like small *Leptura* species. The plants on which the larvae of some species live are still unknown. Like its fellows, the species shown here is not very common. The beetles chiefly frequent the tops of trees, and when the sun shines they are very active. From April to July they can be found on flowering pines. The larvae develop in the wood of pine trees and possibly of other conifers also.

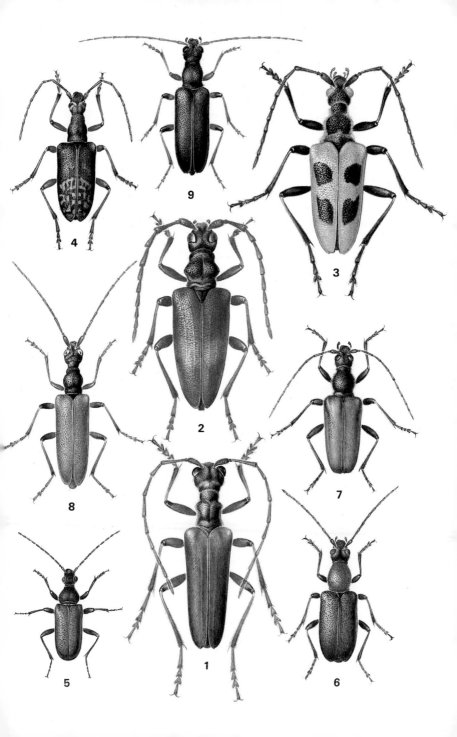

1 *Grammoptera ruficornis, 4.5−7 mm   (23 : 2)
Of the 4 species of this genus in central Europe (3 in Britain), the one depicted here is the most generally abundant; the other 3 are much rarer. *G. ruficornis* is to be found on flowers (especially hawthorn) everywhere in central Europe and the British Isles (except the very north) in May and June; the larvae develop in the twigs of various deciduous trees.

2 *Alosterna tabacicolor, 6−8 mm   (24 : 1)
The single species of *Alosterna* found in central and northern Europe is built similarly to the preceding species, but is immediately distinguishable by its light colour. It is distributed from Europe across Siberia as far as Japan. In central Europe the beetles are abundant everywhere from May to July, when they can be found on flowers, especially in wooded districts. The larvae develop in the bark of various deciduous trees; they display a preference for maples and oaks.

3 *Leptura sexguttata, 7−12 mm   (27 : 2)
The genus *Leptura* is represented by 18 species in central Europe (7 in Britain). Together with the members of the equally large genus *Strangalia,* they represent the most familiar of cerambycids to be seen on flowers. The members of the two genera can best be differentiated by their pronotum, whose posterior corners taper off to points in *Strangalia* species, but not in those of *Leptura.* In the *Leptura* species illustrated here, the reddish yellow spots on the elytra vary. Towards the north the beetles become rarer, and in Britain the species is very rare. They are to be found on flowers from May to July. The larvae develop in oaks and beeches.

4 *Leptura livida, 7−9 mm   (27 : 3)
This is the smallest member of the genus. The beetles are common on flowers everywhere in central Europe from June to August, and the species is also relatively common in southern Britain. The larvae develop in oaks and other deciduous trees.

5 Leptura maculicornis, 8−10 mm   (27 : 9)
Small members of this species resemble those of the preceding species, but the middle segments of their antennae are of a lighter colour at the base, producing a ringed effect. *L. maculicornis* is a boreomontane species, and in June and July in the mountains the beetles can be seen on flowers, generally in large numbers. The larvae develop chiefly in oak, less frequently in other hardwoods, and possibly in conifers.

6 *Leptura rubra − male, 10−14 mm   (27 : 11)
This species is very common in central Europe, but extremely scarce in Britain. From June to September the males can be found on flowers, especially those of Umbelliferae; occasionally they also run about on wood.

7 *Leptura rubra − female, 14−19 mm
The females are not only differently coloured from the males, but are also broader and more robustly built. A whole series of *Leptura* species display similar sex-related differences in colouring. The females are found rather infrequently on flowers and more often on the wood of old conifer stumps, trunks and roots, in which the larvae develop. This species also attacks untreated wooden telegraph poles.

8 *Leptura scutellata, 14−20 mm   (27 : 14)
This species occurs over the whole of central Europe, but nowhere in large numbers. The beetles are to be found mainly in mountainous regions in June and July, on flowers. The larvae develop in the wood of deciduous trees (chiefly beech).

9 Leptura virens, 14−22 mm   (27 : 18)
The black colouring of this beetle's body is often scarcely discernible owing to its coat of long, thick greenish or grey hairs. It is a boreomontane species ranging from northern Europe, through Siberia, to Sakhalin, Korea and Japan. In central Europe the beetles are to be found in the mountains (often at subalpine altitudes) from June to July, sitting on flowers; the larvae develop in conifer wood.

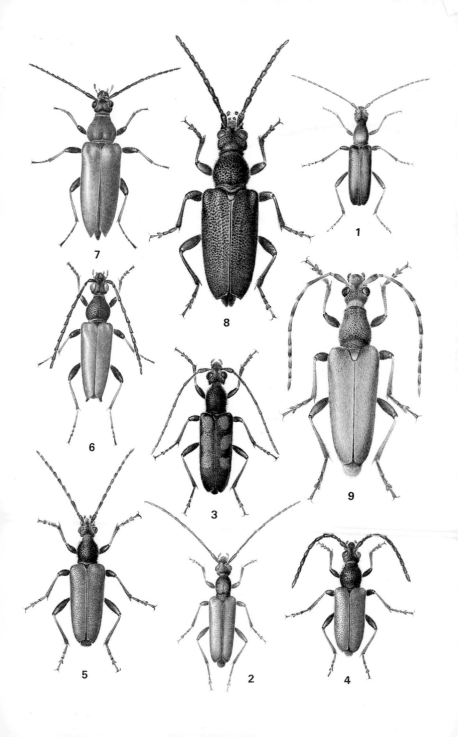

1 *Judolia cerambyciformis, 7−11 mm (28 : 2)
This genus, which used to be regarded as a subgenus of *Leptura,* has 3 species in central Europe, 2 of which also occur in Britain. The beetles are less elongate than *Leptura* and *Strangalia* species and have wider and shorter elytra. The elytra are always yellowish brown with very variable black spots and bars. The species depicted here can be found on flowers from June to August, often in large numbers. Despite this, nothing is known of its developmental stages and its habits; the larvae probably live in the wood of deciduous trees.

2 *Strangalia aethiops,* 10.5−15 mm (29 : 9)
In central Europe there are 14 species of this genus (6 in the British Isles), all of them very slim-bodied insects. Their elytra usually taper off to a point. They have the same habits as *Leptura* species, and have an equal liking for flowers. Some *Strangalia* species are very common in central Europe. The one shown here occurs everywhere and from May to July can be found on flowers in large numbers. The larvae develop in the wood of various deciduous trees.

3 *Strangalia nigra,* 6.5−9 mm (29 : 12)
This much smaller species is not completely black, since at least part of its abdomen is red. In June and July the beetles are present on flowers everywhere in central Europe, often in large numbers. In Britain it is not common and found only in the south. The larvae develop in the wood of deciduous trees.

4 *Strangalia quadrifasciata,* 11−19 mm (29 : 6)
The yellowish red, toothed bands on the beetle's black elytra can be much narrower or still wider than on the specimen depicted here. This species occurs everywhere in central Europe, but usually sporadically. In July and August the beetles are to be found on old wood or on flowers. The larvae develop in old wood of various deciduous trees, particularly willows.

5 *Strangalia maculata,* 14−20 mm (29 : 7)
The beetle's black and yellow markings are very variable and range from almost completely yellow to almost completely black. In central Europe, and also in Britain, this is one of the commonest longhorn beetles, and from May to August it can be found on flowers everywhere. The larvae develop in the wood of various deciduous trees, but also in spruce.

6 *Strangalia arcuata,* 12−17 mm (29 : 8)
This resembles the preceding species; the yellow bands are likewise very variable, but the first one is always hook-shaped. This species is distributed throughout practically the entire palaearctic region. Although recorded from many parts of central Europe, it is generally rare. The beetles can be found on flowers in June and July. The larvae develop mainly in the wood of conifers, but occasionally also in hardwoods.

7 *Strangalia melanura* − male, 6−9 mm (29 : 10)
In this species there are pronounced differences between the sexes, the elytra of the male being a less bright red and with less extensive black markings than those of the female. *Melanura* is one of the commonest cerambycids in central Europe. The beetles are to be found on flowers from May to September. The larvae develop in the wood of both coniferous and deciduous trees.

8 *Strangalia melanura* − female
As in *Leptura rubra,* the females of this species are not only differently coloured from the males, but also have a wider body.

9 *Strangalia attenuata,* 11−15 mm (29 : 14)
Opinions on the systematic position of this species differ. Today it is generally placed in a subgenus of its own, *Strangalina,* belonging to the genus *Strangalia.* In some older works it was segregated in the separate genus *Typocerus.* In central Europe it becomes rarer towards the north. Although once found in Britain, it is now assumed to be extinct. The beetles can be found on flowers from June to August. The larvae develop in various deciduous trees, particularly diseased and damaged oaks.

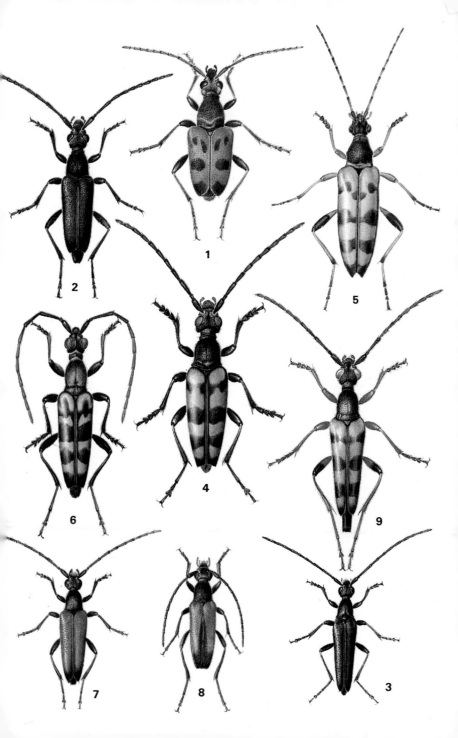

1 *Necydalis major,* 19−32 mm (30 : 1)
The 2 species of this genus found in central Europe can be distinguished by their size, their short elytra and their wasp-like appearance. *Necydalis* species are rare in central Europe. *N. major* can be found in June and July on the brood trees and occasionally on flowers. The larvae develop in various deciduous trees (especially cherry and hornbeam), but sometimes in conifers.

2 *Saphanus piceus,* 14−19 mm (31 : 1)
The single species of this genus found in central Europe occurs only in the mountains in the south-eastern part of the region and even there it is rare. The elytra of males (but not females) taper at the tip. From May to June the beetles can be seen in mountain forests crawling about on felled timber or on the ground; they fly only in the evening. The larvae develop in deciduous trees and conifer roots or stumps.

3 *Cerambyx cerdo,* 24−53 mm (32 : 2)
This genus is represented by 3 species in central Europe. The larvae of the species shown here develop for 3−5 years in oak, where they penetrate to the heart-wood and make it worthless as timber; they are seldom found in other deciduous trees. The beetles fly from May to August, chiefly in the evening and at night. Today they are rare in most parts of central Europe and in some regions they have completely vanished. The species once occurred in Britain but today is extinct.

4 *Trichoferus pallidus,* 14−21 mm (33 : 1)
In older works this genus is called *Hesperandrius* or *Hesperophanes.* The one species found in central Europe occurs only in the south-east and is very rare. The beetles fly in July and August; they are nocturnal insects, but are not attracted by lights. The larvae develop in old oaks.

5 *Gracilia minuta,* 3−7 mm (34 : 1)
This is one of the smallest longhorn beetles and is the only member of the genus found in central Europe. The larvae develop in thin, dry branches of deciduous trees (especially osier stems). At first they tunnel immediately beneath the bark, but later in the wood itself; their development takes 1−2 years. In June and July the adult beetles emerge, often from manufactured wicker articles.

6 *Axinopalpis gracilis,* 6.5−12 mm (36 : 1)
This is the only species of the genus found in central Europe. Its frequency of occurrence diminishes from east to west, where it is very rare or completely absent. From May to July the beetles can be seen on its host trees or on flowers, especially after dusk. The larvae develop in dry oak, lime and maple branches.

7 *Obrium brunneum,* 4−7 mm (37 : 2)
There are 3 species of this genus in central Europe. The beetles are to be found mostly in shady mountain forests on flowers, chiefly of Umbelliferae. The species shown here is by far the commonest member of the genus; towards the north it becomes rarer, and it has been found on only a few occasions in Britain. The beetles can be found on flowers from May to August; the larvae develop in conifer wood (mainly that of spruce and fir).

8 *Nathrius brevipennis,* 3−6 mm (38 : 1)
In older works this genus is named *Leptidea* or *Leptidia.* The adult beetles have abbreviated elytra of characteristic form. They are frequently brought into central Europe in wicker baskets, from which they emerge, together with *Gracilia minuta,* in June and July, often in large numbers. The species has been found in Britain on a number of occasions, but probably does not breed there. The larvae develop in other deciduous trees as well as in willows, and they have also been extracted from pines.

9 *Molorchus minor,* 6−16 mm (39 : 1)
This genus is represented by 4 species in central Europe (2 in Britain). The beetles' short elytra make their identification easy. This species is by far the commonest in central Europe; from May to July, the beetles can be found in abundance on flowers everywhere. Very often they emerge from stacks of firewood. The larvae develop in the bark and sap-wood of conifers (chiefly spruce and pine).

256

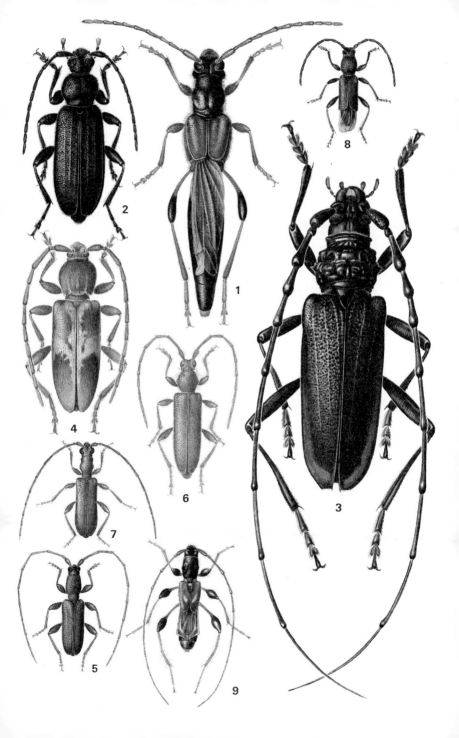

1 *Stenopterus rufus,* 8−16 mm (40 : 2)
The 2 members of this genus found in central Europe, neither of them occurring in Britain, have characteristic elytra with broad shoulders and sharply tapering tips. In the summer the beetles can frequently be found on flowers, in particular on milfoil (yarrow) and wild carrot. The beetles can be found on flowers from May to August, occasionally in large numbers. The larvae develop in various deciduous trees, e.g. oak and walnut.

2 *Callimellum angulatum,* 7−9 mm (42 : 1)
The species shown here is widely distributed in southern Europe, but also occurs in Slovakia, in Austria and (rarely) in south Germany. The beetles can be found from April to June on flowers or on the trees, oaks and beeches, in which the larvae develop.

3 *Deilus fugax,* 6−11 mm (44 : 1)
The only species of this genus (sometimes termed *Dilus*) occurs rarely in Slovakia and Austria. The beetles can be found on flowers or on various shrubs (e.g. *Laburnum,* broom) in which the larvae develop.

4 *Aromia moschata − Musk Beetle, 13−34 mm (45 : 1)
The only member of the genus found in central Europe, this beetle is easily recognisable because of its size and its metallic colouring. It is widely distributed in Continental Europe but of only local occurrence in Britain. The beetles can be found from June to August on willows or on flowers; they release a pungent, aromatic secretion which gives them their name. The larvae develop mainly in willows (chiefly old pollarded trees) and rarely in poplars or alders.

5 *Rosalia alpina,* 15−38 mm (46 : 1)
This sole member of the given genus has distinctive light blue pubescence over a large part of its body. It is still known to exist at a few localities in Germany (Bavaria and Württemberg), but is otherwise extinct in central Europe, where it is now protected by law. From June to September the beetles can be seen on standing or felled beeches. The larvae develop in the wood of diseased beeches, but occasionally also in other deciduous trees, such as maples.

6 *Anisarthron barbipes,* 6−11 mm (47 : 1)
Likewise the only member of its genus known to occur in central Europe, this species is an occasional visitor from southern Europe. The beetles are to be found on the brood trees or on flowering shrubs in June and July. The larvae develop in various damaged deciduous trees, e.g. horse-chestnut, lime, walnut and maple.

7 *Hylotrupes bajulus − House Longhorn, 7−21 mm (48 : 1)
The only member of this genus found in central Europe occurs mainly in houses and seldom in the open. It is among the most feared of insect pests, since the larvae can virtually destroy structural timbers. Their development takes 3−10 years, or even longer, according to the age of the wood. The adult beetles appear from May to September.

8 *Rhopalopus ungaricus,* 16−24 mm (49 : 1)
The incidence of all 5 species of this genus in central Europe is very sporadic and the beetles are all rare. This one (known in older works as *R. hungaricus*) is a rare and exclusively montane species. The beetles can be found on the brood trees from May to July. The larvae develop for 2 years in maple and other hardwoods; at first they live beneath the bark, but later gnaw a curved passage in the wood.

9 *Rhopalopus femoratus,* 8−13 mm (49 : 3)
The distribution of this species is confined to central Europe, where it occurs widely but is not common. The beetles can be found on flowers in May and June; the larvae develop in the wood of various deciduous trees.

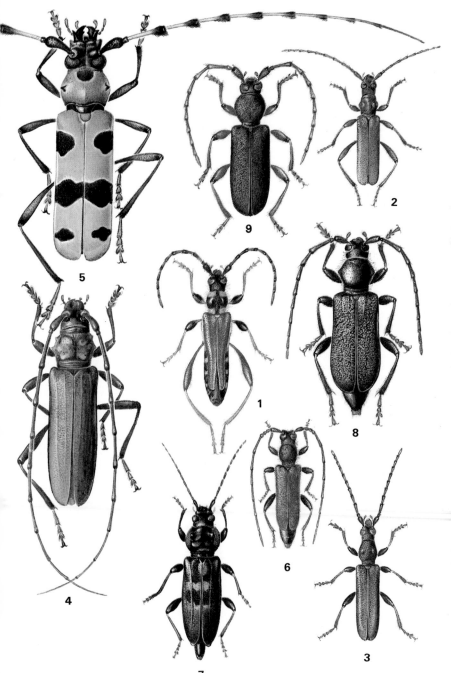

1 *Semanotus undatus,* 7−14 mm (52 : 1)
This genus is represented by 2 species in central Europe. The one depicted here has a boreomontane distribution. It occurs in Austria, the Czech Republic and Slovakia, where, although it is rare or very rare, it is an established member of the local fauna; specimens have been found in Bavaria but it is not clear whether these finds were accidental. The beetles can be found from April to August on the trunks of the brood trees. The larvae develop in the wood of conifers (chiefly pine, fir and spruce); at first they live beneath the bark, but before pupating they burrow into the wood itself.

2 *Callidium violaceum,* 8−16 mm (53 : 2)
The 3 species of this genus found in central Europe are characterized by a broad, flat pronotum. *C. violaceum* occurs everywhere and is generally fairly abundant. The beetles are to be found from May to August on the brood timber. Occasionally they emerge from finished woodwork. The larvae develop in dry conifer wood and rarely in the wood of deciduous trees. At first they feed immediately beneath the bark, but before pupating they excavate a curved passage in the wood.

3 *Callidium aeneum,* 8−15 mm (53 : 3)
This is a primarily montane species in central Europe; towards the north it becomes rarer. The adult beetles can be found from May to July; the larvae develop in the wood of both coniferous and deciduous trees.

4 *Pyrrhidium sanguineum,* 8−12 mm (54 : 1)
The single member of this genus occurring in central Europe resembles *Callidium* species, but is conspicuous by its colouring. The beetles are widely distributed in central Europe and in some places they are quite common, although very rare in Britain. They can be seen on the brood timber from April to June. The larvae develop in oak (dead branches, felled trunks and stumps) and occasionally in other hardwoods. At first they burrow beneath the bark, but pupate up to 6 cm deep in the wood.

5 *Phymatodes testaceus,* 6−17 mm (55 : 1)
The 7 members of this genus found in central Europe, only 2 of which occur in Britain, are longer and of narrower form than those of *Callidium.* This one is exceedingly variably coloured. The beetles are abundant everywhere; they fly after dusk from June to July. The larvae take one year to develop in hardwoods, especially oak. Not infrequently they emerge from stacks of firewood.

6 *Phymatodes glabratus,* 5−9 mm (55 : 2)
This species has been recorded from many parts of central Europe, but is not generally found in large numbers. The larvae develop beneath the bark of junipers and pines.

7 *Phymatodes alni,* 4−6.5 mm (55 : 6)
These small longhorn beetles can be found from April to June, but are somewhat sporadic in their occurrence. Occasionally, however, they are found in profusion. The larvae live under the bark of deciduous trees such as oak, ash, maple and alder.

8 *Xylotrechus rusticus,* 9−20 mm (57 : 1)
None of the 6 species of this genus found in central Europe is very common and they are mostly rather rare. The beetles run about on stacked timber and in warm weather fly quickly and nimbly away. The species shown here occurs everywhere in central Europe, but seems to have been little recorded in recent years. The adult beetles can be found in June and July. The larvae develop in various hardwoods; the pupal chamber is hollowed out in the wood.

9 *Clytus arietis* − Wasp Beetle, 7−14 mm (58 : 3)
There are 4 species of this genus in central Europe. The beetles can be found on stacked timber and on brushwood and occasionally also on flowers. This is by far the commonest member of the genus and occurs everywhere and in quite large numbers in central Europe. It is the only species of the genus found in Britain. The beetles can be found from May to July on wood (especially beech) and flowers. The larvae develop in the wood of various deciduous trees.

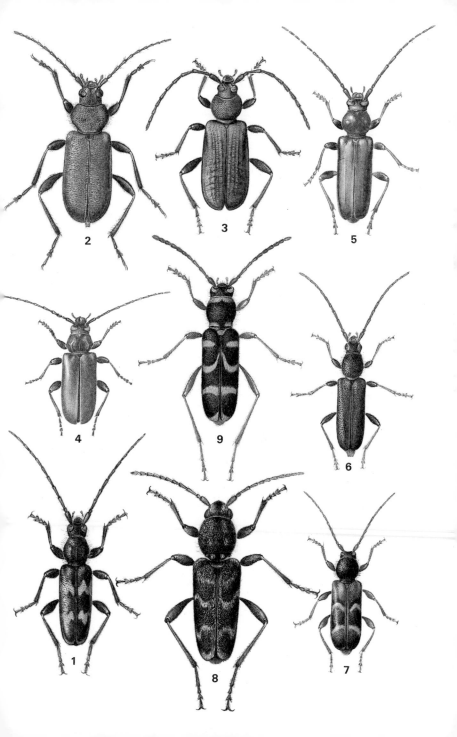

1 *Clytus lama*, 8−14 mm   (58 : 4)
The main difference between this species and the preceding one is that its antennae are more slender at their tips. The beetles have been recorded from most parts of central Europe, but are at all frequent only in the south (towards the north they become rarer or disappear). They are to be found in June and July. The larvae develop in spruces, firs and larches; at first they burrow between the bark and the wood, but later, before pupating, they bore a hook-shaped passage deep in the wood, which thus loses much of its value.

2 *Plagionotus arcuatus*, 6−20 mm   (60 : 2)
Three species of this genus are natives of central Europe. They resemble *Clytus,* but are much more robust. The one depicted here can be found everywhere in central Europe from May to August, often in abundance, running about on the wood of its larval hosts (generally oak, less often other hardwoods). In Britain the species now appears to be extinct. The larvae at first live in the bark, but pupate 7 cm deep in the wood. In a large-scale attack on trunks lying on the ground they can do severe damage.

3 *Plagionotus detritus*, 10−19 mm   (60 : 1)
This species occurs chiefly in the eastern part of central Europe; in the west it becomes rarer or is absent. Its biology resembles that of the preceding species.

4 *Cyrtoclytus capra*, 9−15 mm   (59 : 1)
This, the only member of the genus found in central Europe, closely resembles *Clytus* species, but has distinctive long hairs all over its body. The beetles are to be found in June and July, but they are rare and occur only in the south-eastern part of central Europe and in the Czech and Slovak Republics, Austria and Bavaria. The larvae probably develop in the wood of deciduous trees.

5 *Isotomus speciosus*, 12−22 mm   (62 : 1)
In central Europe, this genus − classified in earlier works as *Caloclytus,* a subgenus of *Clytanthus* − has only one species, which closely resembles the members of the genus *Chlorophorus* (formerly *Clytanthus*). The light spots on the elytra are very variable. The range of this species extends into part of central Europe from the south-east and is found in the Czech Republic, Slovakia and Austria, although rarely. In June and July the beetles can be found on flowers or on old wood, particularly after dusk. The larvae develop in hardwoods − chiefly oak and sweet chestnut.

6 *Anaglyptus mysticus*, 6−13 mm   (63 : 1)
This is the only member of the genus found in central and northern Europe (another species lives in the Mediterranean region). The markings are variable, but their general arrangement is characteristic. In central Europe the beetles appear from May to July; they are to be found everywhere on hawthorn (less often on other flowers) and are generally fairly abundant. The larvae develop in the wood of various deciduous trees.

7 *Chlorophorus sartor*, 5.5−9 mm   (61 : 7)
In earlier works this genus bears the name *Clytanthus;* it is represented by 6 species in central Europe, but none of these occur in Britain. Towards the north *C. sartor* becomes rarer or is absent. The beetles can be found on flowers in June and July. The larvae develop in the wood of various deciduous trees, such as sweet chestnut and *Robinia.*

8 *Chlorophorus figuratus*, 7−13 mm   (61 : 8)
In central Europe this species becomes steadily rarer towards the north and east until it disappears completely. The adult beetles can be found on various flowers from June to August. The larvae develop in various deciduous trees.

9 *Purpuricenus kaehleri*, 9−20 mm   (64 : 1)
The 2 members of this genus found in central Europe have red and black elytra, the extent of the two colours varying considerably. The range of the species shown here extends from the south into the southern part of central Europe, where it is strictly thermophilic and rare. From May to August the beetles can be found on the larval host trees or on flowers; the larvae develop in various deciduous trees (chiefly peach and apricot).

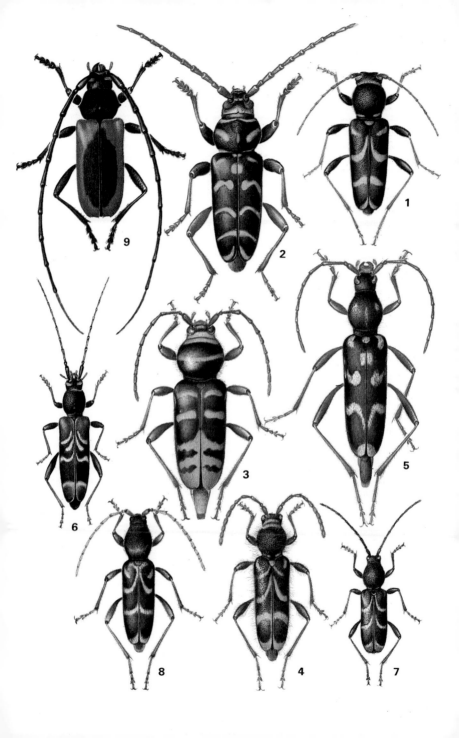

1 *Dorcadion fuliginator,* 10−15 mm (65 : 7)

The members of this genus, which is confined to the palaearctic region, have a very uniform body structure. More than 350 species have been described, from Morocco, across southern Europe, Asia Minor and Siberia as far east as China. The adult beetles are wingless and thus cannot fly. In the spring they crawl about on the ground in grassy places. They are typical of dry grassland and like plenty of warmth. Only 7 species occur in central Europe and none are found in Britain. The larvae develop in the soil on grass roots. The species shown here extends from south-western Europe into central Germany, but is absent in Austria, Poland and Czechoslovakia. The beetles are very variably coloured; they can be found in warm places from April to June, but only here and there and very sporadically.

2 *Dorcadion fulvum,* 13−16 mm (65 : 2)

This species is a native of south-eastern Europe and its range extends from there into the south-eastern part of central Europe. The adult beetles can be found from March to July; in the Czech and Slovak Republics they are often abundant and in Austria they also occur in many places.

3 *Morimus funereus,* 20−38 mm (68 : 1)

This handsome species has another southern relative, which reaches no further north than the south of Switzerland, however. The species shown here is wingless; it is essentially a southern European species, but is found sporadically in the southern part of central Europe, e.g. Austria and the Czech and Slovak Republics. The beetles can be found in May and June on tree stumps, trunks and old wood. The larvae develop in beeches and oaks.

4 *Lamia textor,* 15−30 mm (69 : 1)

This only member of this genus in central Europe has a similar form to the preceding species. The beetles have been recorded from all parts of central Europe, but nowhere in abundance. In Britain the species is very rare and may be virtually extinct. From May to August the adult beetles sit on roots and branches of the brood trees and are not active until the evening. The larvae develop in the trunks and roots of willows and aspens.

5 *Monochamus sutor,* 15−24 mm (70 : 3)

The 4 members of this genus occurring in central Europe are large insects with strikingly long antennae; the one shown here is the commonest, but there are parts of central Europe (especially in the plains) where it is absent. The beetles can be seen on debarked conifer wood from July to September. The larvae develop in conifers (chiefly spruces, but also firs); at first they make burrows beneath the bark, but later they tunnel into the wood and so reduce its value as timber.

6 *Monochamus galloprovincialis,* 12−25 mm (70 : 4)

This species is in general rarer in central Europe than the preceding one, except towards the west. The beetles, which fly from June to September, eat shoots and the bark of young twigs. The larvae develop chiefly in pines, which they damage in the same way as the preceding species damages spruces.

7 *Mesosa nebulosa,* 9−15 mm (71 : 2)

This genus is represented by 2 species in central Europe. *M. nebulosa* has been recorded from all parts of the region, but seldom in large numbers. In Britain it is rare. The beetles can be found from April to August; the larvae develop in dry branches on various deciduous trees (chiefly oaks, limes, elms and walnuts).

8 *Mesosa curculionides,* 10−17 mm (71 : 1)

The biology and distribution of this more strikingly marked species are similar to those of the preceding beetle, but the species itself is rarer. The adult beetles fly from May to September.

9 *Oplosia fennica,* 11−13 mm (73 : 1)

This genus, named *Hoplosia* in earlier works, is represented by only one species in central Europe, where it is to be found in all parts of the region from May to July on dry twigs, although not in large numbers. The larvae develop in old, rotten twigs on various deciduous trees, especially limes.

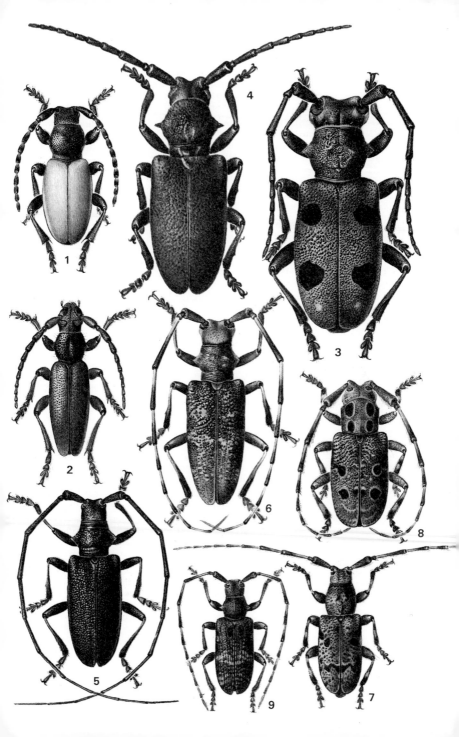

1 *Anaesthetis testacea*, 5−10 mm (74 : 1)

This species closely resembles *Anisarthron barbipes* (p. 258, 6), but the third and fourth segments of its antennae are longer than the rest, while in *Anisarthron* they are distinctly shorter. The species shown here is the only member of the genus in central Europe; it has been recorded there quite frequently, but occurs only sporadically and in small numbers. The beetles sit on twigs during the day and do not fly until the evening. The larvae develop in dry twigs on various deciduous trees, e. g. oak, walnut and chestnut.

2* *Pogonocherus fasciculatus*, 5−8 mm (75 : 6)

The 6 species of this genus found in central Europe (3 in Britain) comprise small beetles characterized by tufts of black hairs on their elytra. The beetles emerge in the autumn, but spend the winter in the wood of the larval host. The species shown here is generally common but, in Britain, is scarce and usually found only in Scotland. The adult beetles can be found on the brood trees from March to October; the larvae develop in conifer wood (chiefly pine and spruce).

3 * *Pogonocherus hispidus*, 4−6 mm (75 : 2)

This species occurs everywhere in central Europe from May to October, but is not very common. The larvae develop in the wood of both deciduous trees and conifers.

4 * *Pogonocherus hispidulus*, 6−7 mm (75 : 1)

The preceding species has a spine on the outer margin of the tip of its elytra; this species has an additional, minute spine at the end of the elytral suture. The beetles can be found everywhere in central Europe from March to July, but not in abundance. The larvae develop in dry twigs on various deciduous trees; a few authors also mention the pine as a brood tree.

5 *Calamobius filum*, 5−11 mm (76 : 1)

The single species of this genus occurring in central Europe is characterized by its slender form and extremely long antennae. Its distribution centres on southern Europe and the Mediterranean region, but it also occurs locally in the southern part of central Europe, e. g. in Slovakia, northern Austria, Bavaria and Baden. Recent records are sporadic, but now and then the beetles appear in abundance; they can be found on grasses from May to July. The larvae develop in the stems of cereal plants and grasses and pupate in the soil.

6 *Acanthoderes clavipes*, 12−17 mm (77 : 1)

The only member of the genus found in central Europe is conspicuous for the club-like thickening of the first segment of its antennae and of its femora. It has been recorded from all parts of central Europe, but is generally rare, except in the mountains. The adult beetles can be found from July to August, running about nimbly on felled trunks. The larvae develop in dry branches on various deciduous trees (chiefly beech and oak).

7 * *Leiopus nebulosus*, 6−10 mm (78 : 1)

Of the 2 central European species of *Leiopus,* the one depicted here is the commonest and it is also one of the commonest species of Cerambycidae in Britain. Adults can be found from May to August on dry branches, most commonly of oak. The larvae develop beneath the bark of various deciduous trees, (e. g. oaks, beeches and fruit-trees); the young beetles spend the winter in the wood.

8 * *Acanthocinus aedilis* − Timberman Beetle − male, 12−20 mm (79 : 1)

There are 5 species of this genus in central Europe. The one shown here, the only species found in Britain, is by far the commonest; the rest are of very local occurrence. The beetles can be seen from March onwards and the next new generation of adults can already be found in the pupal chambers in the autumn. Adult beetles may be found on pine stumps, on stacked timber and under the bark of standing dead or dying pines. The antennae of a male can be five times the length of its body.

9 * *Acanthocinus aedilis* − female, 12−20 mm

The antennae of a female are roughly double the length of its body; females may also be recognised by their prominent ovipositors.

266

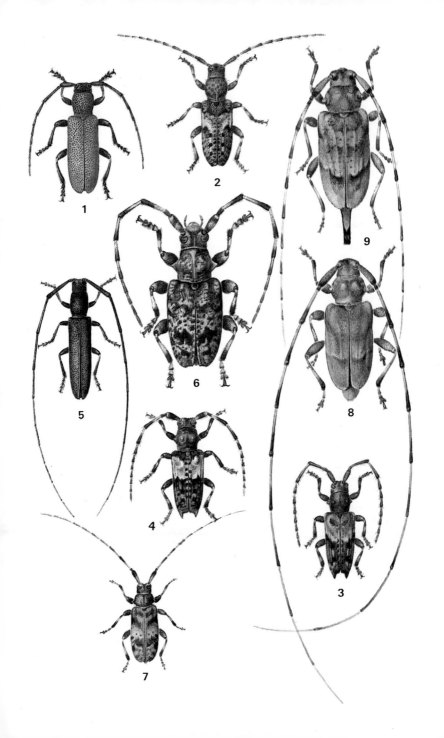

1 *Agapanthia villosoviridescens, 10−22 mm (81 : 3)
Of the 8 species of this genus known to occur in central Europe, this is the only one found in Britain. The adult beetles are to be found, mostly from June to September, on various plants, especially those which act as larval hosts; larvae develop in the stems of various herbaceous plants, particularly thistles.

2 Agapanthia violacea, 8−13 mm (81 : 7)
This species is variably coloured and the adult beetles may be blue, green or violet. They occur everywhere in central Europe, but are not common; they can be found from May to August on flowers. The larvae develop in the stems of various plants, including thistles.

3 Agapanthia cardui, 7−13 mm (81 : 6)
The most characteristic feature of this species is the narrow white hairy stripe along its elytral suture. The beetles occur chiefly in the Mediterranean region, but have also been found regularly in the southern part of central Europe and are occasionally caught as far north as the Rhineland. From May to July the adult beetles may be seen on their brood plants (chiefly thistles), but the larvae also develop in umbelliferous and other herbaceous plants.

4 Exocentrus adspersus, 5−8 mm (80 : 1)
Four species of this genus are natives of central Europe. The adult beetles may be found on dry branches of deciduous trees; they hide during the day and fly about in the evening. None of the species is found in Britain. The species shown here occurs everywhere in central Europe and is generally the commonest member of the genus. The beetles can be found from May to August; the larvae develop in dry branches on deciduous trees (chiefly oaks).

5 *Saperda populnea, 9−15 mm (82 : 3)
This genus is represented by 7 species in central Europe (3 in Britain). The beetles are to be found on shrubs, trees and felled wood; the larvae develop in deciduous trees. This species can be seen everywhere in central Europe from May to July, often in large numbers. In the branches of aspens (and occasionally of other poplars and goat willows) the female makes a cut in the shape of a horseshoe to cut off the supply of sap. It then lays an egg in the incision, which results in the formation of a gall. The larva at first lives in the gall and devours its tissue, but later it burrows its way into the pith; its development takes 2 years.

6 *Saperda carcharias, 20−30 mm (82 : 1)
This is the largest member of the genus and is clothed with yellowish or grey hairs. It occurs everywhere in central Europe and can be locally common. The beetles, which appear on poplars from June to September, betray their presence by the large holes they eat in the leaves. The larvae develop in the wood of the poplars and since their development takes 2 years they can do considerable damage, especially in young trees.

7 *Saperda scalaris, 12−18 mm (82 : 4)
The yellowish green or grey patches of hair on the black elytra of this species are very variable. It occurs everywhere in central Europe and at all altitudes, but is generally found singly. The beetles can be found from April to August, mostly on the brood trees. The larvae develop in various deciduous trees − chiefly in the wood of dead trunks.

8 Saperda similis, 15−22 mm (82 : 2)
Adults of this species resemble small specimens of S. carcharias, but the tips of their elytra are rounded, and not sharpened to a point as in their larger relative. S. similis has been recorded from all parts of central Europe, but is rare. The beetles fly on June and July evenings; the larvae develop in goat willows and aspens (mainly in healthy trees).

9 Saperda perforata, 12−20 mm (82 : 5)
The size and number of the spots on the elytra of this species are variable. The beetles are known to occur in various parts of central Europe, but are generally rare. They fly on June and July evenings and are attracted to artificial light; otherwise they are to be found on the brood trees. The larvae develop in various deciduous trees, but chiefly in poplars.

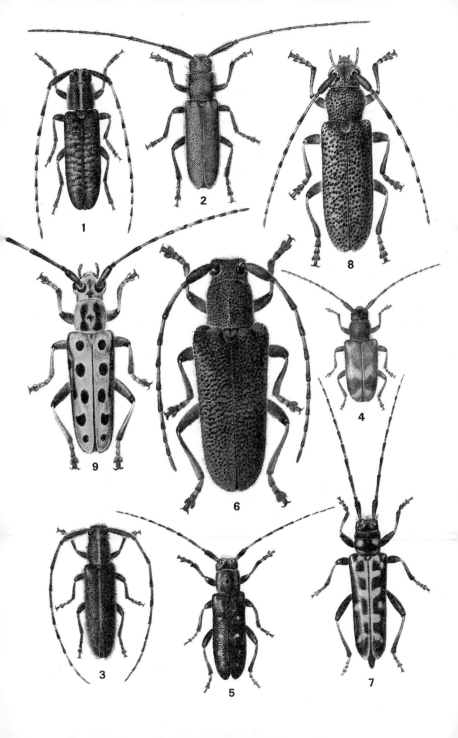

1 *Menesia bipunctata,* 6−9 mm (83 : 1)

This only member of this genus found in central Europe looks like a *Saperda,* but has a square scutellum and a covering of snow-white hairs. The patches of white hair near the tips of the elytra are also characteristic. The beetles can be found in central Europe from May to July, chiefly on alder buckthorn, but are rare, especially in the north. The larvae also develop in common buckthorn and walnut.

2 **Oberea oculata,* 15−21 mm (84 : 3)

The 4 members of this genus found in central Europe are conspicuous for their long, narrow body. Their robust antennae are almost the same length as the body in the male and are longer than the elytra in the female. The species shown here, the only member of the genus found in Britain, is the commonest; it occurs in the mountains, but is rare in the north. The beetles can be found on their larval host plants from June to September; the larvae develop in the switches of various willows.

3 *Oberea linearis,* 11−14 mm (84 : 3)

This species has been recorded throughout central Europe, but is nowhere abundant. The beetles fly after dusk from May to August and can otherwise be found on hazel. The larvae develop in thin, dry hazel branches (less often walnut, lime and elm).

4 *Oberea pupillata,* 16−18 mm (84 : 1)

This species is of local occurrence in central Europe. The beetles can be found from May to July; the larvae develop in honeysuckle.

5 *Stenostola dubia,* 10−13 mm (85 : 1)

The 2 species of this genus occurring in central Europe resemble each other so closely that their names (*dubia* and *ferrea*) are always being confused in the literature, not to mention a third name, *nigripes,* which is now regarded as a synonym of *S. ferrea.* The biology and distribution of the 2 species are also the same. In May and June the beetles are to be found on their host plants everywhere in central Europe, but are generally rare. The larvae develop in limes and also, but less often, in other deciduous trees. *S. ferrea* is found in Britain.

6 *Phytoecia coerulescens,* 8−14 mm (86 : 14)

The 15 members of this genus known in central Europe (only one in Britain) have a cylindrical form. They develop in herbaceous plants on which the beetles are found. This is the commonest member of the genus, but it is nevertheless rare everywhere. The beetles can be found from May to July; the larvae develop in the roots of various plants, such as viper's bugloss and *Lithospermum.*

7 *Phytoecia nigripes,* 10−16 mm (86 : 6)

This species resembles *Oberea oculata,* but is less elongate. It occurs in southern Europe, the Caucasus and Siberia and penetrates central Europe as far as Bavaria and Württemberg, where in some places it is quite abundant. The beetles can be found from May to July; the larvae develop in the stems of various umbelliferous plants and pupate in the roots.

8 *Phytoecia nigricornis,* 8−12 mm (86 : 7)

The distribution of this species stretches from the southern part of northern Europe and from central and southern Europe across the Caucasus to Armenia and Siberia. It has been recorded from many localities in central Europe, but is by no means common. The beetles can be found from May to July; the larvae develop in tansy, golden-rod and mugwort.

9 **Tetrops praeusta,* 3−5 mm (87 : 1)

The 2 species of this genus found in central Europe closely resemble each other, but the one depicted here is commoner and more widely distributed. From April to June the beetles can be found on their larval hosts and on flowers, and are particularly abundant on plum-trees. The larvae develop in dry branches on fruit-trees and other deciduous trees.

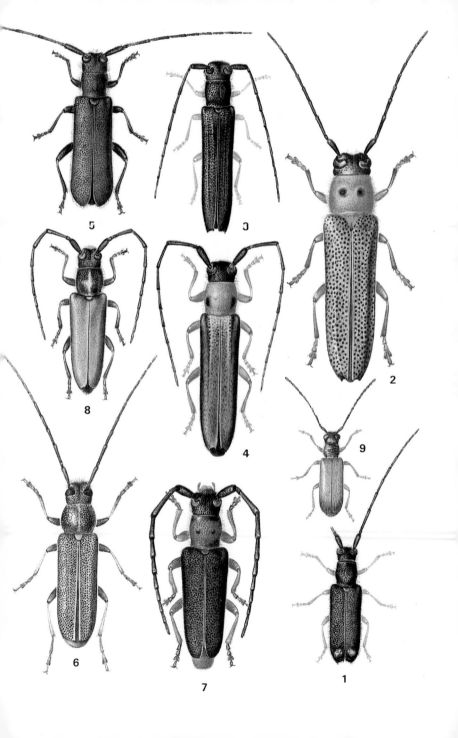

Family Chrysomelidae — leaf beetles

The Chrysomelidae are among the largest of beetle families, with 574 species belonging to 76 genera in central Europe; 256 species occur in Britain. They are related to the longhorn beetles and, like them, feed on plants. Although extremely varied in form, many leaf beetle species are of a convex, oval or more or less rounded shape. The larvae live openly on the surface of leaves or mine within leaves, roots or stems. The larvae of one genus (*Clytra*) live in ants' nests and devour their brood.

1 *Donacia vulgaris, 6−8 mm (2 : 20)
In central Europe there are 21 species of this genus, 15 of which also occur in Britain. The adult beetles can be found on plants standing in or floating on water. The larvae live under water and obtain air from the airways of aquatic plants. The species shown here can be found in May and June on bur-reeds, bulrushes, sedge and reed-grass, but is not very common.

2 **Zeugophora subspinosa*, 3 mm (5 : 2)
There are 4 species of this genus in central Europe (3 in Britain). The beetles are to be found chiefly on poplars, in which the larvae are leaf-miners. This species can be seen from May to September and again in November in comparative abundance on willows, poplars and hazels.

3 *Oulema melanopa, 4−4.5 mm (6 : 5)
The 4 members of this genus found in central and northern Europe, including the British Isles, are either entirely blue or green, or have a red pronotum and legs. The beetles and their larvae attack grass and cereal leaves, chewing them down to a skeleton. Since the larvae have a slimy back, often coated with their own excrement, they can easily be mistaken for tiny slugs. From April to September this species may be found throughout central and northern Europe, often in large numbers. The larvae feed on grasses and cereal plants and the species is sometimes an agricultural pest.

4 **Crioceris asparagi*, 5−6.5 mm (7 : 4)
In all 4 species of this genus found in central Europe, the distribution of the light and dark markings on the elytra is very variable. By rubbing the tip of the abdomen and the under side of their elytra together they are able to produce quite loud chirping sounds. Both the beetles and the larvae live on asparagus and in large numbers can do damage. The species shown here, the only member of the genus found in Britain, is found from April to September.

5 *Crioceris duodecimpunctata*, 5−6.5 mm (7 : 1)
This species occurs in asparagus beds from April to October.

6 *Lilioceris lilii, 6−8 mm (8 : 1)
The 3 members of this genus found in central Europe are related to *Crioceris* species; they are red, however, and live chiefly on lilies, but also on fritillaries, lilies-of-the-valley and onions. The species depicted here, the only member of the genus established in Britain, has been recorded from all parts of central Europe and is fairly common. The beetles can be found on their host plants from April to June; the larvae carry their excreta on their back.

7 **Clytra quadripunctata*, 7−11 mm (12 : 1)
Of the 3 members of this genus found in central Europe, only the one shown here occurs in Britain. The adult beetles may be found on birches, hawthorns, willows and oaks from May to August. The larvae develop in ants' nests, chiefly those of the genus *Formica*.

8 *Gynandrophthalma cyanea*, 4.5−6.5 mm (13 : 1)
There are 6 species of this genus in central Europe, only one of which occurs (very rarely, however) in Britain. From April to August *G. cyanea* can be found, generally not in large numbers, on hawthorns and willows.

9 *Coptocephala unifasciata*, 4−7 mm (15 : 2)
This genus is represented by 4 species in central Europe, but none of these are to be found in Britain. The one illustrated here may be found from April to October on various plants, e. g. wild parsnip, wild parsley and wild carrot. Like in many other bicoloured leaf-beetles, the colour-pattern of its elytra is extremely variable.

1 *Pachybrachys hieroglyphicus*, 3−4.5 mm   (16 : 1)
In central Europe there are 7 species belonging to this genus; none of them occur in Britain. The beetles have black and yellow chequered elytra, but the pattern differs markedly with the species, which live on various shrubs. The species depicted here is to be found from May to July on white willows in the southern part of central Europe.

2 *Cryptocephalus sericeus*, 6−8 mm   (17 : 26)
This genus is represented by 72 species in central Europe, only 19 of which also occur in Britain. The beetles have a cylindrical body with the appearance of having been docked in front and behind. The larvae are protected by a case which they carry about with them. The adult beetles, which are to be found on bushes or flowers, are mostly black, yellow or of a metallic colour, and often have characteristic markings on their head, pronotum and elytra. This species is fairly common everywhere in central Europe. The beetles can be found from May to July on yellow composite flowers.

3 *Cryptocephalus distinguendus*, 5−6 mm   (17 : 9)
This species is known to occur widely in northern and central Europe, but is usually found only in small numbers. The beetles can be found in May on birches.

4 *Cryptocephalus quinquepunctatus*, 4.5−7 mm   (17 : 7)
In earlier works this species is referred to as *C. signatus*. The spots on the elytra are generally separate, but they can merge in different ways to produce very variable markings. This species is generally uncommon in central Europe, and is absent from the northern part of the region. The beetles can be found from May to July, usually on willows, less often on alders.

5 *Cryptocephalus flavipes*, 3−5.5 mm   (17 : 48)
This species is very variable in size, with females sometimes being double the size of the males. In central Europe it is widely distributed and fairly common. The beetles can be found from April to August on hawthorn, oak, hazel and willow.

6 *Cryptocephalus vittatus*, 3−4.5 mm   (17 : 51)
This species is to be found in the southern part of northern Europe, as well as in southern and central Europe. The beetles can be found from May to August on golden daisies (*Chrysanthemum segetum*) and broom.

7 *Lamprosoma concolor*, 2−2.8 mm   (18 : 1)
This is the only species of *Lamprosoma* found in central and northern Europe. The beetles are small, with a convex ovate body. The species has been recorded from all parts of central Europe, but is not common. Towards the north it becomes rarer and in some parts it is completely absent. The beetles can be found on ground elder.

8 *Bromius obscurus*, 5−6 mm   (19 : 1)
This genus, listed in many works as *Adoxus*, is represented by only one species in central Europe which, however, forms two distinct subspecies. The beetle's elytra are mostly black, but can also be reddish. They can be found from May to October and occur over a great part of the entire holarctic region. The larvae develop on rose-bay willowherb and evening primrose and also on the roots of grape-vines, whose young shoots too can be damaged by the adult beetles.

9 *Pachnephorus pilosus*, 2.5−3.5 mm   (20 : 1)
The 3 species of this genus known to occur in central Europe comprise small, elongate beetles, most of which are covered with fine scales. None of them have been recorded from the British Isles. From March to July they crawl about on sand or among short grass beside water. The species shown here is found in southern and central Europe, where it is generally rare. Its most northerly limits are to be found in Silesia, Brandenburg and Hanover.

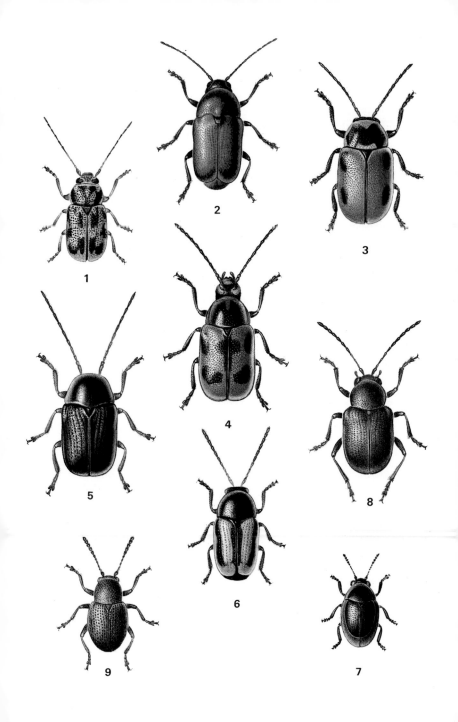

1 *Leptinotarsa decemlineata* – Colorado Beetle, 10 mm (22 : 1)
A native of America, this genus is represented in central Europe by just one species. In Colorado, the beetles and their larvae lived originally on wild *Solanum* species (nightshades), but turned to potatoes when these began to be cultivated there. After spreading to other parts of North America with potato crops they were later carried all over the world. They made their first appearance in central Europe in 1877 where they were successfully wiped out, but in 1922 they gained a firm footing in France. From 1936 they regularly invaded Germany and since 1948 the whole of Germany has been plagued by them. Since then the species has penetrated deep into the parts of the former USSR and it may now be only a question of time before it has colonized the entire holarctic region. If they appear in large numbers, the larvae and beetles can strip whole potato fields bare.

2 *Chrysolina cerealis* – Rainbow Leaf Beetle, 5.5–10 mm (23 : 12)
This genus, listed in many works as *Chrysomela*, has 46 species in central Europe, 16 of which occur in Britain. The males are generally smaller and more elongate than the females. The larvae live openly on their food plants where they eat holes in the leaves. This species forms many subspecies. It has been recorded from many parts of central Europe, but is not very common; towards the north and north-east it becomes rarer and there are regions where it is completely absent. The adult beetles and larvae live on various wild mints and thyme; adults are to be found from June to September. In Britain the species is confined to the area of Snowdonia, where it is protected by law.

3 *Chrysolina polita,* 6.5–8.5 mm (23 : 10)
This species occurs throughout the palaearctic region, and is probably the most generally distributed species of *Chrysolina* in Britain. Adult beetles appear from March to October on water-mint, cat-mint, balm, wolf's-foot, sage, marjoram and ground ivy, and hibernating individuals may be found in moss and leaf-litter during the winter months.

4 *Chrysolina varians,* 4.5–6 mm (23 : 26)
This very variably coloured species is common everywhere in central Europe. The elytra can be green, blue, violet, coppery red or even, on occasion, black. The beetles are to be found on St John's wort from May to September.

5 *Chrysolina fastuosa,* 5–6 mm (24 : 1)
This species is sometimes referred to a separate genus (*Dlochrysa*). It is very widely distributed in continental Europe, but of very local occurrence in Britain. From April to August the adult beetles can be found on hemp-nettle and dead-nettle.

6 *Gastrophysa polygoni,* 4–5 mm (28 : 1)
The 2 species of this genus found in central and northern Europe differ markedly in colour. *G. viridula* is uniformly metallic green, while *G. polygoni* always has a reddish-yellow pronotum. Just before the female lays the eggs it has an extremely swollen abdomen which often bulges beyond the elytra. This species can be seen from May to September on docks and knotgrass and is abundant everywhere.

7 *Phaedon cochleariae,* 3.5–4 mm (29 : 2)
The 6 species of this genus found in central Europe (4 in Britain) comprise small metallic beetles with regular rows of punctures on their elytra. The species shown here is fairly common and can be seen practically the whole year round on watercress and other plants in damp localities.

8 *Hydrothassa glabra,* 3–4 mm (31 : 1)
The elytra of the beetles in the 3 species of this genus found in central and northern Europe generally have a red border. The insects live in damp localities. The species depicted here is also referred to as *H. aucta* in earlier works. From March to August the beetles can be seen on buttercups and other ranunculaceous plants, often in fairly large numbers.

9 *Prasocuris phellandrii,* 5–6 mm (32 : 2)
There are 2 species of this genus in central and northern Europe. The beetles have an almost square pronotum and – for a leaf beetle – an unusually long and narrow body. This species occurs everywhere in central Europe, where the beetles live in damp localities and can be found from February to September and again in November on various umbelliferous plants standing in or beside water. The larvae are presumed to develop in the stems of water hemlock, *Sium* species and water dropwort.

276

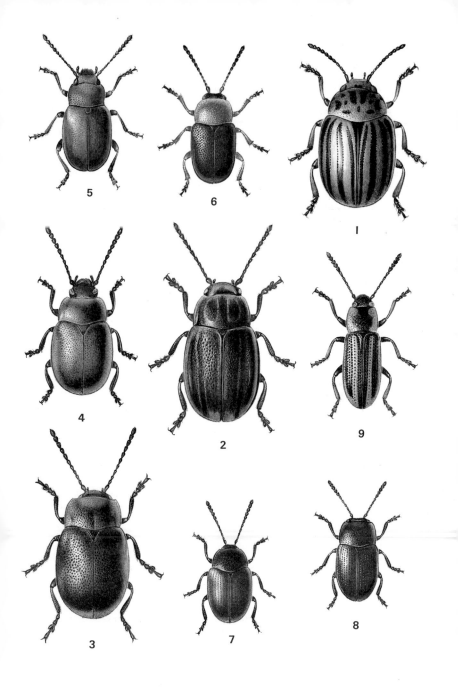

1 *Plagiodera versicolora, 2.5−4.5 mm (33 : 1)
This single species of this genus found in central and northern Europe is very variably coloured and may be blue, green or copper-coloured. It is distributed over a large part of the holarctic region. In central Europe the beetles can be found everywhere from April to September. The larvae attack willows (less often poplars) and frequently eat the leaves down to a skeleton.

2 Chrysomela vigintipunctata 6.5 −8.5 mm (34 : 4)
The 8 species of this genus found in central Europe feed on poplars, willows, birches and alders. The genus, represented by 3 species in Britain, is listed in some works as Melasoma, the name Chrysomela being used for Chrysolina. This species is to be found from April to August on willows, but nowhere in large numbers.

3 *Chrysomela populi − Red Poplar Leaf Beetle, 10−12 mm (34 : 6)
This species is distributed over the whole palaearctic region, and in central Europe can be seen from May to August on willows and poplars in large numbers. Like the other members of the genus, the beetles, when disturbed, release a protective secretory substance smelling strongly of prussic or carbolic acid. This is derived from the salicylic acid in the poplar and willow leaves eaten by the larvae.

4 *Phytodecta viminalis, 5.5−7 mm (35 : 4)
The 14 species of this genus found in central Europe have a similar form to species of Chrysolina and have characteristically spotted elytra. All the species have extremely variable colouring, often varying from a uniform light colour to almost completely black. This sometimes makes differentiation of the species difficult without examination of the male sex organs. The species shown here occurs in northern and central Europe, Siberia and North America. In central Europe the beetles are fairly abundant on willows from May to July.

5 *Phyllodecta vulgatissima, 4−5 mm (36 : 1)
The 6 members of this genus which occur in central Europe (4 in Britain) have an elongate and only moderately domed body. This species occurs widely in Europe, Siberia and North America. In central Europe the beetles can be found on willows from April to October in comparatively large numbers.

6 *Timarcha goettingensis − Bloody-nosed Beetle, 8−11 mm (37 : 2)
Six species of this genus are known to occur in central Europe (2 in Britain). The beetles are conspicuous for their large, almost spherical body and their broad tarsi. Since the central European species are wingless, they are mostly to be found crawling about on the ground or low vegetation, or hiding under moss and stones. The larvae, which are a metallic blue, green or bronze in colour, eat low plants (chiefly bedstraw). This species occurs in western, southern and central Europe, where the beetles can be found from March to October; in the north and east they become rarer. In earlier works this species is referred to as T. coriaria.

7 *Galerucella lineola, 4.5−6 mm (39 : 3)
The 7 central European members of this genus, all but one of which also occur in Britain, are finely pubescent. Both the beetles and the larvae feed on leaves, often eating them away until only the thicker ribs are left. The species shown here is fairly abundant from April to December on willows, hazels, alders and black poplars.

8 *Galeruca tanaceti, 6−10 mm (41 : 1)
In central Europe there are 7 species belonging to this genus. The beetles generally have distinctly ridged elytra. They are mostly to be found in dry, sunny places. This species can be seen from June to September on low plants. Its larval hosts are knapweed and other species of Compositae.

9 *Lochmaea caprea, 4−6 mm (42 : 1)
The 3 central and north European species of this genus somewhat resemble Galerucella but lack their coat of hairs. The various species live on quite different plants, one of them on heather, one on hawthorn, and the species depicted here mostly on willows; the adult beetles of this species can also be found on poplars and birches, from April to September.

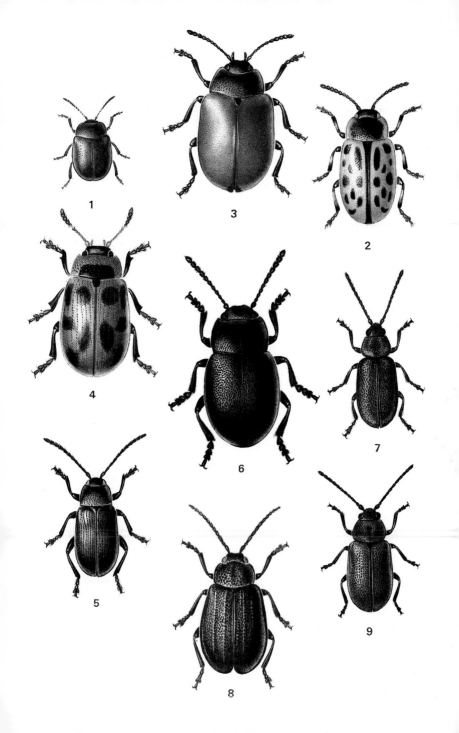

1 *Phyllobrotica quadrimaculata, 5−7 mm (43 : 1)
The two central European members of this genus are both yellow with black spots. The beetles live in damp, shady spots; when disturbed they fold up their legs and drop to the ground. The species depicted here (which is not very common in central Europe) can be seen from June to October on low vegetation. The larvae apparently develop in labiate plants of the genus *Scutellaria*.

2 *Luperus lyperus,* 4−4.5 mm (45 : 8)
There are 7 species of this genus in central Europe, 2 of which are also found in Britain. The beetles are soft and rather delicate, with very long antennae (especially in the narrower male), and they have thin legs. The species shown here occurs chiefly in the west and south of central Europe, becoming rarer towards the north; it can be found on willows from May to July.

3 *Agelastica alni* − Alder Leaf Beetle, 6−7 mm (46 : 1)
The single species of this genus found in central and northern Europe is blue-black or violet in colour. It is very common in most parts of central Europe except the Alps, in parts of which it is absent. In Britain it may now be extinct. The adult beetles and larvae live mainly on alder leaves, which they often eat right down to the large ribs.

4 *Sermylassa halensis,* 5−7 mm (47 : 1)
The only member of this genus occurring in central and northern Europe has gleaming metallic blue, green or (less often) copper-coloured elytra. The beetles can be found from July to September; the larvae live chiefly on bedstraw, but occasionally are found on other plants, such as willows, cow-wheat and roses.

5 *Phyllotreta undulata,* 1.8−2.5 mm (49 : 5)
There are 23 species of this genus in central Europe (15 in Britain). They belong to a group of the leaf beetles known as flea-beetles which possess stout hind femora enabling them to jump long distances. Flea-beetles are economically important, since hibernating beetles often emerge to attack young plants in the spring and may destroy a whole crop. *Phyllotreta* species are uniformly black, sometimes with a metallic sheen, or have broad yellow stripes down their elytra. They live mostly on Cruciferae but one species is found only on wild mignonette. Many are pests of cultivated Cruciferae, such as *Brassica;* their larvae live on roots and stems or are leaf-miners. The species *P. undulata* is found everywhere in central Europe and is generally abundant. From April to August the beetles can be found on various Cruciferae; they often do considerable damage in gardens and to vegetable crops.

6 *Phyllotreta atra,* 1.7−2.6 mm (49 : 14)
This species is common everywhere in central Europe. From March to October it can be found mostly on Cruciferae, but occasionally on other plants. It likewise often does damage to vegetable crops.

7 *Phyllotreta cruciferae* − 1.8−2.5 mm (49 : 15)
This species is distributed from the southern part of northern Europe across central and southern Europe to north and east Africa and across the Caucasus to western and inner Asia. In central Europe it is one of the commonest pests of vegetable crops. The beetles can be found on various Cruciferae from May to October.

8 *Longitarsus anchusae,* 1.5−2.4 mm (51 : 54)
There are 57 species of this genus in central Europe (41 in Britain). In all of the species the tarsus of the hind legs has an unusually long first segment (hence their generic name *Longitarsus*). The adult beetles and larvae live on various plants, especially those belonging to the Boraginaceae, Scrophulariaceae and Labiatae. The species shown here is widely distributed in central Europe, but its numbers diminish towards the north. It lives mainly on Boraginaceae.

9 *Longitarsus pellucidus,* 2−2.5 mm (51 : 1)
This species is found in the southern part of northern Europe, central and southern Europe, the Mediterranean region and Turkestan. In central Europe it becomes less frequent towards the north and in the north itself it is very rare or absent. Adult beetles occur on bindweed, which is presumably the larval host.

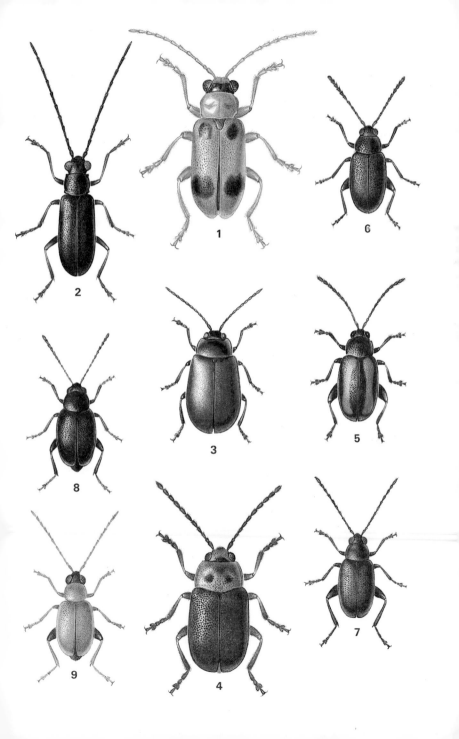

1 *Altica oleracea, 3.2−3.7 mm$\qquad$(52 : 7)

This genus (spelled *Haltica* in many works) is represented by 13 species in central Europe (7 in Britain). Although flea-beetles, none of the members of this genus are serious pests, as their host plants are all wild herbaceous plants and bushes. They are rather large for flea-beetles and the various species, all of them a metallic blue to green in colour, are often very difficult to distinguish from one another. *A. oleracea* is particularly variably coloured. It occurs everywhere in central Europe and is generally fairly common. The free-living larvae are known to feed on various plants, principally rose-bay willowherb and other Onagraceae.

2 *Batophila rubi, 1.4 −2 mm$\qquad$(54 : 2)

In earlier works, this genus, which is represented by 3 species in central Europe (2 in Britain), bears the name *Glyptina*. The beetles have an ovate, convex body and rows of punctures on their elytra. This species is widely distributed in northern and central Europe. From April to October the beetles can be found on blackberry, raspberry and strawberry plants.

3 *Lythraria salicariae, 1.8−2.3 mm$\qquad$(55 : 1)

The single species of this genus found in central and northern Europe is uniformly yellowish brown in colour. In central Europe its numbers diminish towards the south, where it is often to be found only sporadically. The beetles live in damp places on *Lysimachia*.

4 Crepidodera femorata, 3−4.5 mm$\qquad$(57 : 6)

There are 17 species of this genus in central Europe, only 3 of which occur in the British Isles. The beetles have yellow, reddish brown or metallic black, green or blue elytra. This is a boreomontane species ranging from northern and central Europe to Siberia. From May to October the beetles can be found in damp localities on hemp-nettle.

5 *Hippuriphila modeeri, 2−2.5 mm$\qquad$(60 : 1)

The only member of the genus *Hippuriphila* found in central and northern Europe lives in damp places on horsetails. It is distributed over much of Europe and Siberia, and is present everywhere in central Europe, where it is fairly common.

6 *Chaetocnema hortensis, 1.5−2.3 mm$\qquad$(66 : 17)

There are 20 species of this genus in central Europe (9 in Britain), of varying size and colour, many of them living on grasses, sedges or rushes. Since the larvae of some species bore holes at the base of the blades of cereal plants, they can do severe damage to crops. The species shown here (which in older works is referred to as *C. aridella*) occurs widely in Europe, the Mediterranean region and western Siberia. It lives on various grasses and, in central Europe, it is one of the commonest members of the genus and can be found everywhere in abundance.

7 Hispella atra, 3−4 mm$\qquad$(73 : 1)

The sole member of this genus found in central Europe is unmistakable because of its spines. There is a similar, brown species belonging to a related genus that occurs in the Mediterranean region. The species depicted here is to be found in dry localities on grasses. The larvae mine holes in various species, such as meadow-grass and couch-grass. The species becomes rarer towards the north, but reaches to southern Scandinavia, although not the British Isles.

8 *Cassida viridis − Tortoise Beetle, 8.5−10 mm$\qquad$(76 : 1)

This species is one of 28 members of the genus *Cassida* found in central Europe. Twelve species occur in Britain. They all have a flat, wide body beneath which they can retract their legs, head and antennae. The long, spiny larvae live on various herbaceous plants together with the adult beetles. The species shown here is distributed over the entire palaearctic region. When alive, the beetles are green with a narrow silver border at the base of their wings; when dead they are mostly yellow. In central Europe *C. viridis* is fairly abundant on water-mint, and may also be found on sage, woundwort, hemp-nettle, wolf's-foot and various Compositae.

9 *Cassida nebulosa, 6−7 mm$\qquad$(76 : 5)

This species is likewise distributed over the entire palaearctic region. The beetles live on fat-hen and other Chenopodiaceae, and sometimes are pests in beet and turnip fields.

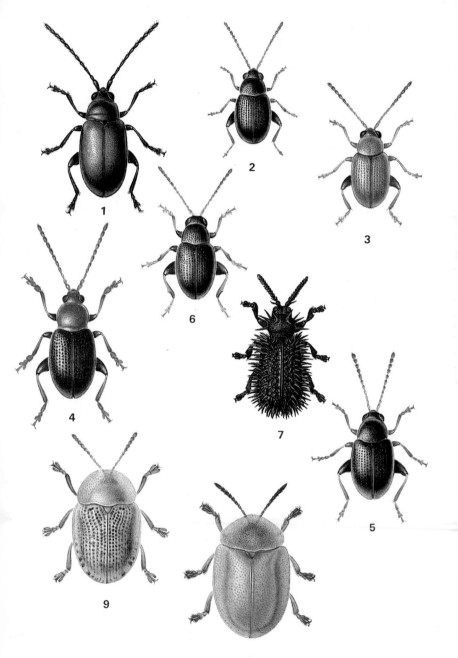

Family Bruchidae — seed beetles or bean weevils

This family (in older works referred to as Lariidae) is represened in central Europe by 8 genera with a total of 35 species, 13 of which occur in the British Isles. The beetles are mostly small and compact; no native species measures more than 5 mm in length. It is characteristic for the elytra not to cover the tip of the abdomen (the pygidium) and for the head to be produced into a short rostrum. The larvae develop in the fruits of leguminous plants. The females of most species lay their eggs on pods ripening in the fields. The newly hatched larvae, which have well-developed legs, penetrate the pod, bore a hole in the seed and develop in that. The first moult gives rise to a quite different, legless larva; this eventually pupates in the seed, and the adult beetle emerges after the seeds have been harvested. Secondary invasion of the seeds by such species is impossible, however. On the other hand various species introduced from other regions to central Europe with imported pulses are able to develop in ripe seeds and may be serious pests of food-stores.

1 *Spermophagus sericeus,* 1.2—2.8 mm (2 : 1)
Only one species of this genus occurs in central Europe; a second one is known in southern Europe. *S. sericeus* (in earlier works referred to as *S. cisti*) is common in central Europe and lives on various types of bindweed.

2 *Bruchus affinis,* 3—5 mm (3 : 6)
This genus (formerly known as *Laria*) has 12 species in central Europe. The one shown here is fairly abundant everywhere in central Europe, where it lives on peas (*Lathyrus* species and *Pisum sativum*).

3 **Bruchus rufipes,* 1.5—2.8 mm (3 : 13)
This is the commonest member of the genus in central Europe. It lives on vetches of the genus *Vicia.*

4 **Bruchus rufimanus,* 4—5 mm (3 : 5)
One of the largest European species of the family, this beetle occurs everywhere in central Europe, where it lives on vetches and *Pisum sativum.*

5 *Bruchus ervi,* 3—3.8 mm (3 : 9)
In central Europe this species is not to be found in the open, but in southern Europe it is found out-of-doors on lentils and sweet peas. Like the related species *B. lentis,* it is constantly being imported to central Europe in lentils.

6 **Bruchus pisorum,* 4—5 mm (3 : 8)
Because of its size, only one beetle of this species can develop in each seed. The larvae attack young pea seeds in the open. The beetles have been recorded from all parts of central Europe, but are not found in large numbers.

7 *Bruchidius marginalis,* 2.8—3.2 mm (4 : 2)
Most of the 13 species of this genus found in central Europe (2 in Britain) are smaller than those of the preceding genus and the males often have markedly serrate or dentate antennae. The species shown here is generally abundant in the southern part and middle of central Europe; in the north it is sporadic or absent. It lives on milk vetch.

8 **Bruchidius ater,* 1.7—3.5 mm (4 : 14)
This species — also known as *B. cisti* in earlier works — is characterized by its particularly variable size. It is abundant everywhere in central Europe and lives on broom.

9 **Acanthoscelides obtectus,* 3.2—4 mm (6 : 1)
This species — also named *A. obsoletus* in older works — is continuously being brought to central Europe in consignments of peas, beans and lentils from warmer parts of the world. Like other members of the genus which are imported *A. obtectus* is a pest of stored pulses in central Europe but has become established, and sometimes develops in the open, especially on beans.

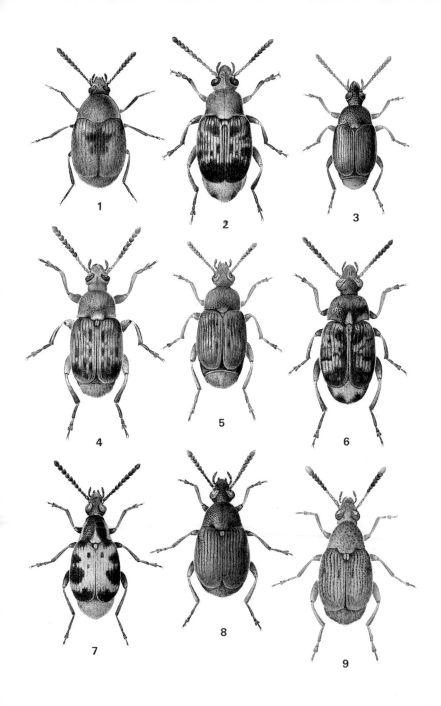

1 *Urodon suturalis*, 2−3 mm   (8 : 1)

There are 5 species of this genus in central Europe. These beetles are often included in the Bruchidae, but probably belong to the Anthribidae. This species occurs in southern and central Europe, becoming rarer towards the north. It develops on wild mignonette. The host plants of other members of the genus are species of *Reseda* and *Iberis*.

Family Anthribidae

Although very numerous in species in the tropics this family is represented by only 25 species in central Europe and only 7 in the British Isles. The beetles generally have a short, compact head produced into a broad rostrum. The majority of species develop in dead wood (branches and stumps), in which the larvae eat irregular passages. The adult beetles are to be found on fungus-infested wood. The genus *Brachytarsus* is an exception, since the larvae live under loose, soft bark and eat scale insects and plant lice.

2 *Tropideres albirostris*, 3−6 mm   (3 : 1)

T. albirostris is to be found chiefly on oaks, but occasionally on beeches also. The beetles occur everywhere in central Europe except in the north-west near the Atlantic; they can be fairly abundant in places.

3 *Platystomos albinus*, 6−12 mm   (10 : 1)

This is the largest and commonest species of the family in central Europe. In the summer the beetles appear on fungus-infested beech and alder stumps (seldom on other deciduous trees). Towards the north they become less frequent and there are places where they are absent altogether.

4 *Anthribus nebulosus*, 1.5−4 mm   (12 : 3)

There are 4 species of this genus in central Europe, of which 2 also occur in Britain. In the spring and summer the beetles can be found mostly on wood and less often on flowers. They hibernate − often gregariously − beneath loose bark. The species shown here is the only one found regularly in central Europe and it is one of the commonest members of the entire family; it is to be found on the wood of deciduous and coniferous trees practically the whole year round.

Family Curculionidae − true weevils or snout beetles

With some 1,200 species recorded from the region (416 in Britain), this is the largest beetle family after the rove beetles in central Europe. In all the species the head is characteristically produced into a rostrum, but this is of very variable length. The larvae, which live in plants, have a short cylindrical body and instead of legs they propel themselves by means of thick ridges on the under side of their body. While the larvae generally live inside plant tissues, the adult beetles generally feed on plants from the outside.

5 *Otiorhynchus niger*, 10−12 mm   (15 : 39)

This is one of the largest weevil genera and in central Europe it is well represented by 170 species. However, only 18 species occur in Britain. Many of them reproduce entirely, or in certain parts of their range only, by parthenogenesis. Where males occur, they are generally narrower than the females. The beetle shown here is a montane to subalpine species in central Europe and does not occur at lower altitudes in the north. The beetles are to be found − sometimes in large numbers − on spruces and on the leaves of small plants.

6 *Otiorhynchus scaber*, 4−6 mm   (15 : 89)

Only females of this species are known. They can be found on conifers, shrubs and herbaceous plants and also, in the Alps, under leaves, moss and stones. This is a fairly common species, especially in the mountains; in gardens it occasionally damages *Primula* species.

7 *Otiorhynchus sulcatus*, 8−10.5 mm   (15 : 126)

This species lives chiefly in flat country and is a frequent pest of agriculture and horticulture. Not infrequently the beetles appear indoors, since the larvae can also develop in the roots of pot-plants. The adult beetles are active after dusk.

8 *Otiorhynchus gemmatus*, 8−12 mm   (15 : 134)

The patches of light-coloured scales on its elytra make this species easy to identify. It chiefly inhabits the eastern Alps, where the beetles are often very common at high altitudes.

9 *Otiorhynchus ligustici*, 8−12 mm   (15 : 11)

This species occurs everywhere in central Europe and in some places it is abundant. It likes dry localities and is occasionally an agricultural pest.

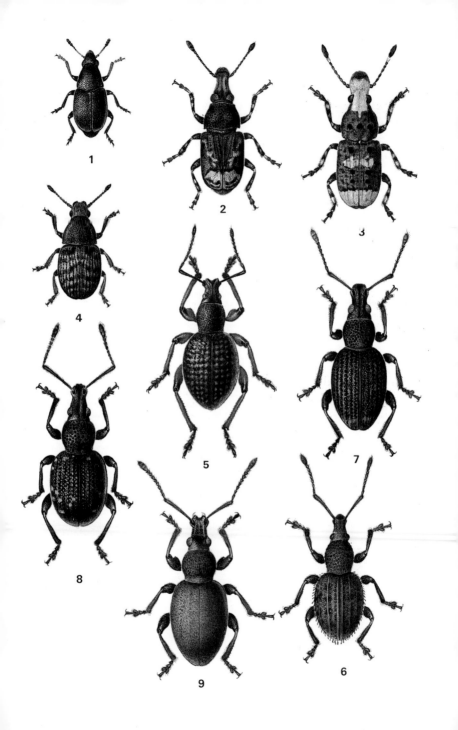

1 *Peritelus leucogrammus,* 2−3.5 mm   (20 : 1)
The 3 species of this genus found in central Europe are polyphagous and live on shrubs and herbaceous plants. This species is to be found chiefly in dry, warm places in the middle and southern parts of central Europe.

2 *Mylacus rotundatum,* 2−3 mm   (23 : 2)
The 3 central European species of this genus are small, round, black beetles covered more or less thickly with grey hairs. They prefer open grassland and can be found in dry, warm places very early in the spring. Like the members of the preceding genus, they are polyphagous and live on a variety of plants. *M. rotundatum* occurs only in the warmer parts of the middle and south of central Europe.

3 *Phyllobius calcaratus,* 7−12 mm   (21 : 15)
This genus is divided into 10 subgenera and is represented by 25 species in central Europe (10 in Britain). The beetles are mostly covered with scales, often of a metallic green colour. They live on trees, shrubs and herbaceous plants and in the spring and early summer they can often be found in large numbers. The larvae live in the soil and eat roots. *P. calcaratus,* which can vary from almost black to green, is common everywhere in central Europe and ascends in the mountains to very high altitudes. Although the beetles are polyphagous, they have a particular preference for alder and birch.

4 *Phyllobius pyri,* 6−7 mm   (21 : 21)
This species is common everywhere in central Europe. The males have a more elongate body than the females and the colouring of the beetles' scales is extremely variable. The adults are found mostly on trees and bushes, but the larvae probably develop on grass roots.

5 *Phyllobius argentatus,* 3.5−6 mm   (21 : 19)
This beetle is thickly covered with gold-green scales. Its antennae and legs are usually red, but the femora (and sometimes the whole leg) can be dark. This species has a very wide range, including the whole of Europe and Siberia east to Japan. In central Europe the beetles are very abundant and can be found on deciduous trees (occasionally on conifers also).

6 *Phyllobius oblongus,* 3−6 mm   (21 : 8)
This is one of the few *Phyllobius* species without scales on its back; instead, the beetles have a thin covering of grey hairs. This species is common everywhere in central Europe. The beetles are to be found on trees and shrubs and although they are polyphagous, they prefer rosaceous trees.

7 *Eusomus ovulum,* 5−7.5 mm   (32 : 1)
The single species of this genus found in central Europe is thickly covered with green scales. The beetles reproduce by parthenogenesis. The most northerly finds have been reported from Westphalia, Saxony, Brandenburg and the Harz mountains. The beetles live on sunny slopes.

8 *Sciaphilus asperatus,* 4.5−6 mm   (33 : 1)
This is the only species of *Sciaphilus* found in central Europe and the British Isles. Its elytra are variably marked and can be marbled grey or brown. It is widespread in Europe, including montane and subalpine areas, but is unknown in olive-growing regions. The beetles prefer damp and shady localities, are polyphagous and live on bushes and herbaceous plants.

9 *Brachysomus echinatus,* 2.2−3 mm   (35 : 6)
This genus has 8 species in central Europe (2 in Britain), all of them small beetles measuring only 1.5−3 mm in length; the females are stouter than the males. The beetles are very sluggish and live under fallen leaves and in moss, often on dry hillsides with short grass. The species shown here, which is common everywhere in central Europe, reproduces parthenogenetically.

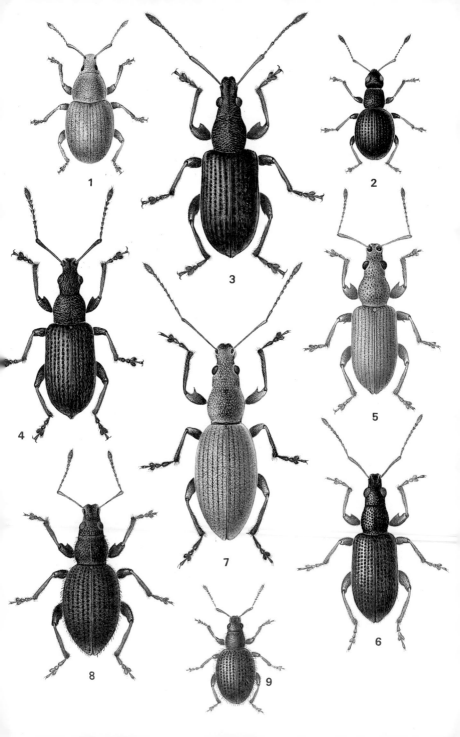

1 *Barypeithes araneiformis, 3−4 mm   (37 : 7)
This genus (spelled *Barypithes* in many works), is represented in central Europe by 16 species and in the British Isles by 5 species. The beetles differ from all their closest relatives by the complete absence of scales on their back, which is bare, shiny and brownish red to black, with only a few sparse hairs on it. The beetles are active at night, when they climb up various plants; by day they hide under leaves and moss. This species is to be found chiefly in the western part of central Europe and becomes rarer towards the east.

2 *Brachyderes incanus*, 7−10.5 mm   (37 : 7)
The only species of *Brachyderes* found in central Europe lives chiefly on moors with pine-trees, on which the beetles hibernate beneath loose flakes of bark. In the spring, the female lays her eggs in the soil. The larvae feed on the roots of pines while the adult beetles feed on the needles. In nurseries with 8- to 15-year-old pine trees the beetles can do severe damage, while the larvae can threaten the very existence of seedling nurseries.

3 *Polydrusus cervinus*, 3.9−5.7 mm   (27 : 11)
This genus, sometimes spelled *Polydrosus,* is represented by 26 species in central Europe (11 in Britain). The adults live on deciduous trees (conifers, shrubs or low plants), while the larvae eat the roots of the host plants. This species occurs everywhere on deciduous trees, especially oaks and birches.

4 *Polydrusus picus*, 2.5−4.5 mm   (27 : 19)
This species occurs chiefly in the eastern part of central Europe, where it can be abundant. The beetles can be found on oaks, birches and beeches.

5 *Liophloeus tessulatus*, 7−11 mm   (29 : 1)
In central Europe there are 2 very variable species belonging to this genus. The large, rather clumsy beetles are active only at night, when they crawl about and feed on low herbaceous plants, especially coltsfoot. They prefer damp localities and have a special liking for the banks of mountain streams. Their wings are rudimentary and they are unable to fly. The species shown here, the only member of the genus found in Britain, is represented by bisexual populations in mountainous areas, but otherwise reproduces by parthenogenesis. The beetles are to be found everywhere, often on ivy.

6 *Strophosoma melanogrammus*, 4−4.5 mm   (40 : 2)
This genus is represented by 6 species in Europe, all of them being found in the British Isles. The adult beetles live mostly on trees or on heather. The one illustrated here is flightless and reproduces by parthenogenesis. It feeds on various deciduous trees and also on conifers. The larvae live on the roots of dock and other herbaceous plants.

7 *Sitona sulcifrons*, 3−4 mm   (44 : 13)
This genus is represented by 25 species in central Europe (20 in Britain). The adult beetles feed on the leaves of various leguminous plants, mainly at night. The larvae live in the nodules which are to be found on the roots of these plants. The species shown here is widely distributed in central Europe, and is quite common in Britain. It lives on lucerne, red and white clover and can be a pest of lucerne and clover crops.

8 *Trachyphloeus bifoveolatus*, 2.8−5 mm   (26 : 8)
None of the 12 members of this genus found in central Europe (8 occur in Britain) measures more than 5 mm. The beetles are polyphagous and live on herbaceous plants, but are generally to be found under grass, leaves and stones, particularly on chalky or sandy ground or on sunny hillsides. They prefer flat, low-lying country to mountains and reproduce parthenogenetically. The species depicted here can be fairly common in places.

9 *Trophiphorus elevatus*, 5.3−7.5 mm   (50 : 4)
As far as is known, members of this genus occur only in Europe, mostly inhabiting the mountains in the north, the Alps and the mountains of the Balkan Peninsula. Nine species are found in central Europe, 3 of these also occurring in Britain. Many species reproduce parthenogenetically — some evidently in only part of their geographical range. The beetles live on many different plants. Nothing is known as yet of the larvae and their mode of life, but they are likely to be root feeders. The species illustrated here, referred to as *T. carinatus* in many works, is the commonest member of the genus and is widely distributed in central Europe; it is known to live on dog's mercury and chervil.

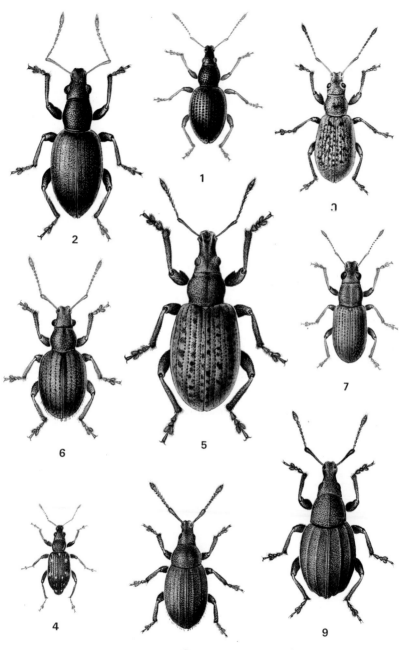

1 *Chlorophanus viridis*, 8−11 mm (49 : 2)

The sides of the pronotum and elytra of the 4 species of this genus found in central Europe are thickly covered with yellowish green scales. The beetles live on various trees, particularly alders and willows. The larvae probably feed on roots, but this still requires confirmation. The species shown here is fairly common and lives chiefly on alders.

2 *Tanymecus palliatus*, 8−12 mm (48 : 2)

Of the 2 species of this genus found in central Europe, the one depicted here is the more widely distributed. It lives on various plants and although polyphagous it prefers thistles and nettles.

3 *Leucosomus pedestris*, 14−18 mm (58 : 1)

This only species of *Leucosomus* found in central Europe can be fairly common in limestone regions. The larvae live on willows.

4 *Chromoderus affinis*, 8−11.5 mm (59 : 1)

Two members of this genus occur in central Europe. This one is commoner in the east and becomes rarer towards the west and south. It is the only species of the genus found in Britain, where it is very rare. The beetles can be found on milfoil and have a predilection for sandy areas, especially on the coast.

5 *Cleonus piger*, 10−16 mm (64 : 1)

Five central European species were formerly included in this genus, but all but *C. piger* have now been allocated to other genera. These large beetles live on various species of thistles, mostly in sandy places; they are commoner in the eastern part of central Europe than in the west.

6 *Lixus elongatus*, 4−11 mm (51 : 23)

This genus is represented by 22 species in central Europe, only 3 of which occur with any certainty in Britain. The males have a shorter rostrum than the females. The adult beetles live on a variety of plants and the larvae develop inside the stems. This species is widely distributed, especially in the south, and is sometimes quite abundant. Towards the north the beetles become rarer and in some regions are not to be found at all.

7 *Larinus planus*, 5−8 mm (52 : 7)

Seven species of this genus inhabit central Europe and 4 others are found in adjacent regions (especially the Mediterranean area). The beetles are of a stouter build than their relatives in the genus *Lixus*. They all live on thistles, but avoid competing with each other by means of a series of specializations. Direct competition has been obviated by specialization of the various species on different groups of thistles (globe thistles, carline thistles or members of the genera *Cirsium* or *Carduus*). Competition on the same plant is avoided by dividing up living space, with some larvae living in the buds or flowers, some in the stems and others in the roots. The length of the rostrum in *Larinus* species varies with the mode of life. When they first emerge, the beetles are often thickly covered with a yellow dust, which can be renewed if it is rubbed off. The species shown here, the only member of the genus found in Britain, is also referred to as *L. carlinae* in earlier works. It is fairly common in the southern part of central Europe, rarer in the middle and completely absent in parts of the north.

8 *Rhinocyllus conicus*, 4−7 mm (54 : 1)

The only species of this genus is more elongate than the related *Larinus* species and has more parallel sides and a very short, angular rostrum. It becomes rarer towards the north, but is found, although very rarely, in Britain.

9 *Donus comatus*, 7−10 mm (124 : 10)

In central Europe there are 11 species of this genus, which was formerly included under *Hypera*. None of them occur in the British Isles. They live on various low plants. This is a montane to subalpine species restricted to central Europe. It is to be found on coltsfoot.

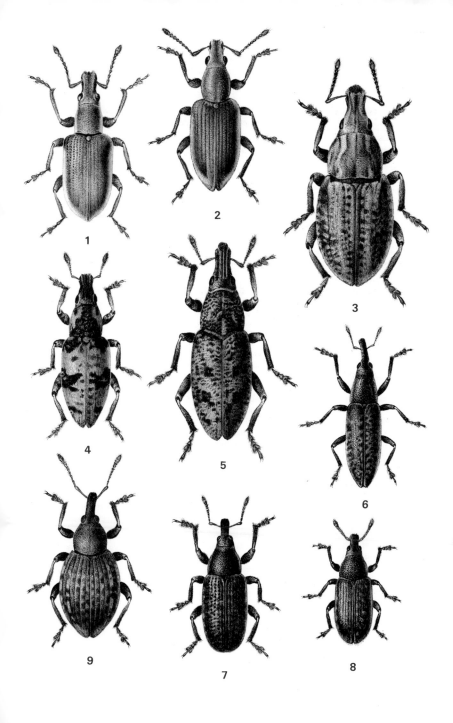

1 *Hypera punctata, 7−10 mm (125 : 1)
This genus (formerly known as *Phytonomus*) is represented by 25 species in central Europe (15 in Britain). The larvae pupate in a transparent cocoon attached to the leaves or stem of their food plant. The species shown here, which in some works is referred to as *Phytonomus zoilus*, is common everywhere in central Europe.

2 *Hypera meles, 3.5−5 mm (125 : 14)
This small species occurs throughout Europe. The adult beetles may be found on clover.

3 *Hypera arator, 5−7 mm (125 : 20)
This species is fairly common everywhere in central and northern Europe, and in the Alps it ascends to very high altitudes. The larvae live on *Dianthus* species (pinks).

4 *Hypera postica, 4.5−5.5 mm (125 : 29)
As indicated by the name (*variabilis*) under which it is known in many works, this species has very variable markings, especially on its back, and can vary from a more or less uniform grey or brown to distinctly variegated. It abounds everywhere in central Europe and can be found high up in the Alps.

5 *Alophus triguttatus, 6.5−8 mm (123 : 3)
Of the 3 species of this genus found in central Europe, this is the most widely distributed, and is the only one known to occur in Britain. The beetles are fairly abundant, but little is known of their life and habits. They can be found under stones and the leaves of various herbaceous plants, especialy in riverside meadows; they have also been found on beets and turnips.

6 *Lepyrus capucinus, 10−12 mm (114 : 4)
Four members of this genus occur in central Europe, where the beetles live on willows. The species depicted here, the only member of the genus recorded from Britain, is fairly common in most parts of central Europe, although reports from Austria describe it as rare.

7 *Hylobius abietis − Large Pine Weevil, 8−14 mm (115 : 2)
Of the 4 species of this genus found in central Europe, this one and the somewhat smaller *Hylobius pinastri* (6−9 mm) are very hard to tell apart and their biology is also similar. The adult beetles appear chiefly from April to June, but can still be found up to September. The females lay their eggs on dying pine and spruce roots. The larvae at first feed on the inner bark, but later they encroach on the sap-wood and finally pupate in a hook-shaped passage in the wood itself; the adult beetles do not emerge until the following year. The larvae do little harm, but the adult beetles cause serious damage since, after leaving their winter quarters, they feed on the cambium and bark of conifers from May to September. Although they are polyphagous, they prefer 3- to 6-year-old pines and spruces; in years of unusual abundance they will also attack younger trees, which wilt and then die. The species illustrated here is very common in central Europe and is considered to be the worst insect pest of young conifers; its smaller cousin is less abundant.

8 Liparus glabirostris, 17−21 mm (116 : 2)
Seven species of this genus are known to occur in central Europe, only one of which is found in Britain. These are the largest of north and central European weevils. They develop in the roots of various umbelliferous plants. This species is a native of central Europe; it lives chiefly in mountainous regions (to subalpine altitudes in the Alps). The adult beetles can be found on coltsfoot. Although this is the commonest species in central Europe, it is found in abundance only in Bavaria and Silesia, and there are many regions, especially in the north, where it has not been reported for years.

9 *Leiosoma deflexum, 2.5−3 mm (117 : 1)
Eight species of this genus occur in central Europe (3 in Britain). The tiny beetles live mostly in mountainous regions on the outskirts of forests. They are to be found in association with *Ranunculus* species, but also under moss and damp fallen leaves. The species shown here is the commonest member of the genus, but its numbers diminish towards the north. The beetles can be found on wood anemone, creeping buttercup and other plants.

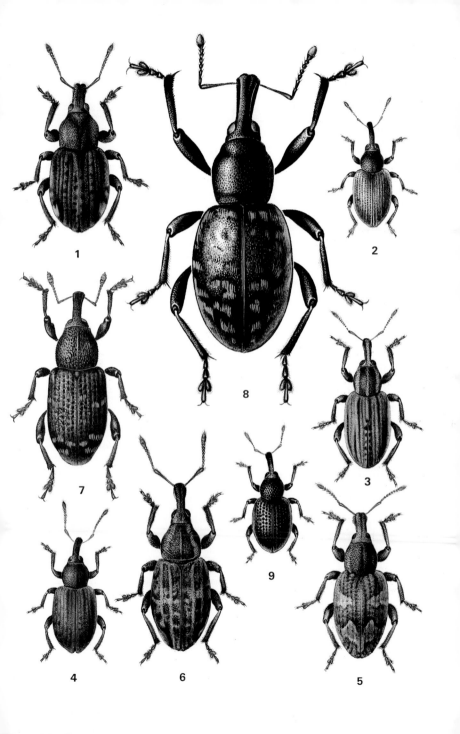

1 *Pissodes piceae,* 7−10 mm (111 : 1)

This genus is represented by 8 species in central Europe, 3 of which occur in Britain. The larvae live beneath the bark of various conifers and pupate in the wood just under the bark in a silken cocoon. The genus comprises some of the most serious forestry pests, each species specializing in its own particular conifer. The one shown here lives on silver firs and is primarily a montane species. After the eggs have been laid the trees look as if they had been sprayed with whitewash, owing to the resin which oozes from the holes bored by the females in the bark. The larvae eat irregular passages in the inner bark. This species prefers 40- to 80-year-old timber; it attacks ailing, damaged or deformed rather than healthy trees, because the latter's stronger resin flow might suffocate the larvae. It may be partially responsible for the gradual disappearance of silver firs.

2 **Pissodes pini,* 7−9 mm (111 : 6)

This beetle has similar habits to the preceding species, but mainly attacks the tops of pines. In central Europe it is common everywhere where pines occur.

3 **Magdalis ruficornis,* 2−3.5 mm (112 : 2)

There are 21 species of this genus in central Europe (8 in Britain). The larvae live in the same way as those of *Pissodes* in branches and young trunks of deciduous and coniferous trees. The pupal chambers often penetrate deep into the wood. The damage caused is also similar to that caused by *Pissodes.* The species shown here lives on fruit-trees and rowan-trees and is common everywhere in central Europe.

4 *Anoplus plantaris,* 2 mm (179 : 1)

This genus is represented by 3 species in central Europe (2 in Britain); *A. plantaris* is found on the leaves of birches, oaks and other young deciduous trees.

5 **Cossonus linearis,* 4.5−5 mm (77 : 3)

The larvae of the 3 species of this genus found in central Europe live in rotting wood on living or dead deciduous and coniferous trees. This species becomes rarer in a south-to-north direction. The beetles are to be found in the trunks of poplar and willow trees.

6 **Rhyncolus chloropus,* 4 mm (78 : 4)

The 6 central European species of this genus, which used to be called *Eremotus,* are to be found on damaged parts of deciduous trees and conifers, where they bore in the outer part of the wood (not in the bark). The species shown here occurs chiefly in the eastern part of central Europe and elsewhere only sporadically. The beetles attack damaged deciduous trees and conifers, and are found chiefly in the parts of the roots showing above the ground.

7 **Hexarthrum exiguum,* 3 mm (82 : 2)

This only member of this genus found in central Europe used to be referred to the genus *Rhyncolus,* and it has the same habits as members of that genus. The species depicted here lives in the inner wood of oaks, beeches and elms. It is not permanently established in most parts of central Europe, but is often imported.

8 **Cryptorrhynchus lapathi,* 5.5−9 mm (134 : 1)

This genus, which is represented by only one species in central and northern Europe, is referred to in many works as *Cryptorrhynchidius.* Alders (less often willows, poplars and birches) provide food for both adults and larvae. The adult beetles feed on the bark, while the larvae first of all feed beneath it and then tunnel into the inner bark, sap-wood and heart-wood. A large-scale attack can kill or deform young trees.

9 **Acalles camelus,* 2.5−4 mm (135 : 6)

Nine species of this genus occur in central Europe (3 in Britain). The beetles live and develop in dead branches on deciduous trees and conifers. They are also to be found on brushwood and dry timber. The species depicted here occurs chiefly in the mountainous parts of central Europe and is thus commoner in the south than in the north, where it is very rare. It is to be found on the bark of old oaks.

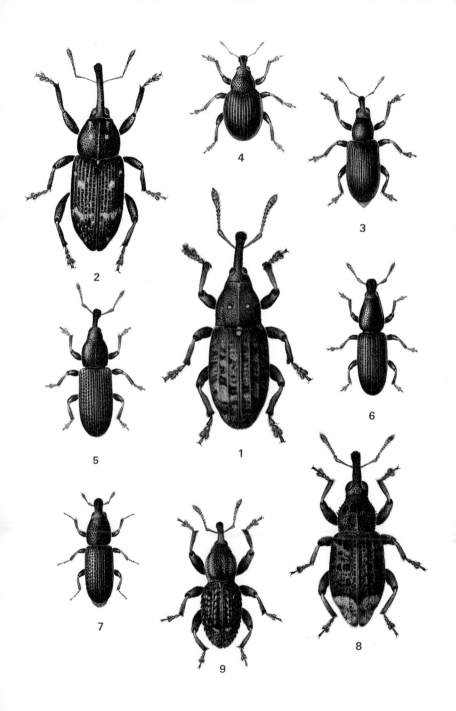

1 *Zacladus geranii, 2−3 mm (160 : 1)
In central and northern Europe, including Britain, there are 2 species of this genus, which in older works is called *Allodactylus*. The beetles live chiefly on species of *Geranium:* they are black and the thorax and elytra lack scales. The species shown here is the commoner member of the genus in central Europe, where it is more abundant in the south. It is to be found on cranesbill.

2 *Coeliodes dryados, 2−2.8 mm (157 : 3)
This genus is represented by 9 species in central Europe, of which 5 occur in Britain. They live on various deciduous trees, especially young oaks. This species (also listed as *C. quercus* in earlier works) occurs on oak foliage everywhere in central Europe and generally in large numbers.

3 *Auleutes epilobii, 2.8 mm (161 : 1)
The only species of this genus found in central Europe was formerly listed under various other generic names, such as *Craponius, Cnemogonus* and *Auletes*. The beetles live on rosebay willowherb and are fairly common everywhere in central Europe.

4 *Cidnorhinus quadrimaculatus, 2−2.5 mm (169 : 1)
This only species of this genus found in central and northern Europe is abundant throughout the region. In the Alps it ascends to subalpine altitudes. The beetles are to be found on stinging-nettles.

5 *Ceutorhynchus floralis, 1.3−1.5 mm (164 : 1)
This species is representative of a group of species sometimes separated from *Ceutorhynchus* as a separate genus − *Neosirocalus*. In Europe there are 9 species of this group, all of which live on various low plants. The one shown here occurs everywhere in central Europe (in the Alps up to subalpine altitudes). The beetles live on various Cruciferae, such as shepherd's purse and charlock, on which they can often be found in large numbers. The larvae develop in the seed-capsules of lady's smock.

6 *Ceuthorhynchidius troglodytes, 2 mm (167 : 1)
The adults of the 6 central European species of this genus resemble those of *Ceutorhynchus*. The species depicted here occurs in abundance in meadows, beside rivers and on embankments, wherever there is plenty of vegetation. The larvae develop in plantains.

7 *Ceutorhynchus geographicus, 4−5 mm (163 : 115)
This genus is represented by 113 species in central Europe and 52 in the British Isles. The beetles live on the herbaceous plants in whose stems or roots the larvae develop. This species is to be found everywhere in central Europe, in relative abundance, on viper's bugloss and alkanet.

8 *Ceutorhynchus cruciger, 3.8−4 mm (163 : 109)
This species becomes less abundant in central Europe from the south towards the north, where there are areas in which it is completely absent. The beetles can be found on hound's tongue in rich, grassy pastures.

9 *Ceutorhynchus litura, 2.8−3.8 mm (163 : 94)
This species feeds on various species of thistles, especially *Carduus nutans* and *Carduus crispus*. They are to be found everywhere and are fairly abundant.

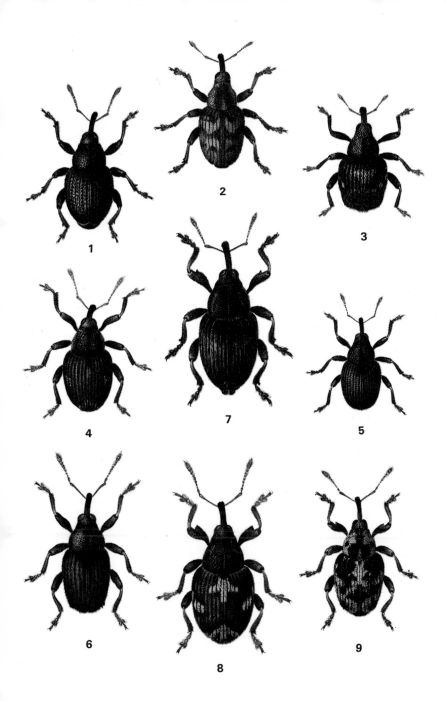

1 *Ceutorhynchus campestris,* 2.2−2.8 mm (163 : 91)

This species occurs in the southern part of northern Europe as well as in central and southern Europe and, in the Alps, is to be found at quite high altitudes. In central Europe the beetles can be found everywhere in large numbers on tansy.

2 *Ceutorhynchus melanostictus,* 2.2−3 mm (163 : 81)

This species is widely distributed in the southern part of northern Europe, central and southern Europe eastwards to Asia Minor. In central Europe the beetles occur chiefly in damp localities, where they can be found mostly on water-mint, often in abundance.

3 *Ceutorhynchus napi,* 3.2−3.8 mm (163 : 38)

This species has a generally similar distribution to the preceding species, but in central Europe the beetles are to be found chiefly in the southern part, where they are fairly common. The beetles live on Cruciferae, in particular winter-cress, garlic mustard and watercress. They also attack *Brassica* species, causing deformation (twisting) of the stems. Only the top and bottom parts of the stems remain unaffected, the remainder being hollowed out by the yellowish white larvae. While the damage caused to rape plants is small, cabbage seedlings can be severely affected.

4 *Ceutorhynchus assimilis,* 2.2−3 mm (163 : 40)

This species inhabits the whole of Europe. It attacks a number of different cruciferous plants, but is a particular pest of oilseed-rape. When the rape buds turn yellow adults of this species emerge from hibernation and appear in the fields. When the female is ready to lay its eggs it bores a hole in the wall of a rape seed-pod and lays an egg on the seed; one larva is capable of destroying up to 10 seeds, so that a mass attack can do considerable damage. The fully-grown larvae bore their way out of the pod, drop to the ground and pupate in the soil.

5 *Ceutorhynchus quadridens,* 2.5−3.2 mm (163 : 23)

This species attacks winter rape at the end of April or the beginning of May. The females lay their eggs at the base of the leaf-stalk; the larvae eat the inside of the leaf-stalk, the midrib and the main and subsidiary ribs. Outwardly the plants look no different, but they are considerably weakened. This species occurs everywhere in central Europe and can also be found on various other Cruciferae.

6 *Ceutorhynchus erysimi,* 1.8−2.3 mm (163 : 3)

This species, which is widely distributed in Europe, Siberia, Asia Minor and the Mediterranean region, is common everywhere in central Europe. The beetles feed on a variety of cruciferous plants.

7 *Rhinoncus pericarpius,* 2−3.5 mm (145 : 4)

There are 8 species of this genus in central Europe (6 in Britain). The beetles are most commonly found in damp localities on knotgrass. The species shown here, which is the commonest member of the genus, is found throughout the palaearctic region and has also been recorded from North America. The beetles live on docks as well as on knotgrass.

8 *Eubrychius velutus,* 1.8−2 mm (142 : 1)

The only species of this genus found in central Europe (also known as *velatus*) used to be included in the genus *Litodactylus.* The beetles have been recorded from all parts of northern and central Europe, but are in general rare. They are to be found in clean stagnant water on the stems of aquatic plants. The larvae develop in the stems of pondweed, water horsetail and water milfoil.

9 *Phytobius comari,* 2−2.5 mm (144 : 1)

This genus in represented in central Europe by 11 species, 8 of which occur in Britain. The beetles are to be found on river banks and beside stagnant water, often running about in the sand. The larvae of most species develop in the stems of various species of *Polygonum.* The species shown here is associated with the marsh cinquefoil; it occurs chiefly in the north and east of central Europe.

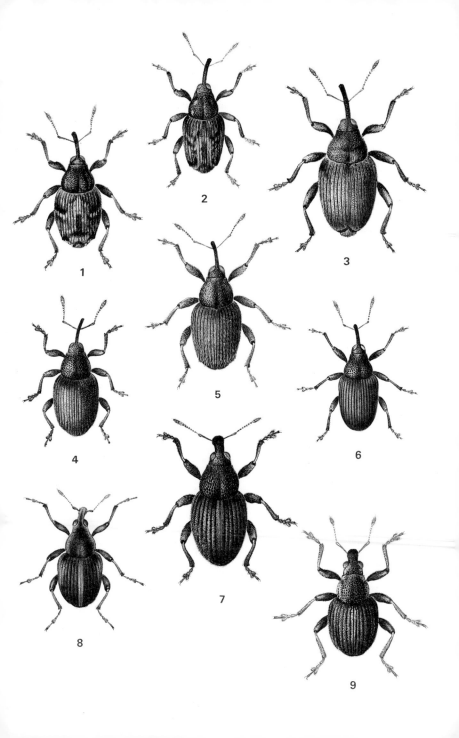

1 *Poophagus sisymbrii*, 2.5–3.5 mm (155 : 1)

In central Europe there are 2 species belonging to this genus. The beetles live on bog plants growing beside water. This species, the only member of the genus found in Britain, is widespread in the southern part of northern Europe and in central Europe, but is often comparatively rare. The larvae develop in the stems of various watercresses and the adult beetles are usually to be found on the same plants.

2 *Mononychus punctumalbum*, 5 mm (141 : 1)

The only central and north European species of this genus has very variable colouring. It occurs regularly in the south of central Europe, where the beetles can be found on yellow flags, but becomes rarer towards the north.

3 *Baris chlorizans*, 3.5–6 mm (137 : 18)

There are 21 species of this genus in central Europe (5 in Britain). The beetles are to be found on various Cruciferae, Compositae and Chenopodiaceae. The beetle depicted here occurs in central and southern Europe. It is found everywhere in central Europe, but is generally not very common; towards the north it becomes rarer.

4 *Sitophilus granarius* – Granary Weevil, 2.3–3.5 mm (131 : 1)

The 2 species of this genus (formerly *Calandra*) found in central Europe are serious pests of stored grain. The original home of the species shown here is unknown, but it seems to have come from the Near East. From there it has spread with trade throughout the temperate regions of the world. Since a tropical or subtropical climate is not favourable to its development, it is of no commercial significance in hot countries. The beetles and their larvae eat grain of any kind, but chiefly wheat and rye. They occur everywhere in central Europe and not infrequently they appear in vast numbers in silos and mills.

5 *Sitophilus oryzae* – Rice Weevil, 2.3–3.5 mm (131 : 2)

This close relative of the Granary Weevil has fully developed wings, whereas those of the Granary Weevil are rudimentary, and that species is unable to fly. The Rice Weevil is cosmopolitan in distribution and, as it is warmth-loving, is an important pest in the tropics. In central Europe it occurs only in warm warehouses and is never to be seen in the open. It attacks all kinds of grain (maize, rye, wheat, millet, etc) as well as rice.

6 *Curculio nucum* – Nut Weevil, 6–9 mm (110 : 5)

This genus (also named *Balaninus* in earlier works) is represented by 11 species in central Europe (8 in Britain). They all have a strikingly long rostrum, which is longer in the female than in the male. The beetles are to be found chiefly on hazels and oaks. The species shown here occurs everywhere in central Europe and is fairly abundant. The females lay the eggs in young hazelnuts, the larvae eat the kernels and, when they are full-grown, bore their way out through the shell, drop to the ground and pupate in the soil.

7 *Curculio glandium* – Acorn Weevil, 4–8 mm (110 : 6)

This close relative of the Nut Weevil occurs chiefly in the southern and middle parts of central Europe and becomes rarer towards the north. Its biology is similar to that of the Nut Weevil, but the larvae develop in acorns.

8 *Curculio villosus*, 4–5 mm (110 : 4)

This species is distributed over the whole of central Europe and is fairly common. The beetles can be found on oak; however, the larvae do not develop in acorns, but in young wasp galls.

9 *Curculio crux*, 2–2.3 mm (110 : 9)

In older works, this and 2 related species were placed in a genus of their own – *Balanobius* – which is today considered to be only a subgenus. The beetles are to be found chiefly on willows; they are abundant everywhere in central Europe.

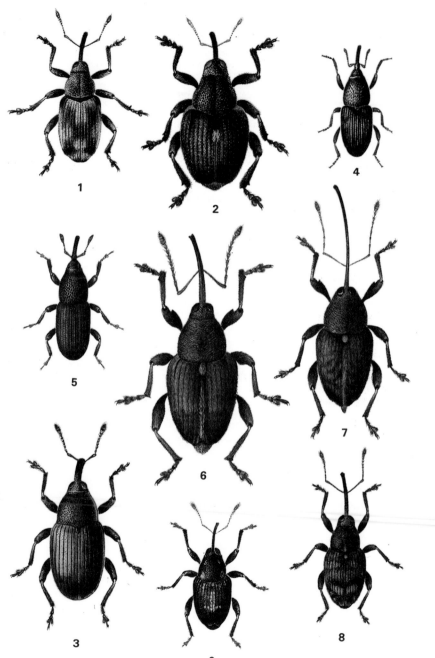

1 *Anthonomus rubi* – Strawberry Blossom Weevil, 2–3 mm (106 : 15)
In central Europe there are 18 species belonging to this genus; 12 are found in the British Isles. The beetles generally hibernate under moss, beneath bark or in the soil; in the spring they leave their hiding-places and make for flowering trees or shrubs, where they mostly eat parts of the flowers and prevent formation of the fruit. The larvae eat out the insides of buds, so that they drop off without opening. When full-grown they leave the buds and pupate in the soil. The species shown here, which is common everywhere in central Europe, lives chiefly on raspberries and strawberries, but also on other *Rubus* species.

2 *Anthonomus pomorum* – Apple Blossom Weevil, 3.5–4.5 mm (106 : 1)
After spending the winter in hiding, the adult beetles of this species emerge in the spring (generally in March) and fly to apple-trees and occasionally pear-trees, where the females lay their eggs on young buds. The larvae eat the buds from inside, damaging the petals, so that the flowers do not open. However, at first the buds go on growing, turning brown as if touched by frost. The Apple Blossom Weevil abounds everywhere in central Europe and in years of abundance it can wreak havoc in orchards.

3 *Dorytomus longimanus,* 4.5–8 mm (90 : 1)
This genus is represented by 22 species in central Europe, 14 of which are found in the British Isles. Both the adult beetles and larvae live on poplars and willows. The beetles hibernate mostly in the fallen leaves of their host tree, but sometimes in cracks in the trunk. The species depicted here, which is very common in central Europe, lives on willows and poplars.

4 *Dorytomus melanophthalmus,* 3–4 mm (90 : 19)
This species has very variable colouring and several aberrations have been described. It is distributed over the whole of Europe, and in central Europe it can be found everywhere in large numbers on willows.

5 *Dorytomus taeniatus,* 4.5–5 mm (90 : 8)
This species is to be found on poplars, willows and birches. In central Europe it is abundant everywhere and in the Alps it is found up to quite high altitudes.

6 *Dorytomus dorsalis,* 3.5–4 mm (90 : 23)
This species is found in northern and central Europe, but is rather patchily distributed. It lives on willows and can be quite abundant in the regions where it does occur.

7 *Notaris scirpi,* 6–8.5 mm (92 : 3)
In central Europe there are 7 species belonging to this genus, 4 of which also occur in Britain. The beetles, which live on waterside or marsh plants, are generally not very abundant. The species illustrated here is distributed over the whole of the palaearctic region from Europe, across Siberia, to Japan and is one of the few common members of the genus. The beetles are to be found on sedges, reeds and rushes at the edge of stagnant water.

8 *Notaris acridulus,* 4–5 mm (92 : 4)
This species is generally also quite common in marshy localities. It lives on sedges. The beetles often hibernate in large numbers in sedge litter, and sometimes under bark, in rotting wood or in fallen leaves.

9 *Grypus equiseti,* 5–7 mm (95 : 1)
Three members of this genus, referred to as *Grypidius* in many earlier works, occur in central Europe. None of the species is very common. The one shown here, which also occurs in North America, lives on horsetails beside stagnant and running water.

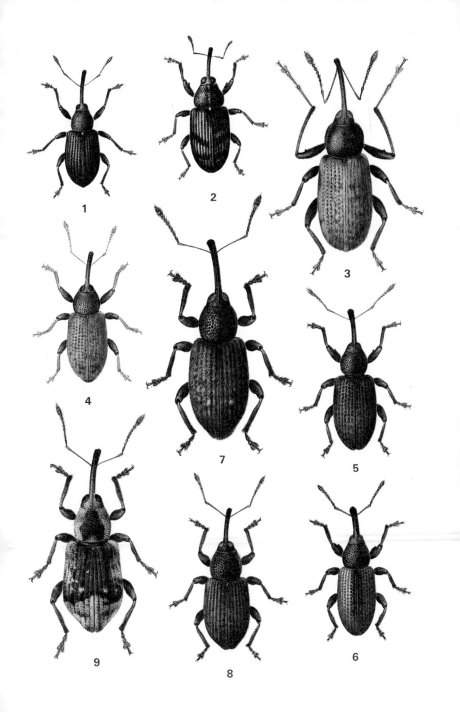

1 *Thryogenes festucae, 4.5−5.5 mm (93 : 3)
In central Europe there are 4 species belonging to this genus, which was formerly known as *Erirrhinus;* 3 of the species are also found in Britain. The beetles live on reed-grasses in swampy localities and on river banks. This species occurs everywhere in central Europe, but is often not at all common. It lives on rushes and sedges.

2 *Bagous glabrirostris, 1.5−3.7 mm (87 : 24)
There are 20 species of this genus in central Europe, and a similar number are to be found in the British Isles. The beetles live in swamps and at the edge of stagnant water − usually on low plants, but occasionally under water, despite the few outward signs of adaptation to this element. The species depicted here occurs beside water and in clay-pits everywhere in central Europe. The larvae live in the stems of pondweed, water-plantain and coltsfoot.

3 *Hydronomus alismatis, 2.5−3.2 mm (88 : 1)
This species occurs beside stagnant water, pools and ditches everywhere in central Europe. Both the adults and larvae live on water-plantain.

4 *Ellescus bipunctatus, 2.5 mm (102 : 2)
Three members of this genus, sometimes spelled *Elleschus,* live in central Europe. The one shown here, the only species found in Britain, can be found throughout central Europe on willows, especially in mountainous regions. The larvae live in the catkins.

5 *Tychius quinquepunctatus, 3.5−4 mm (104 : 1)
This species occurs chiefly in the south and middle of central Europe and is rarer to the north. It lives on various types of wild peas and vetches.

6 *Tychius stephensi, 2−2.5 mm (104 : 20)
The 23 species of this genus found in central Europe (12 in Britain) live on various papilionaceous flowers. This one is common everywhere in central Europe and can be found on melilot and occasionally on other plants.

7 *Miccotrogus picirostris, 2 mm (104 : 19)
This species occurs throughout the whole of central Europe and in the Alps it ascends to subalpine altitudes. It can be found in abundance on various low plants. The larvae mine the leaves of various clovers.

8 Sibina viscariae, 2.5−3 mm (105 : 12)
This genus is represented by 13 species in central Europe, 4 of which occur in the British Isles. The various species live on different low plants. The one depicted here occurs in the southern and middle part of central Europe, where it is generally fairly common. Towards the north and in the Alps it is frequently absent. The beetles can be found on bladder campion and other caryophyllaceous plants.

9 *Rhynchaenus quercus, 2.5−3.5 mm (180 : 5)
In central Europe there are 31 members of this genus, which is listed in some works as *Orchestes;* 14 species occur in Britain. The beetles and their larvae live on various shrubs and trees, where they eat the leaves, sometimes right down to the skeleton. The species shown here is widely distributed in the south of northern Europe and in central and southern Europe. It lives on young oaks, often in large numbers. The larvae mine the leaves in which they finally make a chamber in which to pupate.

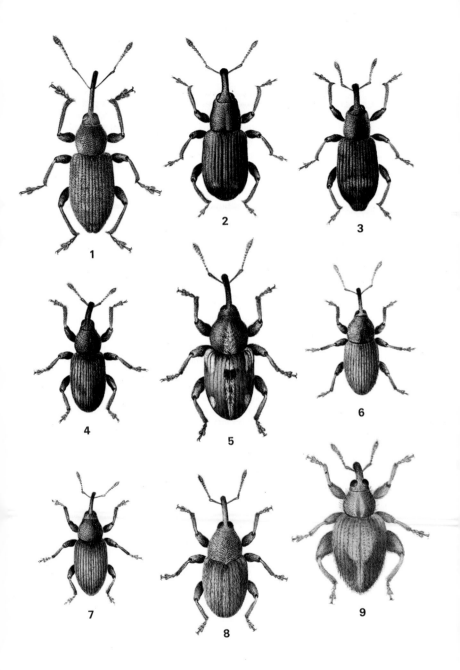

1 *Rhynchaenus fagi, 2—2.5 mm   (180 : 13)
The development of the larvae of this species is bound to the beech, and the beetles' distribution virtually coincides with that of the tree. This species occurs everywhere in central Europe and is often very common. The adults feed on beech leaves, leaf-stalks and flowers, but also visit fruit-trees, bushes and various herbaceous plants. After hibernating, adults appear in the spring to feed on young beech leaves. The females then lay the eggs on the ribs of the leaves, which the larvae mine, making first a tunnel and then a chamber. This is at first pale yellow, but later turns dark brown, so that a severely affected tree looks as though it had been damaged by a late frost.

2 *Rhynchaenus salicis, 2—2.5 mm   (180 : 25)
This species occurs throughout the holarctic region and is abundant everywhere in central Europe. Its biology resembles that of the other members of the genus and it lives on willows.

3 *Rhynchaenus populi, 2—2.5 mm   (180 : 28)
As its name suggests, this very common central European species lives on poplars, but is also to be found on willows.

4 *Gymnetron beccabungae, 1.5—2 mm
This genus has 24 species in central Europe (12 in Britain). The beetles are to be found in the flowers of various low-growing plants; the larvae develop in the base of the flower and of the fruit. This species occurs everywhere in central Europe. It may be found on its larval host — brooklime speedwell, and on other waterside plants.

5 *Gymnetron tetrum, 2.5—3.8 mm
This species, which is found in North America as well as in the palaearctic region, occurs chiefly in the southern and middle part of central Europe. The larvae live in the seed capsules of toadflax, snapdragon, mullein and figwort.

6 *Gymnetron antirrhini, 2.5—3 mm
This species is common everywhere in central Europe. The beetles are to be found on toadflax, while the larvae develop in its seed capsules.

7 *Miarus campanulae, 2.3—3.6 mm
The 9 species of this genus found in central Europe (5 in Britain) live similarly to the members of the genus Gymnetron. The species illustrated here is common everywhere in central Europe. The beetles are to be found in the flowers of Campanula species, ragged robin and other plants.

8 *Cionus scrophulariae, 4—5 mm   (176 : 3)
The 15 species of this genus found in central Europe, of which 6 occur in Britain, live on mullein and figwort. The larvae pupate in a transparent, round, filamentous cocoon on the leaves, where they are very well disguised, since they are taken for fruits. This species is abundant on figwort everywhere in central Europe.

9 *Cionus tuberculosus, 3.5—4 mm   (176 : 2)
This is also a common species on figwort in parts of northern Europe and in central and southern Europe.

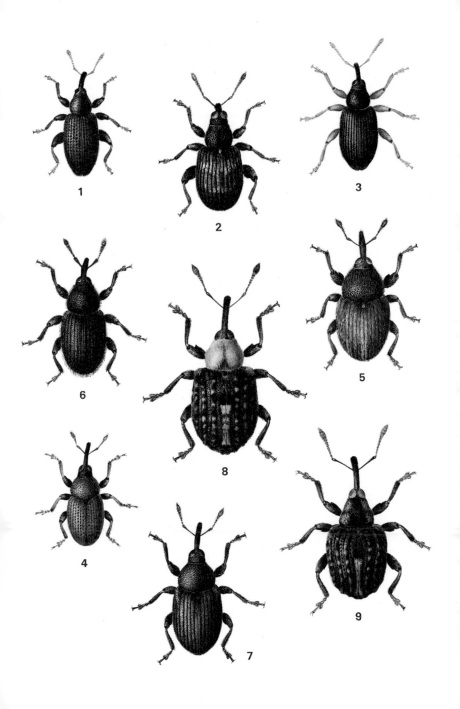

1 *Nanophyes marmoratus,* 1.3−2 mm   (172 : 3)
There are 18 members of this genus in central Europe, only 2 of which occur in Britain. Like *Cionus* species, the larvae live in the base of the flower or fruit or in the stem of various plants, where they cause gall-like swellings and pupate in a netlike cocoon. The adult beetles are to be found in the flowers. The species depicted here is common on purple loosestrife everywhere in central Europe.

2 *Apion pomonae,* 2.5−3.6 mm   (13 : 121)
Apion, with the previous genus, is often separated from the Curculionidae as a separate family − Apionidae. So far there are over 1,000 known species of the genus, 140 of which live in central Europe (84 in Britain). The larvae attack various parts of flowering plants. More than half of the native species live on leguminous plants, but other species have members of Compositae, Polygonaceae, Labiatae, Malvaceae and various other plant families as hosts. Most species hibernate as adults, which emerge in the spring to return to their host plants, but occasionally visit other plants for a meal. The species shown here is common in central Europe. The adult beetles can be found from April to November on wild pea (*Lathyrus*) plants and vetches; the larvae develop in the pods.

3 *Apion apricans,* 2.2−2.7 mm   (13 : 134)
This species, which is distributed over the entire palaearctic region, lives on red clover and is abundant everywhere. The adult beetles can be found on their food plant from April to November; the larvae develop in the flowers and can do considerable damage to crops grown for seed.

4 *Apion frumentarium,* 2.2−3.1 mm   (13 : 3)
Most species of *Apion* are dark, with a metallic sheen, and only a few are reddish, like the one depicted here. *A. frumentarium* abounds on dry ground everywhere in central Europe. The adult beetles can be found from April to September; the larvae develop in the upper part of the root of sheep's sorrel.

5 *Rhinomacer attelaboides,* 3−5 mm   (1 : 1)
The only member of this genus found in central and northern Europe has a somewhat patchy distribution, but is generally commoner in the east than in the west. The beetles are found on pines and may be caught by tapping the apical shoots. The larvae develop in the male flowers, but pupate in the soil. *Rhinomacer* is often placed in a separate family − Nemonychidae.

6 *Deporaus betulae* − Birch Leaf Roller, 3−5 mm   (10 : 4)
There are 4 species of this genus in central Europe (2 in Britain). They belong to a group in which the adults twist leaves into a funnel to make a cradle for the eggs; the larvae live on the wilting tissue. The species shown here is generally common, and makes its cradles chiefly of birch leaves, but occasionally of the leaves of other deciduous trees. The larvae pupate in the soil.

7 *Rhynchites aequatus,* 2.7−4.5 mm   (7 : 5)
This genus is represented by some 20 species in central Europe. *R. aequatus* is found on various rosaceous trees and shrubs, but chiefly on hawthorn. It also occurs on fruit-trees, especially apples, where it lays its eggs in the young fruit.

8 *Byctiscus betulae,* 4.8−7 mm   (9 : 1)
Both the central and north European members of this genus are illustrated here. This species occurs over the whole palaearctic region, from Europe across Siberia to China; in central Europe it is fairly common. Like the Birch Leaf Roller, the females twist leaves to form a cradle for the eggs and the larvae. They use various deciduous trees as brood plants, but since they also attack vines, they can occasionally be a pest.

9 *Byctiscus populi,* 4−5.5 mm   (9 : 2)
The distribution and biology of this species are very similar to those of the preceding one, but in central Europe its most usual hosts are poplars, on which the beetles can be seen from April to October. This genus, together with the two which precede it here (*Deporaus* and *Rhynchites*) and the two which follow are often placed in the Attelabidae, as a family distinct from the Curculionidae.

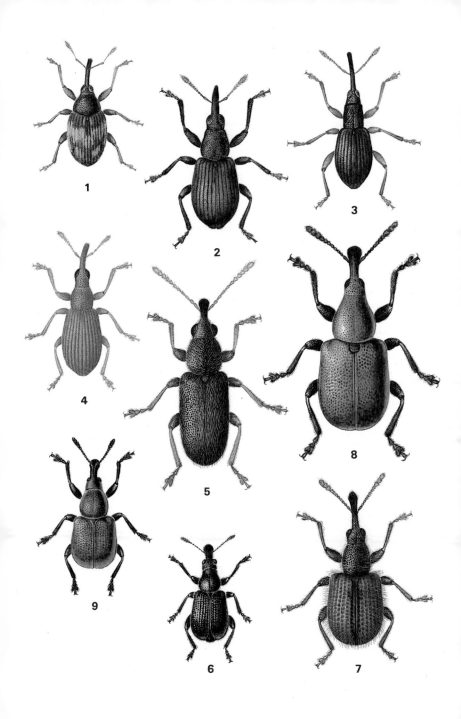

1 *Attelabus nitens* – Oak Leaf Roller, 4—6.5 mm (11 : 1)
The females of this species – which is the only member of the genus found in central Europe – make little leafy containers for their brood. They prefer oaks, but occasionally use sweet chestnut, alder or hazel leaves. This is a common species everywhere in central Europe, where the adult beetles can be found from May to August. The larvae develop in the leaf-rolls, hibernate and pupate in them the following spring.

2 *Apoderus coryli*, 6—8 mm (12 : 1)
Of the 2 species of this genus found in central Europe, the one shown here is by far the commoner and in central Europe it is fairly abundant everywhere. The beetles are to be found from May to September, chiefly on hazels and only rarely on other deciduous trees such as alders and birches. The females construct cradles made from leaves for their brood. In these the larvae develop and pupate; the adult beetles emerge the same summer, before hibernating.

Family Scolytidae — bark and ambrosia beetles

This family – also known under the name Ipidae in older works – is represented by 119 species in central Europe, 57 of which occur in Britain. The majority develop in the twigs, branches and trunks of deciduous and coniferous trees and the family includes some of the most serious forest pests. As well as doing direct damage to the wood, many of them help to transmit plant diseases. Only a few species live in the stems and roots of herbaceous plants or in seeds. The species living on deciduous trees and conifers may develop either in the bark or in the wood itself (see p. 318).

3 *Scolytus scolytus* – Large Elm Bark Beetle, 3.2—5.5 mm (1 : 9)
In earlier works this genus is also listed as *Eccoptogaster*. The 14 species occurring in central Europe (7 in Britain) breed chiefly between the bark and sap-wood of deciduous trees. The one shown here lives mainly on elms, but occasionally on other deciduous trees, and produces 2 generations in a year (May—June and August—September).

4 *Scolytus mali*, 3—4 mm (1 : 4)
This species – which also occurs in North America – is common everywhere in central Europe. It breeds in the branches and trunks of fruit-trees and occasionally of other deciduous trees; it produces 2 generations in a year (May—June and August—September).

5 *Scolytus rugulosus*, 1.8—2.5 mm (1 : 1)
The biology of this smaller relative of *S. mali* is similar to that of its larger cousin. The breeding sites of the two species are not infrequently to be found close together, although *S. rugulosus* generally prefers the twigs and branches of the crown.

6 *Phloeophthorus rhododactylus*, 1.4—1.8 mm (3 : 1)
The only member of this genus found in central and northern Europe breeds chiefly in woody leguminous plants, such as broom. It is present everywhere in the west of central Europe, but becomes rarer towards the east.

7 *Phloeosinus thujae*, 1.5—2.4 mm (17 : 1)
Of the 3 members of this genus found in central Europe, only the one shown here is found in the British Isles. It breeds in various Cupressaceae, including cypresses and juniper.

8 *Hylesinus crenatus*, 4—6 mm (11 : 1)
Two species of this genus occur in central and northern Europe. Both live mainly on ashes and only exceptionally on other deciduous trees. In central Europe they are not very common. The one shown here is the larger of the two.

9 *Leperisinus varius*, 3 mm (12 : 1)
In older works the single central European member of this genus is also known as *Hylesinus fraxini*. It attacks ashes of all ages and only occasionally other deciduous trees. The larvae feed between the bark and the sap-wood. The adult beetles chew at the outside of the bark, giving rise to scabby, cancer-like excrescences.

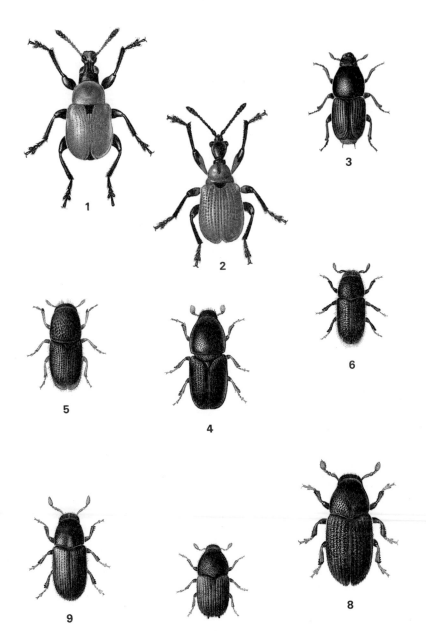

1 *Dendroctonus micans,* 7−9 mm (8 : 1)

The only member of this genus found in central Europe, this is the largest bark beetle in the whole palaearctic region. In central Europe it occurs wherever there are spruces, since they (and only seldom other conifers) are its brood tree. The beetle is to be found in abundance in the entire northern spruce zone, from western Europe to Japan, and is also found in regions where spruce has been introduced.

2 *Tomicus piniperda* – Large Pine Shoot Beetle, 3.5−4.8 mm (6 : 2)

This genus, listed in many works as *Myelophilus* or *Blastophagus,* is represented in central Europe by 2 species, both of which occur on pines. They breed in the bark and seldom attack other conifers. Not only the larvae cause damage, as the adult beetles may chew holes in the tips of the previous year's shoots, with the result that they easily snap off and may be found lying on the ground under the tree. In a mass attack the crown of the tree looks as though it had been trimmed. This species inhabits the whole of the palaearctic region and often occurs in abundance.

3 *Hylurgus ligniperda,* 5−5.7 mm (7 : 1)

The only species of this genus found in central Europe is distributed throughout the whole of the palaearctic region and has been carried to many other parts of the world. The beetles breed in pine bark. The main damage is done by the young adult beetles, which feed on the lower parts of the trunks.

4 *Hylastes cunicularius,* 3.2−4.5 mm (4 : 3)

In central Europe this genus is represented by 6 species, which breed beneath the bark of various conifers. Like the preceding species, the young beetles damage the trees by gnawing the bark. This species is common throughout the palaearctic region. It prefers spruces and only exceptionally breeds in other conifers.

5 *Polygraphus poligraphus,* 2.2−3 mm (10 : 2)

In central Europe there are 3 species of this genus, all of which breed behind the bark of conifers. This species, the only member of the genus found in Britain, is distributed over practically the whole of the holarctic region. It mainly attacks spruces in central Europe, but sometimes pines as well, and in a large-scale attack can cause serious damage.

6 *Crypturgus cinereus,* 1.1−1.5 mm (20 : 1)

There are 3 species of this genus in central Europe, but none of them occur in Britain. *Crypturgus* females make use of the entry holes and passages of other bark beetles as starting points for their own galleries. The species depicted here is widely distributed in the palaearctic region and in central Europe it mainly attacks pines and spruces.

7 *Cryphalus abietis,* 1.2−1.7 mm (26 : 4)

The 4 central European members of this genus breed in the twigs and branches (less often in the trunks) of deciduous and coniferous trees. The larvae pupate in the bark. This species is distributed over the whole conifer belt of the palaearctic region. It is to be found chiefly on spruces, but also on pines, firs and other conifers.

8 *Ernoporus fagi,* 1.5−2 mm (27 : 1)

The three species of this genus occurring in central Europe live in the twigs of deciduous trees. In central Europe, this one breeds in twigs and thin branches of beeches and occasionally of other deciduous trees.

9 *Xyloterus domesticus,* 3.1−3.8 mm (38 : 1)

Three species of this genus live in central and northern Europe. They chiefly attack felled timber (both conifer wood and hardwoods). The larvae do not live on the wood which they scrape away as they make their passages, but on ambrosia fungi growing on the walls of the burrows. The species shown here breeds mainly in beeches, but also in many other hardwoods. In a large-scale attack it can cause severe damage to ailing trees and to felled timber.

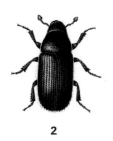

2

1

5

4

3

6

7

8

9

1 *Dryocoetes autographus*, 3.5−4.2 mm (24 : 1)

There are 3 species of this genus in central Europe. This one inhabits the conifer belt of the entire holarctic region. The larvae live in spruce bark and seldom in the bark of other conifers; they pupate in a chamber constructed in the inner bark.

2 *Xyleborus dispar* − male, 1.8−2.1 mm (36 : 1)

Almost all 7 species of this genus found in central Europe live in the wood of deciduous trees and have their brood galleries there. They live not on wood, however, but on ambrosia fungi growing on the walls of the passages. The species shown here is distributed over the whole of the holarctic region and attacks a wide range of trees. Its distinct preference for fruit-trees (chiefly apples and plums) make it a serious pest in orchards. The males are flightless; after mating with the winged female they die on the tree in which they developed.

3 *Xyleborus dispar* − female, 3.2−3.6 mm

After mating, the female flies to a new brood tree, bores its way into the wood, makes brood galleries 1−2 cm long in twigs, branches and trunks and deposits ambrosia fungus in them. The larvae live in these galleries, where they eat the fungus and finally pupate.

4 *Xyleborus monographus*, 2−3.2 mm (36 : 5)

In central Europe this species breeds chiefly in oak and only occasionally in beech, elm and chestnut. Two generations are produced in a year; one appears in March and April and the other in July. The beetles generally attack freshly felled oaks, but sometimes old trees struck by lightning or damaged in some other way.

5 *Pityophthorus pityographus*, 1.1−1.6 mm (29 : 2)

There are 8 members of this genus in central Europe, only 2 of which are found in Britain. The species shown here is referred to as *P. micrographus* in earlier literature; however, the true *micrographus* is a Scandinavian species not represented in the central European fauna. *P. pityographus* breeds in the bark of spruces and other conifers. It generally appears in quite large numbers, but seldom does any serious damage.

6 *Pityogenes chalcographus*, 2−2.3 mm (32 : 1)

All 6 central European species of this genus breed in the bark of twigs and branches of pines and spruces and (occasionally) of other conifers. The one illustrated here is common throughout the entire spruce belt of the palaearctic region. It generally occurs together with *Ips typographus*.

7 *Pityokteines curvidens*, 2.5−3 mm (33 : 2)

The 3 species of this genus found in central Europe are included in earlier literature in the genus *Ips*. This one breeds in the bark of fir-trees and seldom in other conifers. The pupal cell lies up to 1 cm deep in the sap-wood. Since this is a species with a tendency to mass proliferation, the damage it can do is quite considerable. It is partly responsible for the demise of the silver fir.

8 *Ips typographus* − Engraver Beetle, 4.2−5.5 mm (35 : 4)

This genus is represented by 7 species in central Europe (4 in Britain). The one shown here breeds in the bark of spruces and occasionally of pines and larches. The beetle is one of the commonest and most harmful bark beetles, since it has a particularly strong tendency to mass proliferation. It chiefly attacks and kills trees already damaged by gales or snow.

Family Platypodidae

This family is represented in central Europe by only one species.

9 *Platypus cylindrus*, 5−5.5 mm (1 : 1)

This beetle is related to the bark beetles, but can be distinguished from them by its much longer body. It also resembles bark beetles in its biology. It generally breeds in oak, but occasionally in other deciduous trees. Its galleries lead deep into the wood, affecting its value as timber; fortunately, it is not common in central or northern Europe.

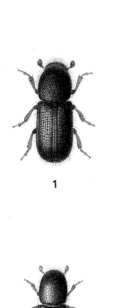

1

2

3

4

8

5

6

9

7

Gallery patterns of various species of bark beetles (Scolytidae)

Apart from the few members of the family which live in seeds or in the stems and roots of herbaceous plants, the galleries formed by Scolytidae are of two types, depending on the way in which the larvae feed. In one type the larvae develop in or just beneath the bark; in the other they develop in the wood. The galleries made by the beetles and larvae form such different and often such characteristic patterns that the species which made them can be identified.

Bark-breeders:

1 *Dendroctonus micans*   (8 : 1)

The female bores its way through the bark, right into the cambium, where it makes a roomy cavity in which it lays little piles of eggs. The larvae form a working column which eats away the cambium on all sides; as they go they leave excrement and powdered wood behind them, blocking up the cavity. Finally, they pupate in the bark.

2 *Cryphalus piceae*   (26 : 1)

In this species the female also makes a wide maternal cavity, sometimes with various bulges on the sides. The larvae do not progress column-wise, however, but eat their way singly into the cambium, giving rise to a radial pattern of tunnels. They likewise pupate in the bark.

3 *Scolytus scolytus* – Large Elm Bark Beetle   (1 : 9)

From the mating chamber in the outer bark or cambium, the female of this species makes a maternal gallery of very variable length (2–10 cm) and lays the eggs along its sides. From here the larvae eat out radiating passages measuring 10–15 cm and finally pupate in the bark or sap-wood.

4 *Leperisinus varius*   (12 : 1)

The female of this species usually makes a two-branched maternal gallery measuring 6–10 cm, from which short larval passages (up to 4 cm) lead roughly at right angles and encroach on the sap-wood. The larvae pupate in the wood.

5 *Pithyophthorus pityographus*   (29 : 2)

The males of this species are polygamous and from the central mating chamber the individual females eat out radiating maternal galleries in which they lay their eggs. The larval passages lead either radially from the maternal galleries, or at right angles to them.

6 *Taphrorynchus villifrons*   (31 : 4)

The males of this species are also polygamous, but the galleries made by individual 'wives' tend to lead in one particular direction. As with all polygamous species, the eggs are laid in niches in the passages at very regular intervals, thereby reducing competition for space – as far as possible – to a minimum.

Wood-breeders:

In the case of wood-breeders, the female bores the brood galleries into the wood itself and deposits fungal spores on the walls. The larvae live in the gallery system, but instead of eating wood they live on the growing ambrosia fungus.

7 *Xyleborus dryographus*   (36 : 7)

In this simplest example of a wood-breeding bark beetle, the female excavates a single maternal gallery, with brood galleries leading from it antler-wise on the same level; in these the eggs are laid at random. The larvae do not widen the passages any further.

8 *Xyleborus dispar*   (36 : 1)

The gallery pattern of this species is three-dimensional and is thus more complicated. Again, the larvae do not widen the passages any further.

9 *Xyloterus lineatus* – Lineate Bark Beetle   (38 : 3)

The female drives a brood gallery into the wood and on either side, at regular intervals, it makes niches, in each of which it lays an egg. The larvae enlarge the niches, in which they feed on ambrosia fungi. Powdered wood and excrement are thrown out into the brood gallery.

318

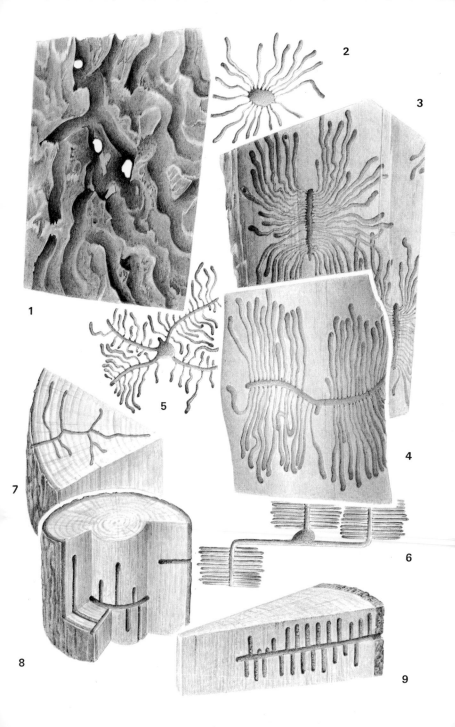

1

2

3

5

4

7

6

8

9

References

Amateur Entomologist's Society, 1975. *A Coleopterist's Handbook.* 142 pp., 62 figs., 18 plates. [2nd Edition].

Böving, A. G. & Craighead, F. C., 1931. *An illustrated synopsis of the principal larval forms of the Order Coleoptera.* Brooklyn, New York (Brooklyn Entomological Society), viii + 351 pp.

Calwers, C.G., 1868. *Käferbuch. Naturgeschichte der Käfer Europas.* Stuttgart (Sprösser & Nägele), 722 pp. [Also in various other editions, from 1858 to 1916].

Crowson, R.A., 1967. *The natural classification of the Families of Coleoptera.* Hampton, Middlesex (Classey), pp. 1–187, 209–214.

Crowson, R.A., 1981. *The Biology of the Coleoptera.* London, etc. (Academic Press), xi + 802 pp.

Fowler, W.W., 1886–1891. *The Coleoptera of the British Islands.* London (Reeve). [5 volumes].

Fowler, W. W. & Donisthorpe, H.StJ.K., 1913. *The Coleoptera of the British Islands,* Volume 6.

Freude, H., Harde, K.W. & Lohse, G.A., 1964-on Editors. *Die Käfer Mitteleuropas.* Krefeld (Goecke & Evers). [An 11 volume work; volumes 1 to 10 already published].

Ganglbauer, L., 1892–1904. *Die Käfer Mitteleuropas.* Vienna [4 volumes].

Hammond, P. M., 1974. *Changes in the British Coleopterous Fauna. The changing flora and fauna of Britain.* Hawksworth, D. L. ed. *Systematics Ass. Special* Volume No. 6: 323–369. London.

Hinton, H.E., 1981. *Biology of Insect Eggs,* Volume 2, pp. 649–703.

Horion, A., 1941–1974. *Faunistik der Mitteleuropäischen Käfer.* [12 volumes; various publishers].

Joy, N.H. 1932. *A Practical Handbook of British Beetles.* (Witherby). 2 volumes, xxvii + 633 pp & 194 pp. [Reprinted 1976, Farringdon (Classey)].

Klausnitzer, B., 1978. *Bestimmungsbücher zur Bodenfauna Europas, Ordnung Coleoptera (Larven).* The Hague (Junk), 378 pp.

Kuhnt, P., 1912. *Illustrierte Bestimmungs-Tabellen der Käfer Deutschlands.* Stuttgart (Nägele & Sprösser), 1138 pp.

Peterson, A., 1951. *The larvae of insects. An introduction to Nearctic species. Coleoptera, Diptera, Neuroptera, Siphonaptera, Mecoptera, Trichoptera. Part II.* Columbus, Ohio (Ohio State University), 416 pp.

Reitter, E., 1908–1916. *Fauna Germanica. Die Käfer des Deutschen Reiches.* Stuttgart (Lutz). [5 volumes].

Index

331